Vampire: The Dark Ages™
A Storytelling Game of Gothic Horror
By Jennifer Hartshorn, Ethan Skemp, Mark Rein•Hagen and Kevin Hassall
Vampire: The Dark Ages™ uses the Storyteller™ game system

CREDITS

Designed by: Jennifer Hartshorn, Ethan Skemp, Mark Rein•Hagen and Kevin Hassall

Based on an original concept by: Mark Rein•Hagen

Developed by: Jennifer Hartshorn and Ethan Skemp

Edited by: Cynthia Summers, Trevor Chase and Ken Cliffe

Written and additional design by: Bill Bridges, Phil Brucato, Ken Cliffe, Richard E. Dansky, Jennifer Hartshorn, Kevin Hassall, Ian Lemke, Mark Rein•Hagen, Kathleen Ryan, Ethan Skemp, Stephen Wieck, Cynthia Summers and Robert Hatch

Additional words by: Brian Campbell

Storyteller System designed by: Mark Rein•Hagen

Vampire: The Masquerade written by: Mark Rein•Hagen, Graeme Davis, Tom Dowd, Lisa Stevens and Stewart Wieck

Vice President of Production and Design: Richard Thomas

Art Directors: Lawrence Snelly and Aileen E. Miles

Art by: John Bolton, Tim Bradstreet, John Cobb, James Daly, Mike Danza, Guy Davis, Tony DiTerlizzi, Jason Felix, Doug Gregory, Anthony Hightower, Leif Jones, Eric Lacombe, Vince Locke, Larry MacDougal, Andrew Robinson, Alex Shiekman, E. Allen Smith, Richard Thomas, Joshua Gabriel Timbrook, Andrew Ritchie, and Kathleen Ryan

Cover Design by: Lawrence Snelly

Vampire: The Dark Ages Logo Designed by: Ash Arnett

Layout and typesetting: Matt Milberger

735 PARK NORTH BLVD.
SUITE 128
CLARKSTON, GA 30021
USA

Check out White Wolf online at http://www.white-wolf.com; alt.games.whitewolf and rec.games.frp.storyteller

PRINTED IN CANADA.

DEDICATION

For C.S. Lewis, medievalist, philosopher and fantasy author.

Attention: Reader discretion is advised. The themes and issues described in this game may be disturbing to some. Though our purpose is not to offend, our use of the vampire as a metaphor and as a channel for storytelling may be misconstrued. To be clear, vampires are not real. The extent to which they may be said to exist is revealed only in what they teach us of the human condition and of the fragility and splendor which we call life.

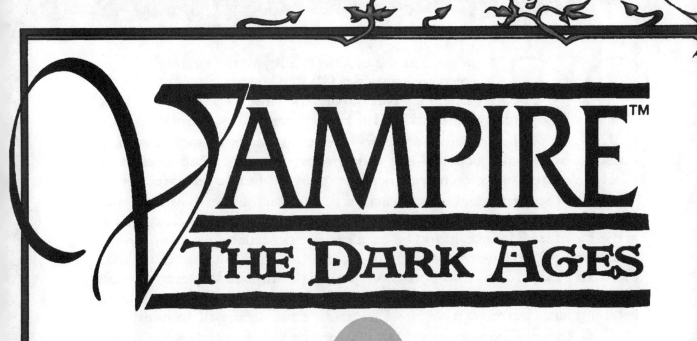

Contents

Will no one rid me of this troublesome priest? One of your kings said that, my dear Geoffrey, thirty years gone. He was hardly the first. I have heard that same complaint uttered in French and Gaulish, and tongues that no one yet living remembers. When you have witnessed as many seasons as I have, you will see that history repeats itself endlessly. There are no new stories, merely new tongues in which to tell the old ones.

One of the very oldest is enclosed for your entertainment and instruction. This type I have seen in the agorae and forums time and again. He is the Hunter of Hunters, and he calls for our destruction in the name of whatever god he worships. I have heard his voice invoke Zeus and Serapis, Adonai and Jesu Christos, even as the flame of the torch danced in his grip. Never have I heard a one of these gods answer, and I have been listening since before barbarous Alexander roused himself to war.

Still, this one has survived his ordeals thus far, which is no mean feat. I would have him, Geoffrey, and I would have you be the instrument of his final degradation.

No, fear not, my childe, I am not thinking of adding him to my brood. You are all the legacy I have desired for centuries, and I would not lay so heavy a burden as that of being a sire upon you yet. There are decades yet before you will be ready, before you know enough of the ways of our kind to teach them to another. You must learn how to bow to the Tzimisce voivode in his castle in the Carpathians, and how to smile even while gazing upon a Nosferatu. There are a thousand things that I must teach you yet before you can teach another.

Besides, there is hardly enough feeding for you in your Londinium. Think of how a ravenous childe might swagger, the mad wolf among the flocks, and leave you starving while the city howls for your blood.

It always makes one feel guilty, destroying one's own childe.

Still, this letter troubles me. I had been meaning to visit you this season in any case, and the missive, which my good friend Monsignor Bernardini was kind enough to turn over to me, provided the necessary impetus. This priest knows too much, and must be turned to our cause. A suicide would serve no purpose, and the taint of Faith may yet turn his blood bitter in your mouth. No, there is a better way.

Turn him, my son, my pride, my joy. Show him the glory and the majesty of what his masters call the Cainite heresy, and let him take communion from our blood and body. Then return him to his abbey, and let him reap wealth from its lands for you. Grant him his sacrament, and then let him serve our will and his God's within the monastery walls. Surely such a strong-willed man will rise in the hierarchy of those who have taken vows. Surely a man strong enough in middle age to defeat one of your elder cousins will live long, and have many years in the seat of power.

I think he'd make a most excellent convert. When I see you in Londinium a fortnight hence, I expect a *fait accompli*.

I did tell you that I felt the urge to travel, did I not? I have been on your green isle for near a month now, traveling posthaste since the good Monsignor placed Friar Offa's record in my hands. Worry not, I've not peered in on you, and the monk still weeps in his cottage. I took great care to ascertain it while hunting down his precious corrupter, his lost Aelfred.

The Aelfred the letter spoke of was a Gangrel of the sort that earn them the sobriquet Animal. He had a certain native cunning, I admit, and given some centuries might have proven to be a most potent member of his clan.

A pity, then, that I did not allow him those centuries.

I entered his forests just after sundown a scant three weeks ago. He was instantly aware of me, as I heard the scuttling claws of his spies leaping branch to branch, hurrying to tell him his doom had come. Faugh! That one of our kind should be reduced to messages brought by diggers of holes and hoarders of acorns.

He knew of my coming, yes, and he fled me. Deep into the trackless wood he scurried, where the canopies of trees are so thick that I could stride them at midday and not fear the kiss of the sun. There are trees there that make me feel young, Geoffrey, and past them Aelfred fled. I suspect his plan was to evade me until dawn, leaving me to seek shelter even as he joined with the earth to slumber. Ever I found signs of his passing, and ever I pursued him. The night wind on my face, the scent of his fear in my nostrils, and the sanguine joy of knowing that a prey worthy of my hunt was before me – ah, what a night! Thrice he was in my grasp, and thrice the gifts of his blood allowed him to elude me. At the last, when my claws would have rent him crotch to crown had I but the time to work my will, the cock's crow heralded the sunrise. Laughing, he sank into the earth.

Laughing, I mimicked his trick. Long ago I learned the secrets of Proteus, of joining with the earth.

For a day, hunter and hunted slept. Then night came again, and we both surged forth from the bosom of the earth to continue our chase.

It was not a chase, but a battle that second night. The second I emerged, he was on me with the savagery of a starved dog. You know that I follow the Road of Heaven; this Aelfred trod the Road of the Beast. There was nothing of the intellect in the dead thing that flung itself on me that night.

It was a nearer thing than I care to remember. His strength was more than his frame should have held, and his claws tore at me. Yet my strength was greater, and I flung him down. He rose and leapt at me again, and so the night was passed, in bloody constraint such that villagers did shut their doors and cry that devils reveled in the wood.

He called to his beasts that night, every thing that the forest held that flew or walked or crept on land, and they came to his succor. I would have my hand at his throat, and lo! from the wood came a wolf to tear at me, or an owl to beat at my face with death-shroud wings. And ever we fought, and ever he tore at me, until the second cock's crow. Again, we sank into earth, but he did not laugh, not on that bloody morning.

Evening, we rose again, and terror was in his eyes. He had called upon the blood often, and I had not allowed him respite in which to feed. And as I am closer to Caine than many, I am capable of going long indeed between draughts.

The hunt was was indeed a hunt this night, as he fled like Actaeon before his own hounds. Eschewing strength, he took the form of a stag. Through the forest he careened, and I after him as a wolf. We went deep into the heart of the wood, into places that no man or beast had trod since before the Romans first laid their roads, and I felt a sleeping presence there that quickened my pace with fear.

But his fear was greater than mine, and he fled before me until, mad with terror, he staggered into a thicket which tangled his antlers like a crown of thorns. Great were his struggles against this prison, and he was made strong indeed by terror, but it was of no avail. The fountain of his strength had run dry, and there was naught left to him but animal ferocity. It did not suffice.

I resumed my own form, and caressed the muzzle of the stag that had been the Cainite who was my prey. "Absalom, my Absalom," I whispered to him, and then I took the edge from my thirst with the shallow pool of his blood.

His ashes scattered on the wind even as I took myself to another hunt that evening. It is foolish, do you not think, for a cotswolder to dwell so far from his neighbors that none can hear his cries for help?

But my tale is done, and all that remains is news. I shall be visiting you in Londinium, as I said, in a fortnight. I expect that you will have turned the priest by that date, and that sufficient refreshment will be available. For the nonce, study the monk's tale. You may learn something of our kind, and much of how we are perceived by our prey.

I look forward to seeing you again and to measuring your progress. I have no doubts that you will make my heart swell with pride. I have been saving a very special flask of vitae, Roman in vintage,` perhaps we shall find cause to celebrate and share it.

A fascinating country, your England. I look forward to the rest of my stay. Do what you will with the messenger who bears this. I wish you *bon apetit*, as the Franks say.

Boukephos, now called Francisco Diego del Belmonte

Monsignor Bernardini:

You may wonder why this epistle is scribed in English. In reply, I would state that I know from our days together under the banner of Edessa that you do speak that tongue, and that many others, even in so learned a city as Rome, do not. While I have no doubts as to the absolute fidelity of the brother I entrust as my courier, misfortune may yet befall him, and such matters as I write on are not for most eyes. It is not often that a man receives the opportunity to document his own damnation, and yet he may not wish to share those details with the vulgate.

I most humbly beseech you to peruse the following missive, and then to take the findings contained within to His Holiness. What I have discovered, what I have recorded in this scroll, what horror I have lived is a matter that threatens the existence of all Christendom. You may scoff, but I speak truth. I am not one of those feeble-minded village priests who sees Our Lord in the cornfields after eating too much moldy grain, nor am I of the sort to hide behind abbey walls from imagined demons in the night. You saw me ride out to the bloody disaster at Hattin before I took holy orders; you saw how I carried myself in tourney and battle. I am told they still speak of me with reverence in the tilting-yards of Acre, and that the Musselmen have not forgotten my name. Are these the deeds, is this the reputation of a shirking coward? I think not. I have since laid down my arms for the shepherd's staff, but I keep my wits and courage about me still. What I tell you is true. I swear it on the body and blood of Christ, if one such as I has any right to mention His holy name.

Do not ask how I came to research this matter; by now I am sure that you have heard how I was disgraced, I know not why, and exiled from the abbey at York. I have been told by friends that it was for my insistence on preaching a sermon whose subject material was most displeasing to Abbot Dafydd. I can think of no such sermon, however, merely a humble piece penned to confront the evils of those who come to church, not to take part in the sacrament but instead to mock those who do. Those who guzzle the blood of Christ, I called these, and I am told that the abbot was most incensed by my choice of theme. In light of what I later learned, his actions seem to be more sinister. Or perhaps I am merely seeing the ghosts of the blood-drinkers where there are none, and I truly deserved to be removed from the company of my brethren.

Regardless, I found myself banished from the abbey and determined to set myself up as a hermit, the better to continue those studies of herbal lore which occupied so much of my time at York. In accordance with this wish, I returned south to the forests of the county of my birth. There I erected a cottage that would serve me both as *domus* and the site of the strangest confession it was ever my misfortune to hear.

The Damned Man's Tale

Most of the information I relate to you here comes from a single source, though one whose reliability I do not doubt. Aelfred was his name, a boy of Saxon blood from my home village of Cheltenham, but an honest and devout boy. He had just started his first growth of beard when he vanished in the wood while hunting. Imagine my surprise, then, to see young Aelfred appear on my doorstep these five years gone, his face framed by the orb of the full moon and looking not a day older than when he vanished.

Not realizing the gravity of the situation, thinking the boy had been perhaps fairy-led, I invited him in. He followed me, gratefully, and sought confession from me for a multitude of sins, the likes of which I could not imagine this simple lad committing. Sins of blood, sins of murder, sins of angelism and theft and blasphemy — to all of these Aelfred confessed. Now I must admit that I could hardly see this downy-cheeked boy committing such grievous sins, any one of which was like to sentence him to the Pit forthwith, and as such I expressed my slight incredulity at his recitation. You are familiar, no doubt, with the sort who claims all sorts of demonic behaviors in confession merely for the enjoyment they receive from their penances, and I feared that Aelfred had become one of this sort. At least, I did until he turned to me with his eyes glowing the red of a beast, and fangs like unto those of a great cat or perhaps a wolf protruding over his barely-bearded lower lip. He laughed then, and no human boy could have made that sound.

With bloody tears rolling down his cheeks, he told me that he had indeed committed that entire litany of sins, and from me he sought first absolution, then death, so that he might not stain his soul any further through the demands of his demonic existence. I made as if to flee from him, but again he laughed and told me that I had nothing to fear from him, because my faith in the Lord was too strong for even his hell-spawned strength to fash out. It was, he said, very different from the last priest he'd spoken to, whose faith had proved to be thin indeed. Aelfred licked his lips at this, and I could not help but shudder at the sight. Then the beast within the child vanished, and I was left with a boy whose brothers and sisters I had baptized, a boy whom I had hoped to help achieve Heaven. Here, then, was my chance.

What else could I have done, Monsignor? Should a fallen angel, even Lucifer himself, truly repent, would not the Lord welcome him back into Heaven? I felt that Aelfred truly sought to repent, and that by denying him this last chance at an unspotted soul I would be the agent of this simple boy's damnation. I granted him absolution, and laid upon him a heavy penance. Part of that penance was for him to relate his tale, and all that he knew of the others of his kind. I trust you do not object.

Of the Nature and Origins of the Cainites

Aelfred told me much that night. He was, he claimed, a *vampyr*, or as the vulgar spell it, vampire. I'm sure you will recognize the term from our brief sojourn with that brotherhood of Slavic knights in Antioch; they told tales of blood-drinking corpses that the peasants labeled with a similar name. These vampires are the descendants of Cain, whom God cursed to wander the earth forever with the mark of His wrath upon him. According to Aelfred, this terrible thirst for blood was God's mark upon Cain, and Adam's son passed the curse down when he, in a mockery of God's act of creation, created his own progeny. All of these vampires, then, are descendants of Cain, walking to and fro on the earth, and up and down in it, bearing his curse and bestowing it upon others. Aelfred even claimed Cain yet walked the earth, and that he had seen him. I pointed out that Cain would be over three thousand years old at this point, and that neither Abraham nor Methuselah had not lived quite so long. Perhaps out of respect, Aelfred did not contradict me.

In any case, I was intrigued as to how Aelfred had become a childe of Cain, as he put it, when I had known both of his parents in Cheltenham. It is a horrifying process, I discovered. The vampire wishing to adopt another into this family of the damned must select and kill his victim, using his fangs to pierce the skin and drink the blood until there is none of the sanguine humour remaining anywhere in the victim's veins. Then, most horrible to consider, the vampire wounds himself and forces his blood down the throat of the victim. Should the victim accept this unholy sacrament, he awakens, dead yet walking, and cursed with Cain's unholy thirst for blood. Some have the strength to refuse the blood when it is offered, and these fortunate souls surely must be granted God's peace. For the others, those who have not the strength of will to turn from the hellish gift offered in that first taste of blood, a new existence awaits them as one of the walking damned.

Aelfred confided in me that when he was first taken and made into a creature of this sort, he awoke with a ravening hunger the likes of which he had not even imagined when alive. As there were no men around to slake his thirst, he pursued some of the king's deer. On foot and without a weapon, he managed to catch two and tear open their throats with his teeth. When I scoffed at this, he left my *domus*, then returned not five minutes later with a brace of pheasants, still living, in his hands. With practiced motion he snapped the neck of the one on the left, laying it out for me. The other… God in Heaven help me, but I watched him as he fed upon it, even as the lamprey or the leech feeds. But no leech devours the way Aelfred took the life from that poor bird, with a look of carnal pleasure on his blood-stained lips. When he finished he called it a poor meal, but that he had no wish to batten upon me even were he able.

I gave the remaining pheasant to the villagers. God and King Richard forgive me, but I could not eat it after witnessing Aelfred's feast.

I must admit that watching Aelfred dine did spark within me some notion of why he must feed as he does. Even in the ruddy torchlight, his countenance was pale and bloodless. Vampirekind must be utterly lacking in the sanguine humour, necessitating them to take it from their victims to replenish their own, ever-diminishing supplies. This imbalance of humours goes a long way towards explaining the mystery of Aelfred. It would also seem that since Aelfred is lacking in sanguine humor and has not aged, that the sanguine humor is in fact the key to aging, and that by thinning the blood one may slow or even halt the aging process.

Of the Benediction of Sun and Torch

After complaining that his meal would certainly not be nearly as pleasing to his taste as mine would be, Aelfred deigned to continue his tale. According to the boy, he had spent his first month alone in the deepest heart of the forest, sleeping in trees with leaves so thick as to block out the benediction of the rays of the sun. His very first day after awakening with this terrible hunger, he had felt a great drowsiness come upon him as dawn arose, but blood-stained as he was, he was still determined to return home.

One step from beneath the canopy of the trees convinced him of his folly, as when sunlight fell upon his flesh it began to smoke as if it were dried wood, held in the fire. Howling, he fled into the forest's depths. Since then he has always slumbered during the day in the deepest hollows and thickets the forest offers. Curiously, I could see no scars from this burning, but he claimed that he and all his kind healed most rapidly from even such grievous wounds as these. Only sunlight, fire, and the claws and teeth of another of his kind, he said, presented any difficulty to him.

Of fire he had learned whilst taking a baby from a cottage. The father, awakened by Divine Providence, thrust a torch into Aelfred's face, wounding him horribly and forcing him to drop the child. The look in Aelfred's eyes was truly awful when he spoke of this, and when he told of the plans for vengeance he had laid upon the innocent cotswolder who had merely defended his child, I must admit I doubted as to whether Aelfred truly sought absolution.

It would seem from Aelfred's record, though, that certain of the Slavs did speak truthfully when telling us their tales of *vampyrs* and, more importantly, how to dispose of them. *Primus*, fire serves as well for vampires as it does for witches. *Secundus*, they cannot stand the light of the sun, suffering the torments of the damned from the slightest exposure to its light. *Tertius*, the sight of the cross wielded by one whose faith is unshaken serves to repel or even wound these beasts in the shapes of men. Even the presence of sufficiently holy men, it would seem, is enough to drive these demons off. Once, I took one of Aelfred's hands in mine, and his very fingers did begin to char and smoke. On the other hand, Aelfred did refute the tales that a stake through the heart is sufficient to slay one of his kind. Such things, he claimed, render the staked vampire unable to move but leave him fully awake and able to use many of his diabolic powers.

My rooster chose this moment to crow, and Aelfred took his leave of me. He claimed that he would return that evening, so that he might finish his tale and his penance. I bid him restful sleep, and he vanished into the greying wood.

Of a Second Eve and Cainite Humours

I was sore troubled that day. By speaking with such a creature as Aelfred had become, did I truck with the very Devil? Was my curiosity a snare set for me, and the knowledge Aelfred offered the bait? On the other hand, did I dare refuse such knowledge as he offered me, knowing the threat that he and his kind were to all the kingdoms of the earth? Even working in my garden did little to soothe my fears, and I must confess a certain distasteful impatience for nightfall and Aelfred's anticipated return.

Return he did, even while the last clouds of the day still bore the clotted-blood stain of the sunset. He seemed eager to finish his confession and have done with his unholy existence. Thankfully, this night he brought nothing upon which to sup.

He entered my *domus* without an invitation this time and perched himself atop my workbench, clearing my pestle and other tools aside to make space for himself. I was reminded of a sparhawk as he crouched there, his eyes darting around the room as if to find something upon which he could pounce. I was thankful his eyes did not fix on me, and I sat transcribing his words at the farthest end of the room.

His words this night rambled. He began by speaking of what he called the clans. Consider this: There are nations of vampires, even as there are nations of men. Just as the humours may mix and balance in different ways to form phlegmatic Frenchmen or sanguine Englishmen, so too do the remaining humours shift their proportions in the bodies of these vampires to create nations among them. Some are in such imbalance that their very features are twisted into a mockery; others could not be distinguished from living men unless goosedown were to be held under their noses to catch their exhalations.

He himself claimed to belong to a nation of Cainites, as he put it, called *Gangrel*. The word is broad Scots, I believe, or perhaps Pictish. He told me of others as well: foul sorcerers called the *Tremere* (from the Latin "to shake," perhaps?), terrible scholars known as *Cappadocians*, itinerant thieves called *Ravnos*, unholy idealists called *Brujah* and more. You may find it of interest, as a fellow veteran of the fighting in the Holy Land, that those rumors we had of the infidel's demonic assassins, the so-called *Hashishin*, are quite true. Aelfred had something akin to fear in his eyes when he spoke of the "Sons of Hassam," and if a creature such as he fears these monsters, then I can no longer fault the bravery of those who fell under their knives. I merely commend their souls to God.

Of Mine Own Peril and the Servants of the Cainite

This second night of confession, Aelfred seemed less at ease, his eyes constantly darting to the nighted windows. Even the smallest noises made him jump, and — I cannot escape the observation — he paced within my hut like a caged animal. A wolf, perhaps, or a great cat that nonetheless knows that the lion waits outside for him. It made for most disagreeable company, and he paused his recitation several times to bolt to the window and gaze into the night. At these moments, I could see quite clearly that his eyes were red-litten, not in the way that a cat's eye will reflect the light of a torch, but rather shining with that unholy glow. Each time he would return to his perch on my table, but the look of the beast took long moments to leave his visage.

At long last I could contain myself no more, and asked him what he feared that dwelled in the night. He replied that he did not fear for himself, but rather for me. Certain of his kind had no love for the Church, nor those who served it, and by burdening me with his confession he may well have exposed me to their ire. I responded that he himself had demonstrated aptly that none of his kind could approach me, whether to do me beneficence or harm. By way of reply, he drew a long dagger from his boot and, ere I could so much as move, hurled it past me to stick, quivering, in the lintel.

The blade came close enough to shear away a lock of my hair, and draw blood from my ear. I am quite certain that, had he wished, Aelfred could have put out either of my eyes with equal facility.

With a cat's smile, Aelfred informed me that no Cainite of any skill had any need to close with me to do me harm, and that even the walking damned were proficient with the crossbow and the dart. Furthermore, they had servants: humans, beasts and things no longer human or beast which Aelfred called *soules*. These *soules* had partaken of the unholy sacrament of Cainite blood, in diabolic parody of the Communion, while yet living, and as such shared certain of their masters' powers. Yet as they were still among those who draw breath, they were not yet completely damned, and could approach even (he said) so holy a man as myself without fear. Indeed, he hinted to me that Thomas a'Becket was dispatched in this manner. When one considers the circumstances surrounding the archbishop's demise, Aelfred's insinuation makes chilling sense.

Still, my narrator was quick to add, it was not just men who could become *soules*, nor were all servants of the Cainites of this sort. Beasts who drank of the vampire's blood grew swift and cunning beyond any natural measure, and hearkened to the commands of those unnatural voices. Men who might be found at matins served the wills of vampiric masters, sometimes willingly, sometimes not. Some of the vampirekind, it seems, have the power to seduce or command as the whim suits them, and their word cannot be resisted. Kings have been commanded to war, princes to treason and parricide, and queens to bastard-spawning adultery by these Cainite voices, and no power under Heaven could have served as an aegis against them.

I must confess that at this, I thought of the behavior of Abbot Dafydd, his anger at me so unseemly in so mild a priest. Could it be that he had been ordered by some dread voice from beyond the tomb to banish me, ere I spoke too long of things that the Cainites did not wish revealed? In faith, I do not know, but I have my fears.

Natural beasts also serve the Cainites, it would seem. The rat and the mouse, the wolf and the falcon, all hear the call of the walking dead and heed it. Aelfred was kind enough to demonstrate such to me. As we spoke of other matters relating to his kind, I became aware of the presence of many eyes in the night, gazing in through the window out of which Aelfred was so fond of peering. Staring into the night, I could see the gleam of eyes — green, orange, yellow, unholy red. The owl looked back at me, as did the stag and the wolf. All manner of beast crouched in silence beyond my window. All were quiet, watching. None tore at another, nor did any seek to flee. They merely sat, waiting, until Aelfred came to the window. Then, in seemly fashion, they dispersed back into the night without so much as a bark or a titter.

God help us, it seems the Devil can make the lion lay down with the lamb as well.

After this display, and Aelfred's earlier warning, I was no longer quite so prideful in my ability to resist the ill-will of these Cainites, should they wish to do me harm. What good my faith that would burn one of these damned souls at a touch if a soulless beast were commanded to take my throat, or should a trio of *goules* seek to do unto me as they did unto the archbishop of blessed memory? I inquired of Aelfred more of those Cainites who, damned as they were, might seek to do injury to even so humble a priest as myself, even as I uncovered and unwrapped the blade which had served me so well in the Holy Land.

Aelfred seemed much disturbed by the retrieval of my blade, and was unable to speak for several minutes. At length he admitted that he had heard tell of certain others of his kind who, even before he sought me out, were displeased with my presence within the wood, and had already held council to discuss excising me from their dominions. Indeed, he confessed with downcast face, his confession of the nature of vampirekind to me was intended in part as protection, that I might know what arms would suffice to defend me from these fiends. Even as we spoke, he was sure that those who wished me harm were plotting against me. His presence might serve as a ward against their depredations for so many nights as his confession continued, but what of the first night after I granted him absolution? He would no longer be able to shelter me from the others of his kind, and the Cainites are nothing if not patient.

His voice dropped to a whisper, and, as a child might ask for permission, he begged for my leave to help me defend myself against the Cainites who sought to do me harm. God forgive me, I granted it.

I knew the moment the words left my mouth that I had erred most grievously. Nay, let me say not erred; say sinned instead. For a sin it was, and it led to greater sins, and I am sinning still against both God and man.

Aelfred lifted his face from his hands, and in that moment certain truths were made plain to me. His visage was a mask of eagerness, and what he proposed then was simply monstrous. Yet the alternative was more monstrous still….

Of Dispatching the Beast

To wit, Aelfred claimed to know the name and *domus* of one of the Cainites whom, he claimed, sought my destruction. Harald Leifsson, a Cainite damned during the days when the Norsemen harried us from Whitby to Southampton, brought himself to earth each day not two miles from where my cottage stood, and his was the loudest voice calling for my destruction. Now, this Harald was centuries in the ways of the vampirekind, and as such a mere stripling such as Aelfred held no hope of staying his wrath once the shades of night fell. Aelfred was but new come into his power; this Harald was old and wise, a cunning serpent from centuries gone.

But, and here was Aelfred's hope, were I to come upon Harald by day, he would scarce be able to rouse and defend himself, and the power of my faith would serve to defend me and weaken my foe. By laying to rest this Cainite, I would protect myself and rid the earth of one who ought to have been in the grave three hundred years gone. Surely there was nothing amiss in either of these aims, yet Aelfred seemed almost overeager that I might agree to his plan.

Made wary, I inquired as to the number and disposition of Harald's guards, as well as to their kind. It would not do for one aged Crusader to find himself confronting a phalanx of the fearsome *goules*, daylight or I would be spitted like a fowl instantly. Aelfred had already thought of this, it seemed, and detailed for me the number and kind of Harald's defenders. It seemed that the old Viking trusted neither men nor *goules* of the usual sort, and instead surrounded his manor with fierce hounds which he fed both with his own blood, and, I shudder to tell it, the flesh of serfs who displeased him.

I at once began considering tactics, for my fear and my hubris had allied in my soul, causing me to agree to this mad plan. My sight swam with visions of fanged fiends hovering outside my door, waiting for me to drop to slumber so that they might devour me. In this mania, I gladly agreed to seek out and destroy this Harald, for fear that he might destroy me first.

Aelfred, ever helpful, suggested a way in which he might aid me in dealing with the hellish hounds which Harald employed. Returning to my window, he stared once again into the night, and ere the candle had time to burn even half a notch lower, a great stag strode forth into the clearing surrounding my *domus*. It stood, expectant and regal, as Ælfred retrieved his blade from my lintel and walked towards it. Silent as ghosts they both were, and Ælfred placed his hand on the proud neck of the beast. This is how it must have been in the Garden ere the Fall, I thought, man and beast *in tranquilitas*. Then came the snapping of the stag's neck, his regal head drooping to the leafy floor, and I knew how far Ælfred had fallen.

Working quickly, he hacked the stag into bloody chunks, all the while explaining that while the *goules* hounds did feast upon Harald's blood, they commonly took more earthly sustenance. They would eat venison were it given to them, no doubt. Now should that venison contain a soporific or, were I to decide that these hellhounds ought to be dispatched, a poison, the hounds would be dealt with forthwith, and I need never draw blade to deal with them. Surely, he said, so accomplished a herbalist as myself would know of a potion that could induce sleep, or more than sleep….

Forgive me for thinking instantly of the oil pressed from the plant we call monkshood.

And so we worked the remainder of the night, hunched over the ruined corpse of the great stag with our gloved hands smeared with blood and poison. I was as a man in a fever, and worked as one to achieve labors in a single night which no man has any business accomplishing. A full hour before the sun rose, I found myself laden with my old sword and a bloody pouch full of tainted venison. The blood must have sung loudly in my veins, for I found Ælfred giving me odd glances as we walked towards the place where the dreaded Harald lay.

We reached Harald's fields just as the sky began to lighten. Ælfred begged my pardon that he could not help me any further, but afore he vanished into the shadows between the trees, he pressed into my hand a scroll which he said I would find useful. Then, like a phantom of the night, he was gone. Fully determined to wait for true dawn ere I began my assault, I unraveled the scroll my young guide had left me. It was a map, cunningly done, of the rooms and corridors of the manse. Included were notes detailing where traps had been laid, certain to catch even the most stealthy thief who had not knowledge of their whereabouts. I took the time that God allotted me before dawn to study this gift, making certain that I knew which floorboards were safe to tread.

It was not until many days later that I began to wonder at how Ælfred came to possess such a map. Certes, neither he nor any in his family ever learned to read.

But such considerations troubled me not, not with the promise of battle and danger singing to me as it had not since the day before we returned, broken and beaten, to Krak des Chevaliers. My lost youth was as a troubadour, and I longed for dawn. Inevitably, it came.

Shall I tell you of that day's bloody work? Of the great fire-eyed hounds that were conjured the second I set foot on the lawns of Harald's manor? Of the way they fell upon the poisoned gift I gave them, and of the almost human cries they made as the monkshood did its work? Shall I tell you of the treasures of antiquity that house held, the Byzantine and Babylonian? Idols and icons, all jumbled with treasures stolen from Saracen and Christian alike? Shall I tell you that Ælfred's intelligence was not of the best, and that there was a human servant treading the halls who set upon me with a scramasax, even as I sought his master's tomb?

Shall I tell you I killed a man in cold blood? Bless me, Father, for I have sinned, and there can be no absolution.

Of the Bed and What Lay Upon It

Eventually I came to where Harald lay, stretched out on a wooden bed adorned with the pagan images of his old gods. Tror, Wodan and others I cannot name; their bearded visages laughed at me as I reached within my bloody pouch for the wooden stake with which to still my prey.

It was a boy that lay on that bed. Not a beardless youth, such as Ælfred, but a boy. He was eight, perhaps nine years old, with the golden hair of the Swedes and a visage to make angels weep. Pale was his cheek, and he wore a simple shift of white. He breathed not in his slumber, laying on blankets richly woven, nor did he stir. A doll of rags, such as any child might have, lay by his side, and his head rested on a pillow of scarlet silk.

This could not be a monster, I thought. Only a boy, an innocent boy was lying here. My blade clattered to the floor, and he did not stir. I reached forth my hand, the one that held not the stake, and placed it, gently, on his forehead to see if he lived.

It was then that his eyes opened, and even so great a fool as I knew with what I dealt. For there was age in those eyes, blue as the icy sea he must once have sailed, older than the trees and colder than the ice. Age was there, and I read centuries of hateful existence in that one moment. With my hand yet on his brow, he opened those ancient eyes and saw me, and this vision of angelic beauty *hissed* at me. A serpent's hiss, even as his perfect face began to char under my touch.

God be praised my other hand still held the stake. I am certain that had I used my sword instead, he might have withstood the blow and done me grievous harm. Yet the stake I still held, and I plunged it deep into his breast. 'Twas not enough; he clawed and scrabbled at my face even as rivers of blood poured from his chest and made a ruin of his bed. Howling like a madman he was, and I howling with him, but none to hear us but the dead. Again I lifted the stake, and again I brought it down, yet this time he twisted, that I struck him in the side. I wounded him sore, though, for his thrashings grew more frantic as he tore at the hand that made a ruin of his brow.

A third time I raised the stake and brought it down, and this time, God be praised, he ceased to struggle. His eyes were yet open, though, *mirabile dictu*, and I knew with a perfect faith that he could see and understand all that happened, even with a stout oaken stake plunged deep into his heart. Had I any claim to wisdom, I would have carried this monster, this Harald outside into the blessed sunlight, and tested Aelfred's claims once and for all. I knew that was what the boy feared, for there were neither windows nor sources of flame in his chamber. Only rich furnishings, dimly lit and now stained with twice-used blood.

Yet a voice whispered to me, the Tempter's voice. Unprecedented opportunity lay before me to gain knowledge of the Cainites that no other man might know. My findings would be relayed to the Church, for the good of all Christian men, so that they might defend themselves better against this threat. Did we not study the Saracens so that we might fare better against them in battle? Did we not gaze upon their fortresses and learn? Wherefore should we not do the same with the Cainites, who were a greater threat than Saladin and ten others I could name combined? Nay, better to bring this beast called Harald back where I might study him, and learn how mere men might yet triumph over these creatures of the Adversary.

In bloody blankets I wrapped him, careful not to dislodge the stake which I had planted in his breast. In many folds he was covered, til I was certain that not a single ray of sun might singe his flesh. My own proximity was enough, it seemed, to raise blisters. I was loath to expose my prize to greater perils. And even as I trussed him like a deer taken in the hunt, he did not so much as move. Only his eyes gave any indication that I dealt with more than a shell, for in them I read undying hatred and all of the malice three centuries could muster.

I resolved then to end my researches quickly and dispatch this poor soul, first offering him a last confession.

Suffice it to say that I was able to return to my *domus* with my prize, unseen by any man or creature, before the sun sank below the trees. The cloth I had swaddled Harald in proved thick enough, and when I cleared my worktable and unwrapped him he proved to be only somewhat the worse for wear. I immediately tied him down with straps of broad leather, so that he might not escape or threaten me in my sleep, then burned the bloody rags in the fire.

I was still at this chore when Aelfred reappeared. He seemed ecstatic that I was well, and inquired after the day's sally. Before I had fairly begun my account, he stood within my *domus*, gazing upon the dread Harald with the same cat's smile he had shown me aforetimes.

He did not seem at all surprised to see his rival, stretched out and impaled. Gratified, rather.

Of the Binding of the Cainite

He immediately set about making the straps tighter, explaining as he did so that it would seem that Harald had expended most of his ill-gotten blood and was near to being harmless. It would seem that while Cainites lack the sanguine humor, it is the fuel for their inhuman feats. Deprived of it, they fall into slumber or worse; fed a trickle, they are merely sustained. It was long minutes ere he was finished, long indeed, and all the while that poor mad boy's eyes looked up at me with the blackest hatred imaginable.

When Aelfred had completed his work with the straps, he turned to me and shrugged ruefully. We had come, he said, to the end of his knowledge about his Cainite kind; all that he had left to tell me was rumors and hearsay. But, if I wished, a greater source of knowledge lay before me in the form of the helpless Harald. I could, he explained, learn much from the so-called child who lay bound before me. I could deprive him of blood and watch his reactions, or provoke him to rage and test his limits.

I objected on moral grounds, that torturing even one such as this Harald was purported to be (for I had grown to trust Aelfred's word less since the incident with the unfortunate servant) was no fit occupation for a man of God, and that enough blood had been shed by me this day. I sought to see no more.

Yet Aelfred persisted still. Surely this unnatural creature had no claim on God's mercy or on mine, having existed unnaturally since the days of Aethelred the Unready. During those long centuries, he had committed acts of such an unspeakable nature that even now, other Cainites shuddered at his name. It was even rumored that Harald had, in imitation of blind Oedipus, slain his own sire and drunk dry the well from which he had sprung. Whole villages had fallen to his depredations, fed either to his ravenous appetites or to those dogs whose corpses lay stiffening in the evening's breeze.

Besides, he continued, and here I recognized the voice of the Tempter I had heard within the walls of Harald's manse, I should think upon the uses the knowledge I would gain. Knowledge of ways to stymie the vampire, his weaknesses and flaws. For even such as Harald's kind had weaknesses, and it lay within my grasp to discover them. Such secrets would serve me well, Aelfred noted, should any of Harald's companions or childer discover my whereabouts. As I had slain one of the vampirekind, I would surely be marked for vengeance by any who sought to avenge Harald.

So this, then, was my wyrd. I had slain a vampire; now I must plunge deeper in to their world of madness and blood ere I be slain in turn. I had killed a man; the only absolution I could perform would be to grant a great gift unto all of mankind. I had undertaken this task to save Aelfred's soul; now perhaps I might be able to save mine and the misbegotten Harald's as well. I knew that, even should I grant Harald final peace at this moment, my prior existence could never be regained. I would forever fear the night and what it contained, and no more would I be able to merely labor in my garden without seeing the guilty herbs that laid low Harald's watchdogs. No, I could not go back, and to stand still would be to invite death. I could but go forward and pray that God's mercy holds room for even one such as myself.

Shuddering with self-loathing, I assented. Thus did I seal my own damnation, thus are Aelfred's black soul and mine linked in eternal perdition. With a wolfish smile, Aelfred handed me his knife, still stained with the blood of the stag whose flesh had gone to feed the dogs their last supper. The stripped corpse still lay beyond my door. In the silence of the night the flies buzzed loudly.

Still, it is better that someone enjoys the fruits of my damnation. Let me relate to you what we discovered, Aelfred and I, as we subjected Harald to the torments of the very Pit itself. Perhaps you, or one of your superiors shall take my account and because of it, be better armed against the Cainite foe. Perhaps then will my actions have a saving grace.

OF THE ORGANS AND *SANGUINIS* OF THE CAINITE

What we learned that night was repellent beyond measure, but also fascinating. Having Aelfred make an incision in the chest of the boy Harald (for my touch still provoked agony and char), I was able to examine his entrails and to find them shriveled nearly to dust. Had a Roman augur found such within a sacrificial beast, 'twould be a certainty that the Emperor would lay dead on the morrow. The only exception to the general desiccation was the stomach, which pulsed a ruddy red. Even as I cut, the tissues attempted to mend themselves. Aelfred assured me that this would be so until Harald completely exhausted his supply of *sanguinis*, at which point there would be no more healing as the fuel which stoked the flame of his body would be lacking.

I remonstrated at this knowledge, as my researches would have a rapid ending indeed were I to be dealing with a dried-out husk within the space of a brace of nights. Harald must be fed, I argued, else his suffering would be worse than useless, and I would grant him the *misericordia* at that moment.

Aelfred relented at this, but demanded to know from what source would Harald's nourishment come. Not me, certes; my blood would burn on his very lips. Not the beasts of the field, Aelfred argued; in Harald's weakened state such thin blood would not serve to nourish at all. Not any other specimen of mankind, I held firm, for even in the depths to which I had sunk I would not give over another man, no matter how base, to the foul appetites of these dark creatures. Aelfred swore and cursed me, but I stood firm, and at last he muttered darkly that he would take it upon himself to feed our prisoner.

In horrified fascination I watched as Aelfred took the bespattered knife in one hand, the still-erect stake in the other. Even as I realized his intention, he pulled the stake forth with the sound of a stick being pulled from the mire. Harald at once began to strain mightily against his bonds, but even at his first motion, Aelfred had taken the knife and drawn it across his own wrist. The blood cascaded down as Aelfred pressed his wrist to the boy's mouth, a look that I can but describe with the word "lascivious" crossing his face.

Harald's reaction was curious. One would think that these Cainites would relish any blood that they might be able to inbibe, yet at first he sought to spit the *sanguinis* offered him upon the floor. Soon, though, his struggles ceased and he sucked greedily at Aelfred's wrist. I was reminded of a babe at its mother's teat, so rapturous was the expression on the boy's face. It made for odd contrast with Aelfred's lustful visage, and I found myself wondering again whether he sought absolution, or something darker from me.

At length he pulled free, and with a serpent-like tongue licked the place where he had cut himself, then replaced the gore-rimed stake in Harald's chest. Of more interest to me, alas, was the result of this unholy feeding upon the gaping rents that Aelfred's knife had made in the boy's form. Before my unbelieving eyes, the very place where the blade had bitten not an hour before healed without so much as a scar. Not a mark remained, and for the remainder of the evening Aelfred, for his amusement and my edification, made ever more horrendous wounds in Harald's supine shell, so that we might watch the rate at which they healed. Some took as long as three days, I noted, and multiple quaffs from the font at Aelfred's wrist.

At dawn Aelfred left, and I sank into an uneasy slumber. My vegetables I neglected that day, and my sleep was full of fallen angels bearing Harald's face. I awoke as a sun the color of the bloody spittle on Harald's lips disappeared below the trees. Aelfred was at my door within the hour, and we continued our grisly work.

Oh, that I had never granted him entry, and that I had hardened my heart against his entreaties! This child, whose brothers I had taught their catechism, became my teacher in the ways of the Cainites. He inducted me into the mysteries of the vampiric flesh, and I dwelt more and more as he did, a creature of sundown to sunrise.

One night he resolved to demonstrate for me what is termed in barbarous German, the *Rotschreck*. We took turns, Aelfred and I, moving a lit torch closer and closer to Harald's still-burned face and waiting for him to explode into contortions of fear. I paid careful heed to the necessary distance to provoke this reaction; you will find those notes also enclosed with this missive. The terror in Harald's eyes quickly turned to madness, and then something else I dare not name, but to see it was truly terrible.

Aelfred later explained that many Cainites held that they had an inner Beast, which I can only take to mean a personal devil who travels with them and tempts them into even more evil than they might craft otherwise. Aelfred corrected me, calling the Beast the animal that lives in all men, and allowing that the Cainite nature made it possible for the Beast to surface far more violently than any human temper might. So another series of evenings was spent poking and prodding at Harald's Beast, seeing what would cause it to snap and what would make it cower. I was reminded inevitably of the spectacle of bear-beating, but even the chained bear has to him more dignity than we allowed Harald.

Of course, Harald needed to be fed in the wake of our work, and Aelfred was always happy to oblige. The two nights after the first, Harald fought against his supper, finding something more distasteful in Aelfred's blood than even the wounds which my partner in damnation had inflicted upon him. After the third instance, however, his manner abruptly changed, and there was liquid adoration in his eyes as he gazed up at his Cainite tormentor.

For me, of course, there was the old hatred, richly deserved.

We tested many things: how many nights Harald could go without being fed and what might the results of starving him be; whether the removal of any of his organs might impair his functioning; how long it would take him to grow back severed fingers, hands, and even limbs — oh, the tortures we devised, all in the name of knowledge, that I might gift the Church with the truth of the secret ways of vampires.

Yet my conscience, long numbed, grew restless even as my sleep grew troubled. Once the great rush of discovery had fled, I found myself worrying anew for Harald's soul — and even Aelfred's. Taking care to cover the windows with heavy cloth, I found myself doing something quite rash: removing the stake from Harald's breast in the middle of the day, and waking him that we might converse.

Of an Oath of Blood

He was grossy, of course, as one might expect of a demon wakened at midday. He hated me as well, and cursed me in all the tongues that three hundred years had taught him. He strained against his bonds, but wearily, like a man who had drunk too much wine. Eventually I was forced to threaten him with the light of the sun, and he desisted sullenly.

This was not what I wanted, however. I wished to hear from Harald's lips the same words that I had heard from Aelfred's, that I might know that my first Cainite acquaintance had told me true. So I cajoled and wheedled, and obtained for him certain small animals upon which he might feed. For the last he grudgingly thanked me, until I mentioned that I had previously refrained from feeding him such because Aelfred had claimed that it would not sustain him. From that point forth he would not partake of the meals I brought him.

This secrecy went on for many days. By night I would direct Aelfred's hands, or at least think I did; by day I made efforts to reach Harald, that I might see for his salvation. It was if I had become two men, one for the night hours and one for the day. And still Harald loved Aelfred, his tormentor, and still he hated me.

I did at last pry the secret from him one particularly brilliant May morning. I know not what possessed me that day, only that I threatened to snatch down every piece of cloth that might shelter Harald from the sun, and then expose him to its cleansing rays without so much as a chance for final confession. Harald relented then, and told me of the source of his undying love for my monstrous Aelfred.

It would seem that there is witchery in the *sanguinis* that the Cainites bear in their veins. Three tastes of it, and your passions are inextricably bound up in the one whose blood you have drunk. *Goules* and great *vampyrs* are equally susceptible to this Blood Oath, as it is called, though to name it an oath is a mockery. Those feedings in the heart of the savagery, those actions which I thought had been the wings of mercy beating in Aelfred's struggling soul, had been merely his means to procuring the unbreakable love of his rival.

The scales fell from my eyes at that instant. All was revealed to me, how all of Aelfred's false declarations of contrition were merely the carrot held before me as if I were some old cart-horse that only required a treat to move in the desired direction. My every action from the moment I had first spied Aelfred's face had been directed towards the moment when Harald's devotion would be his. Through the love engendered by the Blood Oath, Aelfred would have a servant more powerful than himself whose loyalty was absolutely unquestionable. And in all this, mine was the responsibility.

I resolved that day to end matters. I offered Harald a final confession, which he refused, and destroyed him. Within an hour of my removal of his head with my spade, his body was ash upon the table. One monster was destroyed; there remained the other. Heedless of my safety, I would seize upon Aelfred that night as he entered my *domus*, and with the power of my faith protecting me, remove that scourge from the earth. As for myself, I would take myself to Canterbury on pilgrimage, and perhaps thence to the Holy Land, to spend the rest of my days in good works and repentance. I hear that Saladin allows Christian pilgrims yet to seek Jerusalem.

Of Endings

It was a good plan, I think. Had I been the man I was when this nightmare first seized me, it would have succeeded admirably. Alas, I am not that man. Aelfred entered that night and, without a word, I clasped my hands to his face in hopes of burning out his accursed red eyes.

Nothing happened, save that he took my hands and gently removed them, laughing. He told me that we had countered each other; I had destroyed his valued slave, but he had destroyed me. My faith was gone, he said, and lo, I could not find it within myself. And so we stood there, Cainite and faithless priest, in the dark of the night in a hut strewn with the ashes of a child three hundred years dead.

I had thought, once my faith was revealed to be a sham, that Aelfred would destroy me. Instead, he smiled his wolf-smile and asked that I serve as his confessor. Defeated, I agreed. What mattered if this monster's confession was heard by one who belonged not in the clergy? It was God's will, not mine, that might grant this wretch absolution. So I began the ritual, taking comfort in its familiar words and phrasings. Aelfred still remembered somewhat of his living days, and waited until I asked him to enumerate his sins before betraying his wickedness.

I have lied many times, Father, were his last words to me. *Jesu's wounds, but I have lied.*

Then, laughing, he strode off into the night. Behind him, in a dusty, bloody room, sat a broken priest.

I have since taken quill to parchment to record my experiences, in the hopes that my knowledge will be of some use to Mother Church and the Christian kings of Europe in annihilating the race of Cainites. By the Rood, if they all bear resemblance to Aelfred and Harald, the sooner the last is scattered to dust, the happier the lot of mere man on earth will be.

As for myself, I still sit in my ruined *domus*, Harald's ash sifting on the breeze. I cannot go back to what I have done; the villagers have branded me "the Black Priest", and murmur fearfully of nigromancy and diabolism. I expect them to haul me to the pyre ere long, should Harald's kin not find me first. As for Aelfred, he still watches me from afar. Nights do come when I can see the blaze of red eyes in the darkness, and the silent circle of beasts reforms outside my door.

Do what you think best with this information, Monsignor. All Christendom may rest in your hands.

Vale

Fr. Offa

BOOK ONE: FLESH AND BLOOD

In the Year of Our Lord 1148, I took up sword and shield to march to Edessa. I was unlettered and ignorant, and believed that I understood all beneath God's Heaven, knew all the secrets to the earthly and mundane. I was young.

Long before our tattered army set foot on the Eastern deserts, we made war on our own. The armies of the Second Crusade bickered among ourselves, and the Moslems broke us before we had arrived. I was lucky to survive. Ravens choked the skies.

I walked the long road home, with a sword that had tasted blood only once: the blood of a man of 15 years, who had run at me with a spear. I was tired, but strong enough to take or steal food on the way back. I carried my sword like a scar, and few on the road challenged me. My faith was lessened, and I was older. Still, it seemed that my life's trial was past. I had killed. I could do so again, and so I feared the coming days a little less.

How was I ever to know what God had designed for me?

Chapter One: Introduction

This world is but a thurghfare ful of woo,
And we ben pilgrimes, passinge to and fro:
Deeth is an ende of every worldly sore.
—Chaucer, "The Knight's Tale"

Vampire: The Dark Ages is set at the close of the 12th century in medieval Europe — the darker, nastier Europe that existed in the past of the World of Darkness. The Dark Medieval world is fairly similar to its counterpart in the real world, so if you want more information you can look into the history collections of your local library or bookstore.

Although the end of the 12th century is the primary time in which Vampire: The Dark Ages is set, you can set your own chronicle in any era. Most of the information in this book applies to Europe up until the first stirrings of the Renaissance, though the technology varries depending on the period. Don't feel constrained by the history of the "real world," however — it's your game, so make it what you will!

For those familiar with **Vampire: The Masquerade** and the other 20th century games, you will find both familiar and new aspects to the Dark Ages. Much changed between the 12th and 20th centuries, so don't assume that the same things hold true.

ROLEPLAYING

Vampire: The Dark Ages is not only a storytelling game, but a roleplaying game as well. You not only tell stories, but actually act through them by taking on the roles of its central characters. It's a lot like acting, only you make up the lines.

Roleplaying is equal parts improvisational acting and Cowboys and Indians, a set of rules laid out over a story that everyone in the game is involved in telling. Think back to the games you played as a child; every time you imagined yourself as a knight in shining armor or an Indian on the warpath, you were roleplaying. Every time you chased dragons around the backyard or headed the bad guys off at the pass, you were roleplaying. It's something you've all been doing all along; now you have a name for it. Besides, not everything you did as a child was inherently childish; by allowing us to try on other people's skins, even for a little while, these games helped us understand them (and ourselves) better.

Of course, we're a long way from hiding behind the swingset and arguing "Is not! Is too!" over whether the arrow was faster than the six-shooter. That's why there are rules to this sort of roleplaying, to provide a structure and a framework for the stories that you tell. By using the basic rules that are provided in Chapter Six, you can resolve conflicts and define the capacities of the characters in the stories you tell.

In **Vampire: The Dark Ages**, it is best to play with only a few players, five at the very most. It is far too personal a game to make it very enjoyable with a large group. Much of its mystery and flavor is lost when players must compete for attention. Indeed, we have found that storytelling games of this sort work best with a Storyteller and a troupe of only three players.

THE STORYTELLER

Vampire: The Dark Ages is structured a little differently from the games you might be used to. In the first place, there is no board or cards. Second, one player needs to be the Storyteller — the person who creates and guides the stories. The Storyteller describes what happens as a result of what the players say and do, and must decide if the characters succeed or fail, suffer or prosper, live or die. It is a very demanding task, but it's also a rewarding one, for the Storyteller is a weaver of dreams.

The Storyteller's primary duty is to make sure the other players have a good time. The way to do that is to tell a good tale. Unlike traditional storytellers, however, she doesn't simply tell the story; instead, she must create the skeleton of a story and then let the players flesh it out by living the roles of its leading characters. It is a careful balance between narration and adjudication, story and game. Sometimes she must set the scene or describe what occurs (such as when the characters are asleep), but mostly she must decide what occurs in reaction to the words and actions of the characters — as realistically, impartially and creatively as she possibly can.

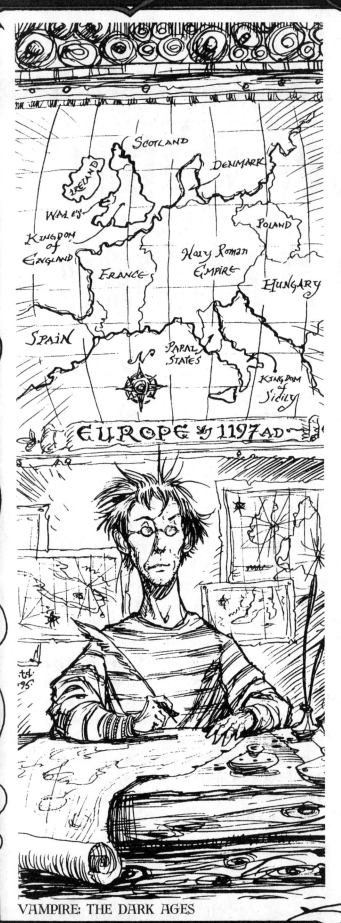

EUROPE 1197 AD

As the Storyteller, you are in charge of interpreting and enforcing the rules, yet you are also an entertainer — you must struggle to balance your two roles. Most of this book was written to help you do just that. It won't make being a Storyteller easy, because it never will be, but it will make you better at it.

The role of the Storyteller is explained in much more detail in Chapter Eight.

The Players

Most of the people who play this game will not be Storytellers, but rather players, who assume the roles of the central characters in the story. Being a player does not require as much responsibility as being a Storyteller, but just as much effort and concentration.

As a player in a **Vampire: The Dark Ages** chronicle, you will take on the persona and role of a vampire or Cainite, whom you invent and then roleplay over the course of a story. The life of your character is in your hands, for it is you who decides what the character says and does. You decide what risks to accept or decline. Everything you say and do when you play your character has an effect on the world.

You must be both an actor and a player. As an actor, you speak for your character and act out whatever you wish your character to do or say. Whatever you say, your character says, unless you are specifically asking a question of the Storyteller or are describing your actions. By announcing and describing to the other players what you are doing, you become a part of the ongoing story.

As a player, you try to do things that allow your character to succeed, so as to "win the game." This strategy element is essential, for it is what so often creates the thrill and excitement of a dramatic moment.

Often after describing the actions "you" want to take, you will need to make dice rolls to see if you succeed in doing what you have illustrated with words. Your Character Traits, descriptions of your strengths and weaknesses, dictate how well you can do certain things. Actions are a basic element of storytelling games, for they describe how characters change the world and affect the course of the story.

Characters are central to a story, for they create and direct the plot; without characters you can't have a story. As the story flows, it is the characters who direct and energize the progress of the plot, not the decisions of the Storyteller.

To some extent, you are a Storyteller as well as a player, and should feel free to add ideas and elements to the story, though the storyteller may accept or reject them as she sees fit. In the end, it is the story, not your character, which is the most important. The character is a tool for telling a good story, not the other way around.

Characters

On a basic level, each of us is a character, composed of mannerisms and memories, behaviors and experiences. Everything we are and everywhere we've been are reflected in each word and action we make. When playing **Vampire: The Dark Ages**, though, we are asked to set aside our memories and masks, and to pick up someone else's, even if only for a little while. This can be incredibly enjoyable, providing us the opportunity to achieve feats that are forever beyond us in our daily lives. After all, how many of us get to stalk castle battlements or ride to the hunt in the twilight mist every day?

This is the reward of roleplaying: the magical and impossible achievements that are within our grasp when we pretend we're someone else. And here lies the great difficulty of roleplaying — the creation of a believable character.

Your characters will have part of you in them. This is inescapable, and if there's nothing of your life in them, then there's nothing you can do to bring them to life. On the other hand, to be enjoyable to play a character has to be more than just a part of yourself. You're yourself every day, after all; where's the fun in being just yourself when you finally have the chance to be someone else? To make characters believable, you have to give them memories and motives that they can draw upon, unique desires and quirks that make them more than just aspects of your personality given a voice. Each character should be unique, equal parts of experience and fantasy.

Vampire: The Dark Ages characters are easy to create. It takes only a few minutes to work out all the Traits and the basic numbers. It takes more effort to make this collection of numbers into a living, breathing character. You must reach deep inside of yourself to find enough that is real and true to produce a complete character. Dr. Frankenstein's monster was easily assembled from available body parts. It was infusing the breath of life that proved difficult.

Character creation is discussed in greater detail in Chapter Five.

Coteries

It is assumed that all the characters will be allies, and that during the game they will operate as a group. This is not to say that they will always get along, but they will watch each other's backs and will share a few common ambitions. Called coteries, such groups of vampires can be found from the halls of power to the dankest slums. In most cases, the coterie of player characters will comprise all the young vampires in a given area, unless it is one of the largest cities such as Venice or Constantinople. Whether the group is drawn together by a common interest, a common enemy or mere survival, it is not hard to see that there is safety in numbers. A single young Cainite alone will face hardships beyond those of a group, and it is this group that each and every character will come to depend upon. It is the coterie that unites the characters and enables the players to work together throughout the story.

Playing Aids

For the most part, **Vampire: The Dark Ages** was designed to be played around a table. Though it does not require a board, there are a number of props which require a table — or at least a flat surface — to use properly. You will need dice, pencils and paper, and photocopies of the character sheets. The dice required are 10-sided, which you can find in any game store. The Storyteller may also want to have paper on hand in order to sketch out a setting (so as to describe it more easily to the players), as well as a few other props to show the players what the characters are seeing (sketches, candles, scarves — anything to make the experience more vivid).

WINNER AND LOSERS

There is no single "winner" of **Vampire: The Dark Ages**, since the object is not to defeat the other players. To win at all, you need to cooperate with the other players. Because this is a storytelling game, there is no way for one person to claim victory. In fact, **Vampire** is a game in which you are likely to lose, for it is difficult to do anything to slow your character's inexorable descent into madness. The whole idea is to hang on as long as possible and eke out the most drama from the ongoing tragedy.

The only true measure of success in **Vampire** is survival. However, if the character has some overwhelming motivation, such as a need for vengeance, accomplishing it is also a measure of success. Additionally, stories have conclusions that either benefit or harm the characters. If the characters learn that a presumed murderer is really a vampire and manage to halt his rampage, then they "win." If they never even find out who was behind the murders (much less manage to stop him), then they lose, though they may not know it until too late.

In order to achieve even a partial victory, the characters must usually become friends. They look out for one another and have a modicum of trust in each other. The Dark Medieval world is so dangerous that trustworthy allies are essential.

LIVE-ACTION

Live-Action roleplaying can be the most dynamic and fun part of playing **Vampire: The Dark Ages**. Live-Action roleplaying is similar to improvisational theatre; the actors (the players) act through the scenes created and introduced by the Storyteller. This creates a much more intense and immediate storytelling experience.

Players in a roleplaying game generally describe what their characters do and even say. During Live-Action roleplaying, however, players actually do what their characters do and say what their characters say (within limits). They can stand up, walk around, hold up a letter, shake hands or rush to a window to see what is going on. Imagination is still important, and the Storyteller may still interrupt the action to describe objects and special situations.

No dice are used during Live-Action sessions; alternate rules, like those given in White Wolf's **Mind's Eye Theatre** line of Live-Action products, take the place of dice when needed. For the most part, everything is decided through acting. The Storyteller simply uses the characters' Traits to decide how well they manage to perform certain mechanical actions (such as picking a lock). The Storyteller also decides how the other Storyteller-run characters react to the players' characters.

RULES

You must follow a few basic rules to ensure that Live-Action roleplaying progresses smoothly and safely. These rules must be obeyed if you intend to run any Live-Action roleplaying at all. Safety is always a primary concern.

- **Don't Touch:** A player should never actually strike or grapple another member of the troupe. No sort of combat should ever be performed — that is one thing you should leave for the dice to decide. If players or Storyteller assistants get too rambunctious in their roles, the Storyteller should call a time-out from the acting and remind everyone of the rules of play. Repeat offenders should be asked to leave, or the action should be returned to a table and conflicts resolved through dice rolls.

- **No Weapons:** No props can be used if they must touch another player to be effective. No real weapons of any sort can ever be handled at any time during Live-Action roleplaying. Not even prop swords can be used. The "no touch" rules must always be in effect.

- **Play Inside:** Play inside your own home or in whatever private area the game normally takes place. Make sure that everyone else in the area understands what you are doing. Never perform Live-Action if passersby may be confused or frightened by the event. If you play outside, such as in the woods behind your house, make sure privacy is maintained.

- **Know When to Stop:** When the Storyteller calls for a time-out, all action must immediately stop. Even during Live-Action (*especially* during Live-Action), the Storyteller's word is final.

THE BECOMING

The moment a human becomes a vampire is never forgotten, for the transformation is usually painful and traumatic. A vampire is created when an existing vampire drains all the blood from a mortal, killing him. However, just before final and absolute death sets in, the sire pierces open her own skin and releases a small amount of blood into the victim's mouth. This rouses him somewhat, and he begins to drink from the sire's open wound. All it takes for the transformation to occur is the absence of one's own blood and the tiniest bit of vampiric blood.

Most characters take on the lineage of their sires, and are therefore of the same clans. The clan membership affects what Disciplines a character can have at the beginning of the game; it also delineates a special weakness of the character. Often characters of the same clan will be allies and will strive to support one another, though this is not always the case.

For the next few years or decades, the newly created childe remains with his sire. He may be taught nothing or everything, nurtured or abused, restricted or granted full freedom. But until he is released by his sire and presented to the prince of the fiefdom, he is not accepted in vampire society.

THE HUNGER

Vampires must feed; this fact is the lowest common denominator of their existence. Hunger is not merely a need, it is an all-consuming passion. The thirst for blood is a primal instinct for survival, for only through blood may the vampire survive. The blood need not be human, and even if it is mortal vitæ, the death of the vessel is not required (although the bloodlust often causes vampires to lose their restraint when they begin to feed, and thus to drain all life from their victims). Vampire teeth leave only a small wound, and even this disappears if the vampire licks the wound.

Because the sire never returns to the childe *all* of the blood she withdrew, the young vampire is soon consumed by a ravenous hunger for blood. As the childe has no experience with this overwhelming urge, it is as total as it is immediate. The fledgling cannot fight the urge except through a constant exertion of Willpower, and even then frenzy might overcome him if fresh blood comes within smelling distance. Vampires need to feed regularly, usually once or twice a week.

NATURE OF THE BEAST

What does it mean to be a vampire? Cainites are not, despite their appearance, human — they have an alien nature and differ from mortals in many fundamental ways. One may start with the picture of a human, but it is a lethal mistake to think vampires are exactly like us. Yet they are similar enough to us that they can be compared and contrasted to humanity. By comparing vampires to humans, it is possible to discover what their capabilities and limitations are.

It is important to keep in mind that, because a vampire's basic needs differ so completely, other desires vary as well. Food other than blood is no longer necessary — but unfortunately, one can't just purchase blood at the local farmer's market either. Vampires are predatory beasts by nature, and though the desire for temporal power over the world of Cainites and kine alike often distracts them for a time, they cannot deny what they truly are.

Most vampires who survive more than a few years develop a kind of philosophy that allows them to continue on each night, to balance their own souls with the needs and desires of the Beast within. Many call these systems of belief Roads or Via, for they help to guide the vampire through unlife, establishing a code of ethics and beliefs that remain constant in a chaotic world.

SOCIETY OF THE NIGHT

Caine's childer are relatively numerous in the Middle Ages. A city of 10,000 mortals may have a dozen resident vampires, with half a dozen more in the surrounding towns and villages. Princes often have only loose control over their subjects, and cannot easily restrict the number of neonates who are sired. And some Cainites exist without ever hunting a mortal, instead establishing willing herds in isolated communities or feeding from easily available animal vitae.

This is a grand but terrifying age in which to be a vampire. On one hand, it is a time of fear and superstition, of blind obedience and casual brutality. If an isolated cottage is too far from the nearest village for the screams of its inhabitants to be heard, then the withered husks within may not be discovered for a season or more. Life is cheap and for the taking, and few gainsay the right of the strong to subdue — or destroy — the weak. On the other hand, it is also a time of terror for Cainites. There are few places to hide from the sun and the torch, and the roads are made perilous by brigands and ravening Lupines. It is an age of faith as well, and the lowliest peasant might hold in her heart the power to thwart even the mightiest vampire lord. Great rewards and great perils fill the nights and days of the Cainite. From the Nile Delta to the Iberian Peninsula, from Moslem Jerusalem to the Teutonic barbarisms of the Schwarzwald, it is an age of darkness, lit by the flickering of torches and the gleam of red eyes in the night.

CHAPTER ONE: INTRODUCTION

25

PROBLEMS AND POWERS

It might seem at first that the Cainites in the Middle Ages are in a much stronger position than their 20th-century descendants. They are vampires of earlier generations, far more powerful than those Embraced 800 years later. They need not worry about foes with high-tech communications or weaponry. They need not fear being photographed and are not obliged to maintain a strict Masquerade.

However, they also have a great number of disadvantages. First, settlements are smaller. Most cities have fewer than 10,000 inhabitants, so that an unfamiliar face is easily spotted, and there are no faceless millions for them to feed upon. Curfews are commonplace. Naked fires burn in every home, while candles and torches provide lighting in easily flammable buildings. Travel is difficult for vampires, as all common forms of transport expose the traveler to the sun.

Further, the Cainites lack many of the conveniences that 20th-century vampires enjoy. This is a world where all trade is done in the daylight, with no 24-hour stores. It is a world without telephones or faxes, answering machines or computers; if a vampire wants to speak with any mortal, she must do so face-to-face. Most importantly, the Cainites live in a society that knows they exist and claims that they are the Devil's pawns. Worse still, the beliefs of the people lend power to the Church's rituals, and so many churchmen have real power to harm or even destroy vampires.

And then, of course, vampires must beware of the Lupines — far more powerful than in the 20th century and sworn enemies of vampires — unpredictable faeries, restless ghosts and scheming mages.

ORGANIZATION

Travel through medieval Europe is slow and dangerous, and so communications are limited. Information and orders are difficult to relay. There are no large sects overseeing the Cainites. There are simply individual clan elders and princes, all exerting influence on their neighbors for their own disparate ends.

THE CLANS

The most important clans, both the most numerous and most powerful, are Clans Ventrue, Tzimisce, Lasombra, Brujah, Nosferatu, Malkavian, Cappadocian and Gangrel. In addition, the newly formed Tremere clan, the Setites, the Assamites and the Toreador are each established in small portions of Europe. Ravnos vampires visit occasionally from the East, and the remnants of the demonic Baali remain in hiding somewhere on the continent.

CAINITES AND MORTALS

There are few large cities in Dark Medieval Europe, and even those such as Madrid, Venice and Constantiople contain but a fraction of the number of kine in modern Paris, London or New York. Few people stray from their houses after dark, instead waking with sunrise and sleeping at sunset, echoing the cycles of the vampires who would prey upon them. The Church wields the powers of Faith against all creatures of the night, especially undead creatures who would steal the lifeblood of their parishoners. One would think that these factors would mean but a few vampires would be found in each city…but this is not the case.

Certainly, vampires are not found in the same numbers during this age as in later periods, but overpopulation is becoming a serious threat to the survival of Cainites during this period. Many ride the night as dark lords, using their power to control and frighten the local folk into timid obedience. Territory is fiercely guarded, and to feed from another vampire's herd is a quick path toward Final Death, if discovered.

Vampire politics are heated, with a great many Cainites competing for scant resources. Vampire princes struggle to keep hunting and feuds among their subjects from drawing the attention of mortal authorities, but this is often difficult. It is not hard to see why the Inquisition formed not long after this period, in an attempt to curtail the perceived flood of undead who threatened the good folk of the Church.

Moreover, because vampires are unable to participate in normal mortal life — whether commerce or leisure — those who want power in mortal society must act through proxies and attend the few feasts and fetes held after sunset in the noble houses while the common folk are fast asleep. In this night and age, Cainites' relations with their ghouls, herds, allies and retainers become more important.

Lexicon

There exists among the Cainites a distinct *patois*, drawing on many tongues and giving new shades of meaning to certain mortal words. One can often tell what generation a vampire is by listening to the parlance that she employs. There is a sharp distinction between the words used by neonates and those of elders. The wrong word in the wrong circumstances is often considered a serious breach of etiquette.

Common Parlance

These are the terms that are most commonly used among vampires during the Dark Ages.

Becoming, The	The moment one becomes a vampire; the metamorphosis from mortal to Cainite. Also called *The Embrace*
Book of Nod, The	The "sacred" book of the Cainites, tracing the race's origins and early history. It has never been published in its entirety, although fragments are known to exist in various languages.
Beast, The	The drives and urges that prompt a vampire to become entirely a monster. Vide *Man* infra.
Blood	The vampire's heritage. That which makes a vampire a vampire.
Blood Oath	The most potent bond that can exist between vampires; the receiving of blood in an acknowledgment of mastery. This grants a mystical power over the one who is bound.
Caitiff	A vampire with no clan; frequently used in a derogatory fashion. To be clanless is not a virtue among the Cainites.

Childe	A term used for a young, inexperienced or foolish vampire. The plural form is *Childer*.
Clan	A group of vampires who share certain mystical and physical characteristics.
Domain	The fiefdom claimed by a vampire.
Elder	A vampire 300 years of age or older. Elders consider themselves the most powerful Cainites and usually engage in their own Jyhad.
Elysium	The name given for the places where the elders meet and gather, commonly public places of culture.
Embrace, The	The act of transforming a mortal into a vampire by draining the mortal's blood and replacing it with a small amount of the vampire's own blood.
Fledgling	A young, newly created vampire. Vide *Neonate*, *Whelp*.
Generation	The number of steps between a vampire and the mythical Caine. Caine's get were the second generation, their brood the third, and so on.
Gehenna	The end of the Third Cycle; the impending Armageddon when the Antediluvians shall awaken and devour all vampires.
Ghoul	A servant created by allowing a mortal to drink Cainite blood without the draining that would give rise to a *progeny*.
Haven	The home of a vampire or the place where it sleeps.
Hunger, The	As with mortals and other animals, the drive to feed. For vampires, though, it is much more intense, and takes the place of every other drive, urge and pleasure.
Jyhad, The	The secret war being waged between the few surviving vampires of the third generation, using younger vampires as pawns. Also used to describe any sort of conflict or warfare among vampires.
Kiss	To take the blood of a mortal, or the act of taking blood in general.
Lupine	A werewolf, the mortal enemy of the vampires.
Man, The	The element of Humanity which remains in a vampire, and which strives against the base urgings of the *Beast* (qv).
Prince	A vampire who has established a claim to rulership over an area, sometimes called a fief, and is able to support that claim. Though prince is the most common term, some rulers are referred to as the overlord, suzerain, baron or sheik of the area. The feminine form is still prince.
Sire	The parent-creator of a vampire, used as both the female and male form.
Vessel	A potential or past source of blood, typically a human.

OLD FORM

These are the words used by the elders and other vampires of antiquity. Though these terms are rarely used by the newly created, they are still the fashionable vernacular among the more sophisticated Cainites. Elders may often be identified simply by their vocabulary.

Amaranth — The act of drinking the blood of other Cainites.

Ancilla — An "adolescent" vampire; one who is no longer a neonate, but is also not an elder.

Antediluvian — One of the eldest Cainites, a member of the third generation. A warlord of the Jyhad.

Autarkis — A vampire who refuses to be a part of Cainite society and does not recognize the domain of a prince.

Cainite — A vampire.

Canaille — The mortal populace, especially that element of it which is the most unsavory and lacking in culture (whom the Cainites largely feed upon).

Coterie — A group of Cainites who protect and support one another against all outsiders. Vide *Brood*.

Consanguineus — One of the same lineage (usually a younger member).

Diablerie — The act of feeding upon other vampires, out of either need or perversion. Vide *Rogue*.

Golconda — The state of being to which many vampires aspire, in which a balance is found between opposing urges and scruples. Many Cainites see it as the only path to salvation. Like the mortals' Nirvana, it is often spoken of, but seldom achieved.

Kine — A contemptuous term for mortals, often used in opposition to *Cainite*.

Lextalionis — The code of vampires, allegedly created by Caine. It suggests biblical justice — an eye for an eye, a tooth for a tooth.

Lineage — The bloodline of a vampire, traced by Embrace.

Methuselah — An elder who no longer lives among the other Cainites. Many Methuselah belong to the Inconnu.

Neonate — A young, newly created Cainite. Vide *Fledgling*, *Whelp*.

Osiris — A vampire who surrounds himself with mortal or ghoul followers in a cult or coven to better obtain sustenance. The practice is less common than it once was.

Progeny — A collective term for all the vampires created by one sire. Less formal, and less flattering, is *Get*.

Praxis — The right of princes to rule, as well as the rules, laws and customs enforced by a particular prince.

Regnant — One who has a Blood Oath over another Cainite, through giving said Cainite blood three times. Vide *Blood Oath*.

Retainers — Humans who serve a vampire master. They are generally either ghouls or mentally dominated by their vampire master. This control is sometimes so complete that the mortals are unable to take any action of their own volition.

Siren — A vampire who seduces mortals, but does not kill them and takes only a little blood after putting the mortal into a deep sleep.

Suspire — The dream dance during the final stage of the quest for Golconda.

Third Mortal — Caine, the progenitor of all vampires, according to the *Book of Nod* (qv).

Thrall — A vampire who is held under a Blood Oath, and thus under the control of another Cainite.

Vitæ — Blood.

Whelp — A contemptuous term for one's own progeny.

HOW TO USE THIS BOOK

This book is designed as a guide, a jumping-off point from which you will create your own stories. Remember that it is not meant to be the final authority — that job is left to the Storyteller. Use what you find here as the basis on which to build your own chronicle, and let your imagination be your guide.

The book is further divided into Books One, Two and Three. Book One describes the world in which **Vampire: The Dark Ages** takes place. Book Two contains all the information you need to create a beginning character and start playing. Book Three is information for the Storyteller, including suggestions for how to resolve difficult rules situations, how to structure a chronicle, and what sorts of antagonists the player characters may run into.

Chapter Two: Setting describes the world of Dark Medieval Europe, combining the history of the real world during this period with the sinister goings on in the World of Darkness.

Chapter Three: The Clans details the bloodlines of vampires present during this period, and their relations to each other.

Chapter Four: Character demonstrates how to create a character and explains the Abilities and Attributes that will be used to describe your character.

Chapter Five: Disciplines explains the supernatural powers vampires possess.

Chapter Six: Rules covers the basics of how to play the game, converting ideas and situations into die rolls.

Chapter Seven: Systems outlines a number of different ways to resolve conflicts in the game, as well as showing how the characters' Traits can increase or decrease as the game goes on.

Chapter Eight: Storytelling is intended as an introduction to the art of storytelling, giving both new and experienced Storytellers ideas for chronicles and advice on how to keep things moving.

Chapter Nine: Antagonists provides a range of potential enemies and other characters for the Cainites to interact with, including mortals, beasts fantastical and mundane, faeries, spirits, werewolves and mages.

RESOURCES

MOVIES AND TELEVISION

• *The Name of the Rose* is perhaps the best Dark Medieval movie — and the book is even better, if you can wade through the depth and detail.

• *Robin and Marian* (starring Sean Connery and Audrey Hepburn) is a good, earthy story with a suitably dismal ending.

• *Jabberwocky* may be comedy, but the foul city streets and brutal fight scenes are very much in keeping with the Dark Medieval world.

• The "Brother Cadfael" episodes of PBS' *Mystery!*, starring Sir Derek Jacobi, have a suitable feel and good visual reference. If they aren't available, look for the original novels by Ellis Peters. These books are rich with vivid characters and historical detail. Many of the episodes are also available in video stores.

• *Robin of Sherwood* (made in the '80s, first staring Michael Praed and then Jason Connery). The *Robin of Sherwood* episodes have plenty of good ideas on incorporating supernatural elements into medieval stories. Some nonfiction books may also provide you with inspiration.

• *The Pit and the Pendulum*, a 1991 Corman film giving a particularly nasty view of the Inquisition.

• *Ladyhawke*, a tale of lovers cursed by a wicked bishop to live as shapeshifters, has a more high fantasy feel, but is still good material for flavor or background.

• *Bram Stoker's Dracula* by Francis Ford Coppola may be a less-than-sparkling adaptation of the novel, but it's a fantastic source for mood and visual images. Especially note the medieval flashback scenes.

BOOKS

The Medieval Reader, Norman F. Cantor

The Art of Courtly Love, Andreas Cappelanus

Dictionary of Witchcraft and Demonology, R. H. Robbins

Magic in the Middle Ages, Richard Kieckhefer

Standards of Living in the Later Middle Ages, Christopher Dyer

England in the Thirteenth Century, Alan Harding

Life in a Medieval City, Joseph and Frances Gies

The "Brother Cadfael" Mysteries, Ellis Peters

Most recent medieval history textbooks are good references for basic facts, and they're often available secondhand for a discount at college and university bookstores at the end of a term. While older books will give you most of the same information, many of the more recent books are more readable, and may provide a different perspective on the period than older references, particularly with regard to the role of women, minorities and other disenfranchised groups during this period.

OTHER SOURCES

Bear in mind that historical sources are not the only sources of inspiration for a Dark Medieval chronicle; most games will include elements of both history and fantasy, which is part of the appeal of this setting. Feel free to draw on novels, movies and music that represent your own view of the Dark Medieval period, as well as the more historical sources. By combining all these things with a healthy dose of imagination, you will be able to create a world that is entirely your own.

GAMES

Countless other roleplaying games have covered fantasy worlds, and sourcebooks for these games can provide new ideas to bring into your **Dark Ages** chronicle.

Pendragon, Chaosium

Dungeons and Dragons (especially the **Ravenloft** setting), TSR

Ars Magica, White Wolf/Wizards of the Coast

GURPS Medieval, GURPS Fantasy, Steve Jackson Games

Warhammer, Games Workshop

MERP, Iron Crown Enterprises

Chapter Two: The Dark Ages

Me miserable! which way shall I fly
Infinite wrath and infinite despair?
Which way I fly is Hell; myself am Hell;
And, in the lowest deep, a lower deep
Still threatening to devour me opens wide,
To which the Hell I suffer seems a Heaven.
—Milton, Paradise Lost

Vampire: The Dark Ages takes you to the nights of long ago, when vampires were the true monsters of castle and graveyard and peasants huddled in their homes, clutching their rosaries in frenzied prayer. Enter an age when the Damned rode through the darkness as black knights, playing Machiavellian games with the nobles of Europe and traveling to the mysterious lands of the East to pursue an ages-old war.

This is the Dark Medieval world, in which the shadowy sides of fantasy and reality meet. Things are a little more sinister, and the wind blows a little colder on a moonless winter's night. But it is an exciting time to be alive, nonetheless...and an even more exciting time to be among the walking dead.

On the surface, little differs from the real medieval age; castles serve as both homes and fortresses to the nobility, while most peasants count themselves lucky to live with their families in drafty one-room buildings. Wars are fought in the name of God and man, and to speak out against one's liege is both blasphemy and treason. But in the darkest hours of the night, undead spirits in the shape of men walk in the shadows....

This chapter describes the setting of **Vampire: The Dark Ages**: the culture and society of both the mortal masses and the undead vampire lords who prey upon them.

The Dark Medieval World

"Dark Medieval" is the phrase we use to describe the world of **Vampire: The Dark Ages**. It is a world in which vampires and werewolves prowl the night, and the powers of magic and faith bring the spark of the supernatural into the lives of everyone, from the nobility to the peasants tilling the fields. Priests still bless the fields, and village wise women are consulted for every worry, from matchmaking and fertility to curing warts. Many folk still pay homage to the "Fair Folk," or to older pagan gods.

But this is not a J.R.R. Tolkien fantasy land — elves, dwarves and the like are mere children's stories, and the few who claim to have seen such mysterious beings in the deepest forests are

dismissed as madmen. Plagues threaten entire cities with the spectre of death, and while the Church wields tremendous temporal power, only the most devout saints can perform miracles.

The so-called Dark Ages of our world was the period between the fall of the Roman Empire and the beginning of the Renaissance. The glory that was Rome crumbled, and the roads and bureaucracy the Empire had brought to the continent quickly fell apart. Trade decreased, and most people were too busy simply trying to survive to spend time learning to read and write. Knowledge of science and technology common during Roman occupation was forgotten, and a cloud of superstition descended on the Western world.

Times were difficult for the common man during this period. Marauding armies sacked towns and pillaged villages. Cities lay in ruins. Most of the art produced during this time was portable and often practical, such as jewelry and pottery. Even some rulers were illiterate, and only in scattered Christian monasteries did reading, writing and academic learning continue. Most people were farmers, never blessed with the luxuries of art or learning, living hard, short lives, more at risk from disease and starvation than from invasions.

But the "dark" part of Dark Medieval means something more, and is not restricted to a single decade or century. The shadow that has fallen across much of Europe is a moral darkness, a rejection of the spiritual. Respect for one's fellow man has been eclipsed by the day-to-day struggle to survive. Many commoners obey the laws of God and man more out of fear of the consequences than from any real belief in what is "good" or "right." The vampires who hold much of the power rule unchecked, and rarely face the consequences of their actions. But the mortal world will not live in fear forever, and the day may come when the living will rise up against the predators in their midst.

In the end, you will decide what the Dark Medieval world is like in your chronicle. It may not be as dark as we've portrayed it, or it may be a living Hell on earth. It can be historical or fantastic, a world of violence or intrigue, and will probably be all of these things at one point or another. Use the tools in this book with your own imagination to create a world that is uniquely your own.

MONSTERS IN THE NIGHT

Believed to be descended from Caine, the first murderer, vampires are cursed forever to shun the sunlight and live off the blood of the living. Yet the curse of God is tempered by the love of Lilith, and through her blessings vampires possess many great and powerful abilities beyond the ken of mortal man.

Mortals know that vampires exist, just as they know witches, faeries, goblins, ogres and lycanthropes exist. While not all people have seen them, they know better than to tempt fate. But the monsters people fear often come in guises they don't expect: monks, lords, hermits, beggars, pilgrims and countless other have been undead predators in disguise. To the medieval mind, anyone could be an agent of the Devil, and the wise man takes no chances.

FEEDING

Vampires need blood to survive, for they are unable to produce any of their own. Many Cainites have pools of mortals they feed from regularly, sometimes referred to as herds. Some feed from the animals of the fields and forests, but many vampires feel that the blood of these lower beasts is salty and bitter, unlike the sweet nectar that flows through the veins of humanity.

Feeding need not always cause the death of the vessel. Wounds caused by a vampire's fangs may be closed cleanly by licking the wound. Many vampires possess the ability to make their victims forget what happened, or perhaps only remember a passionate kiss in the alleyway outside the tavern. Still others feed only upon the sleeping and the wounded, thus avoiding the risk of discovery.

PRIVATE WARS

Like the chieftains and noble families who rule over the mortal world, vampire society is divided into a number of clans, based on lineage. Each clan has certain characteristics and defining traits, which influence the kinds of people who are chosen to join the ranks. As with vampires' mortal counterparts, scheming and backstabbing are legendary. So too is internal loyalty, for in many cases the ties of blood are stronger among the undead than among any mortal bloodline.

Thirteen clans are present in Europe during this age, though a few scattered minor bloodlines may be encountered from time to time. More information on the clans, their internal dynamics and external relations can be found in Chapter Three: The Clans.

OVERPOPULATION

Vampires have existed for millennia, preying upon mortals like the parasites they are. The eldest vampires say that in Caine's First City, his childer ruled as kings and gods over the mortal population. But then came the Flood, and Caine saw the folly in what he had done. He forbade those few remaining to beget more of their kind, and left on a journey from which he has never been known to return. But those of the second and third generations had not the wisdom of their great father, and each sought to produce a brood of its own, in mockery of the families that the sons and daughters of Seth now brought into the world. So it was that the clans were created and have flourished until the Dark Ages, where our story begins.

Unlike mortals, who must struggle day after day to ensure they have sufficient food to eat, vampires are surrounded by unwitting prey. Without fear of the diseases and starvation that strike down so many mortals, Cainites flourish. Abundant food and few predators have produced an overabundance of vampires the likes of which the world has never seen. As a result, competition for domain is fierce. Many vampires foolishly believe that they have nothing to fear from mortals, and openly display their supernatural powers. Others warn that this overconfidence may lead to the downfall of all Caine's childer, and urge caution. Only time will tell which faction will survive.

THE GATHERING STORM

In the centuries that follow the Dark Ages, vampires learn the importance of hiding themselves away from mortal eyes. Inquisitions of Church and state decimate the Cainite population, and only those who are able to blend into mortal society survive.

But those days seem distant in the Dark Ages. In the minds of most mortals, vampires are creatures of the Devil, to be feared — and either fought by the Church or avoided entirely. With the power of their vampiric Disciplines and a cunning born from centuries of experience, some vampires set themselves up as lords of outlying areas, taking their tithes of blood from any unfortunates who pass by. Others control the mortal rulers of the land, through potent Blood Oaths and the work of their half-mortal ghouls.

DESCENT INTO MADNESS

For characters raised in the devout atmosphere of the Dark Medieval world, to become a vampire is to become cursed by God, afflicted with the mark of Caine and forever damned. Unlike their jaded descendants of later centuries, medieval vampires take the notions of salvation and damnation very seriously. Most find it exceedingly difficult to continue on, night after night, in the knowledge that they are damned.

To slow the downward spiral into madness and despair, most vampires adopt a philosophy, called the Via or Road. A vampire's Road is the path she seeks to guide her through existence, the principles upon which her unlife is based.

Variations among Roads are widespread. Some seek only to survive, living on instinct and the needs of their bestial souls. Many take the Church's teachings to heart, and conclude that they are indeed Hell's creatures. Reflective Cainites might muse that their undying states are Satan's attempts to mimic God's promise of eternal life. Since they cannot believe that they are maintained by any holy power, many Cainites conclude that they owe their lives to Hell: the Church, after all, teaches that all power comes from either God or Satan. In some cases this provokes extreme feelings of guilt or self-loathing. Others consciously attempt to serve Hell, in thanks for their immortality, in the hopes of gaining further favors, or simply out of awe and fear.

GOLCONDA

Some vampires speak of a mythic state of enlightenment in which the forces of instinct and self-control are in harmony. The vampire learns to accept what he has become, and thereby gains control of the Beast within. Those who still believe such stories speak of how those who achieve this state are freed from Caine's curse, no longer forced to live on the blood of the living.

But in the Dark Ages, many vampires believe that forgiveness may only come through the mercy of God. Those who search for Golconda are berated as having turned away from both God and Satan, selfishly believing that self-acceptance is more important to salvation than is the mercy of God. As a result, fewer 12th century vampires seek Golconda than their pre-Christian predecessors.

SOCIAL DISTINCTIONS

As in the mortal world, certain levels of social status exist within vampire society. Most of these are based on age, though some denote an individual's rejection of vampire society.

• **Caitiff:** Very rare in the Dark Medieval world, Caitiff are clanless vampires. Whether they were abandoned by their sires or they rejected their own clans, Caitiff exist outside the political structure of vampire society. Without the protection of sire or clan, they are in the lowest social position of any Cainites.

• **Childe:** Vampires bearing this title are newly created, and have not yet been released by their sires. They are not considered to be full members of vampire society, and are thus shown little respect. They are treated as children until they prove themselves ready to be released into the world. In the Dark Medieval period, most childer remain with their sires for several decades, learning how to make their way in the world.

The term "childe" is sometimes used as an epithet to denote a weak or foolish vampire.

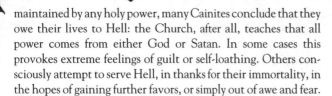

GENERATIONS

CAINE

Tradition holds that Caine, the Biblical slayer of his brother Abel, is the Sire of All Vampires. This tenet engenders much controversy within the Cainite community, for none still exist who can claim with utter certainty to have met Caine. Certainly, those of the second generation would know, but they're not talking. Some of the fourth generation who yet exist claim to have met a being who may have been Caine, though this could simply have been a powerful Cainite of the second generation.

It is an unresolved question — a mystery of heritage.

SECOND GENERATION

The existing translations of the *Book of Nod*, the sacred book of vampire mythology, place the number of second generation vampires at three. Caine in his sorrow created them to live with him in his great city of Enoch. Little is known about these beings.

One can assume, based on the *Book of Nod*, that they were slain either during the Deluge or in the First War following the Flood. As one might expect, ancient vampires are reluctant to speak of their sires and the great strife that overcame them all. Undoubtedly, some know more than they choose to reveal.

Were any of the second generation still in existence today, they would possess power equivalent to that of the fabled demigods of antiquity.

THIRD GENERATION

It is believed that seven members of the third generation are still active, though the names of only two, Lucian and Mekhet, are widely known. In common argot, they are referred to as the Antediluvians, and they are the founders of the 13 vampire clans. All remain hidden in the workings of the Jyhad, a war that has lasted nearly as long as recorded history. The war continues, but now instead of open fighting on the battlefield, the Antediluvians use subterfuge, guile and outright deceit. Their primary activities seem to be tracing the activities of each other and thwarting whatever moves their opponents make.

These moves range from things as petty as the acquisition of pieces of artwork or property to grand schemes involving the fates of nations. Those of the third generation see themselves as manipulators and dominators, split between those who would live within the mortal world and those who would live without. It is unclear if this reflects the origins of the Jyhad, or is merely what it has degenerated into. There are other suspicions, based on the origins of the word *Jyhad*. Some among the third generation may indeed have reached Golconda and are attempting to assist others of their kind to reach this state. They must war with the other Antediluvians, who do not want this to come to pass.

Like their sires, Caine's grandchilder are powerful beings, with abilities and powers only guessed at by their descendants. Some say they are the last vampires to have true mastery over the powers of life and death, and can only die the Final Death if they choose it or are slain by one of equal power. Is this, perhaps, the Jyhad? A maneuvering to see who will be the last of their kind?

- **Neonate:** These are vampires who have not yet made names for themselves in vampire society. Neonates are often the "doers" of the vampiric world, as they attempt to carve niches for themselves in the hierarchy. Neonates who survive for a century after leaving the protection of their sires are considered ancillæ.

- **Ancilla:** These vampires are still comparatively young, but have proven themselves to the elders. Ancillæ are up-and-coming Cainites, the ones who play by the rules (mostly) to achieve greater power. This is the rank between neonate and elder, wherein the vampire is given increasing respect, power and responsibility. In some areas, a vampire is not considered to be an ancilla until she has served another for "six years, six days and six acts of courage." Most ancillæ have existed for one or more centuries since their Becomings.

- **Autarkis:** Outlaws among their kind, these vampires refuse to recognize the authority of any prince. Though they are without a true place in the hierarchy of vampire society, their sheer power grants them respect akin to most ancillæ. Less powerful Autarkis suffer swift demises.

- **Elder:** When vampires reach a certain age, few other beings can still hold power over them. The elders are those Cainites who are in control and who seek to dominate all the others. Elders are normally between 200 and 1000 years old, but as with all things undead, this can vary immensely.

- **Methuselah:** Somewhere between 1000 and 2000 immortal years, a profound change invariably overtakes a vampire. It has long been argued whether this change is mystical, physical or is in fact spiritual, brought about through new needs and desires. Certainly by the time a vampire reaches this age, boredom and melancholy set in, as does an increased paranoia. Those who are weak, take risks or unconsciously desire suicide do not survive to this age — only the very strongest attain the rank of Methuselah.

As a means of self-preservation, most Methuselahs retreat from the world and those younger than they. The constant danger of facing the young reckless ones, who seek power through the blood of their elders, grows numbing. Eventually some ancilla will get lucky and dispatch the ancient. Thus the only option is to

Fourth and Fifth Generations

These vampires are known as the Methuselahs, for they are nearly as powerful and secretive as the Antediluvians. Those of the fourth and fifth generations are most often the pawns of choice in the Jyhad, as they may have political power among the Cainites. As a result, their numbers have dwindled significantly, as they fall in one scheme or another. Accordingly, few of this generation remain active, and many have distanced themselves from vampire society out of fear of the Jyhad and Amaranth. Still, some of the more powerful princes are of the fifth generation. And there are those among the fourth generation, feeling themselves under threat from the Antediluvians, who have made attempts at organizing all vampires under their rule — to date all such attempts have failed.

Though the blood of Caine begins to dilute somewhat at this distance, those of the fourth and fifth generations are still extremely powerful. It can be assumed that they have reached their maximum potential in two or three Disciplines.

Sixth and Seventh Generations

These are among the most powerful vampires likely to be encountered by other Cainites. They are considered to be the elders of Cainite society (though some eighth-generation vampires would contend this). Vampires of these generations are confident that they can resist the manipulations of their elders, and so remain active in Cainite society. Many of these vampires maintain very influential positions. In fact, most of the princes of medieval Europe are of these generations.

Eight and Ninth Generations

Still considered elders by some, these Cainites nonetheless associate themselves primarily with members of the younger generations. Members of these generations are often called ancillæ, though of course this is based on age more than generation. Occasionally a vampire of this generation will claim the title of prince in one of Europe's outlying regions, though this is extremely rare. More commonly they are vassal princes or subordinate nobles under a prince's rule.

Tenth and Eleventh Generations

Often referred to as neonates, these are the most recent generations of Cainites. Though still powerful creatures, their blood has thinned because it is so far removed from that of Caine. Most of this generation have been Embraced within the past century, and so are the most in touch with the modern medieval world.

Twelfth and Thirteenth Generations

There are exceedingly few vampires of these generations, and even fewer beyond. Cainites of these generations are considered beneath contempt, not even worthy of notice. It is rumored that the blood of those beyond these generations is too weak to pass on the Curse.

retreat fully from society and enter torpor. Some Methuselahs remain involved in power struggles and the Jyhad of the Cainites, but do so in complete anonymity.

• **Antediluvian:** These are the most ancient vampires, and are among the most powerful creatures in the world. From these 13 ancient vampires, the clans and bloodlines of the present were formed. They are reputed to be the grandchilder of Caine, and are of the third generation. When they do involve themselves in the affairs of vampires, they seldom leave things untarnished by their touch. The mere word of an Antediluvian is enough to provoke enormous strife and conflict among vampires. Their eternal struggle for supremacy, the Jyhad, affects vampires everywhere.

Social Mobility

Unlike mortal society during the Dark Ages, a fair amount of social mobility is available to vampires. Part of what determines status is a vampire's age, so those who survive the longest inevitably gain more prestige and power. The other factor is generation, or how far removed a vampire is from Caine. If a vampire commits Amaranth upon another vampire of a lower generation, draining the victim of every last drop of her lifeblood, the attacker will effectively lower himself one generation.

With few rigidly enforced rules to govern their feeding, vampires in populated towns have the most to gain (and fear) from Amaranth. With death by disease, fire, murder and countless other causes so common in overcrowded towns, vampires can feed to their hearts' content. However, the childer they create can just as easily prey upon their elders without retribution.

Though no less intimidating, Amaranth is perhaps less of a threat in the countryside. There are limits to which a vampire can abuse her power in the lands of fields and manors. Travel is limited, so most vampires in a rural area know each other. If the local lord is a vampire and is diablerized, the locals will initiate a Blood Hunt for his killer, even if they don't realize the cause of his death. If the culprit is a local Cainite, he will certainly be exposed to the hunt, if not drawn into or made a target of it.

The Cainite who seeks to diablerize his elders, or abuse any of his powers in a countryside estate, therefore runs the risk of marking himself for destruction. Perhaps the wisest way to exist and gain power in the countryside is to feed carefully and perform Amaranth only on those vampires who pass through with the same purpose in mind. Vampires who follow such practices will surely survive and perhaps share their wisdom to create a broader, more controlled Cainite society in the future.

The Prince

Since time immemorial, the eldest vampire in a domain has served as its leader, mediating disputes and rallying the Cainites of the area should danger threaten. The title has varied from one area to the next, usually mimicking the titles of mortal nobility. Emperors, kings, marquis, barons, viscounts, thanes, grand dukes and countless others have led their fellow vampires, but in recent years the title of prince has predominated in western Europe. This is undoubtedly due to the appearance of eternal youth that Cainites are able to maintain, as well as the prestige attached to such a title.

Though the prince of a given area is traditionally the eldest Cainite in the area, there are exceptions. Sometimes the eldest vampire will choose to abdicate and name his progeny as his successor; the power of the sire backs that of the progeny, and allows the elder to pursue his own interests. Still, a prince must be able to enforce his rule, and few childer are able to do this effectively. Unless they are backed by a single powerful elder or group of elders, they will rarely have the strength to hold their positions. Of course, what elder trusts his progeny so completely as to hand over the reins of power?

In some areas, other titles denote vassals of the prince. In particular, the title of sheriff or seneschal has come into common use in Britain, denoting a prince's lieutenant in charge of keeping the peace among the fief's vampires. Other areas have adopted similar titles as befits the mortal culture surrounding them, partly because the neonates of the Dark Ages seem to value titles and status even more than land and fortresses. It is far easier to invent an honorific title to reward a vassal than to further divide a domain already whittled down by elders over the centuries.

Fealty

When one prince acknowledges another as his superior, he swears "fealty" to her. This is much like a mortal knight swearing fealty to a baron, or a baron swearing fealty to a king. The lesser (thence called the vassal or vassal prince) acknowledges his inferiority, and swears to obey the greater prince. This is not uncommon.

Sometimes a prince who swears fealty is indeed expected to serve the greater vampire dutifully, and may swear a Blood Oath to her new overlord. Sometimes swearing fealty has no real consequences — it just bolsters the ego and prestige of the stronger prince. In most cases there are a few mild restrictions placed upon a prince who swears fealty.

• The vassal may not aid the enemies of the greater prince. She may not allow them to hunt or establish havens in her fief.

• A Blood Hunt called in the greater prince's fief is also in effect throughout the vassal's fief.

• The vassal may not form alliances with other princes.

The Prince's Powers

Cainite society has yet to evolve any common assumptions of how a prince might behave or what limits she might have to her power. Instead, a prince's power is determined by practical considerations.

• How much support does the prince have from her subjects? Acting with her subjects' support, even a weak prince can enforce her will over dissenters.

• How independent are her subjects? Free-spirited Cainites will resist strict princes.

• How much more powerful than her subjects is the prince? A really tough prince can do what she likes, safe in the knowledge that she can crush any opposition.

RITCHIE

• How strong is the Church in the area? How tough are the werewolves? And what of the mages and faeries? External threats might unite Cainites around their princes, but a draconian prince might be betrayed to these enemies by malcontents.

Some princes wield vast powers — declaring Blood Hunts on a whim, banning other Cainites from creating ghouls or neonates, strictly regulating what allies their subjects might have, determining hunting grounds, closely watching visiting Cainites, etc. Others are nearly powerless: they must call councils of all their subjects to declare Blood Hunts; other Cainites may Embrace mortals, strike alliances or create ghouls at will; subjects may hunt or establish havens where they wish; and foreign Cainites come and go unchecked.

Ghouls and Childer

Permission to create ghoul servants may be obtained only from the prince of the fief. Too many, and the Silence of the Blood is threatened. Nor is permission to work the Becoming on a mortal taken lightly, though in recent years more and more vampires have ignored this rule. The princes of the Dark Medieval world do not want their enemies, or potential enemies, to build up hordes of ghouls to work against them; nor do they want a plague of uncontrolled neonates terrifying the mortal population and competing with them for hunting rights.

Princes often demand that their subjects ask permission before either Embracing a mortal or creating a ghoul, and if a ghoul or neonate causes trouble, the prince is likely to hold her creator responsible. Of course, most princes can't really monitor all their subjects, and so disobedient Cainites might create neonates or ghouls despite their princes' restrictions. Princes, however, are aware of this. If they can't be sure to discover disobedient Cainites, they usually make certain that those who do get caught are punished severely. Any vampire who Embraces a mortal against the will of her prince can expect to be killed. Blood Hunts may also be called against those who repeatedly create ghouls against their prince's wishes.

Domain

Vampires divide their territory much as mortals do, forming their own domains and city-states, which are often referred to as fiefs. But while mortals value fertile farmland to maintain their people, vampires are creatures of the city, where prey is more easily found and an unfamiliar face is less likely to attract attention. Still, cities of the medieval age are but shadows of their modern counterparts, with a scant 5,000 souls making up a good-sized city. This means that few vampires can successfully hunt and hide in each city. In fact, many are reduced to prowling the outlying villages and towns. But in most cities, many vampires compete for little prey, increasing the risk of discovery by mortals. Worse, many vampires see little need to hide their powers from humanity; after all, what can a few peasants do against a mighty vampire lord?

ON THE HORIZON

It is not hard to see how the overconfidence and overpopulation of this period leads to inquisitions and revolutions, in vampire society as well as in the mortal world. Two centuries from now, Cainites will divide themselves into three factions: the Camarilla, which champions those who would retain some degree of Humanity; the Sabbat, which revels in their status as monsters of the night; and the anarchs, who reject both other groups as oppressive, and want simply to be able to do as they please without regard for vampiric or mortal authority. But for now, Cainites live in a world without restrictions, in which personal power is the only law.

THE TRADITIONS

Since the time of the second generation, a code of unwritten laws has shaped vampire society. Over time some are forgotten and others "discovered," though for the most part, these traditions have stood the test of time. Most sires require their progeny to commit the Six Traditions to memory, though this is more common among vampires created in the Roman era and before than those Embraced in the medieval age.

THE FIRST TRADITION: THE LEGACY

Like the restrictions on class in the mortal world, the legacy of Caine places vampires in a particular role in society — that of the predator. To try to change the hierarchy God (or Satan, according to some Cainites) has created is a nigh-unforgivable crime, for to do so presumes that one possesses divine wisdom. To become a mere beast, living solely to feed, is as great a crime as seeking to return to the mortal life left behind with the Embrace.

THE SECOND TRADITION: DESTRUCTION

Like the Legacy, the Tradition of Destruction puts all vampires in a hierarchy, but in this case it structures vampiric society. By giving the right of destruction only to the elders, this tradition ensures that they remain powerful. It also makes patricide a capital offense among vampires, thereby discouraging rebellion among the young.

THE THIRD TRADITION: PROGENY

This tradition has fallen into disuse in many areas, and some sires no longer teach it to their offspring. It may be in part due to this that so many childer have been created in recent centuries, as not all Cainites know the reasoning behind this tradition. Some claim that it is merely a tool of the elders to keep their offspring weak and unable to rally forces against their elders. This is certainly true, but by limiting the number of progeny created in a fief, the prince may also ensure that all within have sufficient mortals to feed on.

THE FOURTH TRADITION: ACCOUNTING

This tradition attempts to ensure that Cainites will choose wisely when selecting mortals for the Becoming. It also encourages sires to force their offspring to swear Blood Oaths, guaranteeing their loyalty.

The First Tradition: The Legacy

Thy blood is that of Caine, cursed by God and blessed by Lilith. To seek to change your state or to return to that of your mortal life is a sin against thy Father and Mother, and against thy God.

The Second Tradition: Destruction

Thou art forbidden to destroy another of thy kind who is thy elder. Those closer to Caine know his will, and may destroy any childer who are unfit in his sight. It is forbidden for those of weaker blood to rise up against their elders.

The Third Tradition: Progeny

Thou shalt only sire another with the permission of thy elder. If thou createst another without thine elder's leave, both thou and thy progeny shall be slain.

The Fourth Tradition: Accounting

Those thou create are thine own childer. Until thy progeny shall be released, thou shalt command them in all things. Their sins are thine to endure.

The Fifth Tradition: Domain

Thy domain is thine own concern. All others owe thee respect while in it. None may challenge thy word while in thy domain. When thou comest to the fief of another, thou shalt present thyself to the one who ruleth there.

The Sixth Tradition: The Silence of Blood

Thou shalt not reveal thy true nature to those not of the Blood. Doing so shall renounce thy claims of Blood.

The Fifth Tradition: Domain

Even the Tradition of Domain is called in to question in the Dark Ages, as vampires realize that there are limits to the mortal population upon which they feed. Those with the most populous domains must now struggle to defend them from neonates who wish to claim their own territory.

The Sixth Tradition: The Silence of Blood

The Silence of the Blood, or "Masquerade" as it will one night be called, is an unofficial conspiracy born of expediency. No vampire could hope to stand against the power of the Church or the armies of the great nobles. Thus it is necessary for the vampires to hide themselves away.

Because every mortal knows that vampires and other monsters exist, few Cainites care if individual vampires reveal themselves to mortals. Reckless indiscretions, however, are not tolerated. If a vampire publicly displays its power in such a way that frightened mortals begin to hunt for others, or if a vampire reveals the identities or havens of others, princes and other Cainites will not stand for it. Any vampire who puts his own kind in peril will not be tolerated, and one who leads mortals to realize just how many vampires really do exist earns the enmity of all Cainites.

Moreover, many mortals are convinced that these creatures — from Cainites to lupines to infernal sorcerers — are irredeemably evil, drawing their power from Lucifer himself. It is therefore still vital for the Cainites to hide themselves from mortals. If any vampire is discovered, she can expect no mercy from medieval mortals. If the kine ever realize how numerous the Cainites are, a wave of hunts and inquisitions will follow, and no sensible vampire would want that.

Sects

Several different sects have arisen within the Cainites of the era. Each sect maintains power in a different way. Some are informal groupings of convenience, while others are highly ritualized societies unto themselves. Together they compose the main political forces in Cainite society.

Inconnu

The Inconnu are the remnants of the Roman era of Cainites. They are patrician in demeanor, and still have a great deal of influence over the older vampires of Europe. They are rumored to live beneath the ancient Roman cities, such as Paris, Constantinople and Venice. Apparently Rome is their chief stronghold. The Inconnu are opposed by younger Cainites, who have adopted a feudal system as more appropriate to the age. Not all of the clans are associated with this group; for instance, the Toreador, Tzimisce and Brujah are never part of the Inconnu, and few in those clans speak well of it. Their memory of what the Inconnu did to Carthage and Dacia remains vivid.

The Inconnu tend to be concerned with the ancient ways, and many of them strongly believe that humans should be treated as fairly as possible. However, they have their share of inner conflict, just as any group of Cainites would. Among the Inconnu, there is little middle ground except for their common desire to suppress those younger than they.

The Furores

This sect's members have a reputation for being the outlaws of the Cainites. Condemned by most princes as thieves and troublemakers, they exist on the fringes of vampire society, scratching out a meager existence like their mortal counterparts.

The Furores are considered chaotic, disorganized and ignorant of even the base rules that govern all Cainites. Such talk comes more from those not familiar with the sect's internal workings. Many of the Furores are quite familiar with the Six Traditions, but have chosen to throw their lots in with those who walk on the shadow's edge. They are frequently second or third childer, unable to compete with their elder siblings for their sires' attention, and so they set out to make their own ways. In Furores, vampires may shine based on their own merits, not those of their sires, and they need not worry about elder siblings crowding them out.

Furores may be found among cathedral-builders and city burghers, as well as merchant caravans. Most city-based coteries are considered by default to be Furores, unless one or more of them has some standing with the local prince. Indeed, the Furores tend to Embrace those who function outside the rigid structure of Church or feudal state: thieves, merchants, artisans, performers and laborers. Though few would admit it, there are some coteries of Furores who pay tithes to local princes in exchange for autonomy.

Though they shun the hierarchy of princes and vassals, the Furores have a certain structure to their society. They have arranged themselves much like a guild, and any who pass their initiation rites are welcomed, regardless of clan. Most of the cities currently emerging into prominence are, for all intents and purposes, their Domains. The Toreador and Brujah among them often view merchants, scholars, and guildsmen as the promise of a brighter future, a time when learning and knowledge will again reign supreme.

Granted, the Furores do have few scruples about theft — the Ravnos among them have taught them some of their worse habits. Many of them spend as much time practicing sleight of hand and stealth as they do collecting "rent" from their merchant vassals.

The Furores generally have heavily shuttered meeting places, where they discuss issues of mutual concern (attacks by the Lupines, political maneuverings of foreign princes). Violence there is generally frowned upon as a distraction. The cities they govern tend to have more artisans and merchants than most, and they eagerly accept new ideas, rather than shun them as the work of Satan. Their rule is not one of fear, but of subtlety, and they take pride in their ability to get things done quietly. They insinuate themselves into the ranks of burghers, guildmasters and merchants, as a means of exerting tighter control over growing cities.

The Order of the Bitter Ashes

Legends speak of these mighty yet mysterious vampires, saying that they began as a band of mortal crusaders sent to the Holy Land. During their journey, they were set upon by a powerful vampire bearing a strange mark on his forehead. He Embraced them to a man and sent them on a quest for the cup of Christ, the Holy Grail. Their mysterious sire told them that one draught from the true Grail would purify their blood of Caine's curse, and could become the salvation for all Caine's childer.

Many of the Order are said to have fought strange creatures of the night and to have overcome much opposition — even from within their own ranks — to find the sacred cup, whereupon they all partook of the vitæ of Christ. It is said that all those who drank of the cup underwent a strange, miraculous transformation, of which they have been reluctant to discuss. Now their bodies gleam like the moon, and their blades unerringly strike down those who follow the creatures of Hell. The Baali have become some of their most hated foes, an enmity which the Baali return a thousandfold.

The Order is known for its mighty horses, fleet with Celerity from their masters' blood. Each newly made sword is quenched in its maker's blood and purified with incense before it may be wielded. The knights' strange luminescence is frequently masked by their armor, creating an eerie glow beneath their helms, and no doubt giving rise to some strange tales of phantom warriors.

Although the band has supposedly been scattered since the days of the Second Crusade, some have been known to allow other vampires to drink of their pure blood (rumored to replenish without the need to feed on humans). Those who do drink of the Order are said to gain their luminescence and potent powers in destroying the Baali and other Infernalists, for a span of one moon cycle.

The Order is named for a number of legends about how Caine was cursed to "eat only bitter ashes." The Order has little overall organization, although there are rumors that it has formed a strange alliance with the Knights Templar. Humanity in general is regarded with disinterest, although some of the Order look on the devout with pity, that they will never know the blessing of the Cup.

While it was the Grail that gave the Order its miraculous powers, the cup is no longer in the knights' possession. Circumstances surrounding this are vague at best. Speculations suggest that the knights entombed it somewhere in the Middle East, with one remaining to guard it, while others mutter that it was stolen, perhaps by the very vampire who Embraced the group.

Autarkis

The Autarkis are young vampires who have declared open rebellion against the Inconnu and the withdrawn elders of the clans. Most are usually found among neonates and malcontents within Cainite society. They seek freedom, plain and simple, and rebel against the authority of their elders and the rule of any prince. They are often derisively known as the "plague flies," for it is whispered that they travel from outbreak to outbreak of plagues and feed upon the dead and dying. Many of them are rumored to travel in large ravenous packs, looting and destroying all in their path.

The Promethians

It is said that in Carthage, Cainites lived alongside humanity in peace. In the Dark Ages, those days are only a distant memory, and most think that such a society would be an affront to God and Caine. Others argue that such a thing is possible; indeed, that it may be necessary if vampires are to survive. They fear that the ancients now think of themselves as gods, and view mortals and younger Cainites alike as their slaves and vessels. It is thought that only by living in peace and unity with mortals will the vampires of the current age survive the manipulations and wars of the Inconnu.

This group has taken its name from Prometheus, who braved the wrath of the gods to bring fire to humanity. These vampires claim that the Inconnu ignore the potential of the Via Humanitas for allowing self-restraint, and claim further that the Traditions have been corrupted by the Inconnu. The Promethians speak of Caine's wickedness, of how they tire of listening to the commands of the Inconnu, and teach that to overthrow the hidden elders is the only road to true security. Some speak of founding a society based on valuing mortals as their near-equals, as was hoped for in Carthage.

Still, the Promethians are in the minority now, their voices often reduced to whispers, and their dream of a peaceful vampire and human society is only a dream. For the time being, their pleas for humanity fall on deaf ears, but others predict that their day will come, if not now then in the future.

The *Manus Nigrum*

There is one sect so secretive that some Cainites are unaware of its existence. Its members call themselves the *manus nigrum*.

From its origins as a mortal death cult in the ancient world, the *manus nigrum* went on to discover the secret of immortal life from vampires. Hundreds of years ago, the *manus nigrum* split over disagreements regarding the future of the sect. Since then, the two halves, while not at war, have kept an uncommunicative peace. The Eastern Hand, known only in whispers as the Tal'mahe'Ra, devotes its energies to the study of Hell and Purgatory, where the souls of the unholy go after death. The western half of the *manus nigrum*, however, has taken a keen interest in medieval politics. Those few elders who know of the *manus nigrum* say that they work to destroy the Baali, though apparently some members of Clan Tzimisce have somehow offended this sect. The more passive purpose of observation leads to the long-range goal of the *manus nigrum*.

The *manus nigrum* believes that the existence of so many vampires in the Dark Medieval age is detrimental, and seeks to thin out the undead ranks. To this end, they have begun compiling information about every Cainite they encounter, in the hopes

of making their elimination as complete as possible. The *manus* may be instrumental in the death of certain among the Antediluvians. In the meantime, any upheaval that allows them to destroy elders will be used to the utmost, and they frequently attach themselves to the Autarkis for this purpose.

The *manus nigrum* are compiling a sort of Domesday Book, a record of names and havens of every known Cainite. Once assembled, the book will be laid aside and presented to the Antediluvians when the Ancients awaken, that they may know where to seek their childer. If a member of the *manus nigrum* is captured, he explains that he is but a shadow of the coming darkness… and dies saying nothing more.

Elysium

Once a widely held belief, the notion of a neutral meeting place where all the vampires in an area might meet in safety for more genteel pursuits passed away with the Roman era. The changes in mortal society, particularly "barbaric" Northern Europe, contributes a great deal to this, but in truth few Cainites have time for such niceties. Like the mortals they feed upon, most Cainites are engaged in a struggle to survive, and have little time or need for such pleasures. Meetings between vampires are generally terse affairs, wherein business is the only real concern, or ritualized ceremonies of homage and diplomacy.

Cities blessed with long warm nights, like the Italian city-states or Constantinople, still play host to an Elysium. The elders of the cities periodically gather to engage in many of the same pleasures shared by the kine, including discussions of art, philosophy and culture. Physical violence is frowned upon, and anyone wishing to settle a dispute is asked to do so elsewhere. Elysium is looked on by young vampires as an outdated ritual of a time long past, but tradition-minded elders insist that it is only through such events that vampires remain "civilized," and above base creatures that exist purely to survive.

Platitudes aside, age can sour the palate, and many jaded elders in their search for new diversions have sunk to excesses and debauchery at Elysiums. Unfortunate mortals are selected for refreshments based on their "vintage." Some elders stage freakish passion plays in mockery of the Church and mortal society. Some have even sunk to lows that would shock even the most debauched rake, torturing Lupines or forcing Thralls and Dominated kine to perform *tableaux vivants*. Those younger vampires who speak of the wickedness of the elders have seen such Elysiums, and the wild sadism and near-frenzy of the normally staid elders terrifies many into action.

Labyrinths

Since time immemorial, vampires have feared the light of day. For equally long centuries, many have hidden from it beneath the earth. In these dark and tempestuous times, when so many have been dragged out into the sun to die, refuge under cold rock is highly valued.

What began long ago as a tradition of sleeping in caves has developed slowly into a fetish for security. It is not enough simply to sleep beneath the ground; vampires must ensure no one can drag them out. Some say that the Methuselahs long ago built enormous underground tombs, where they now lie guarded by legions of ghouls, magical guardians and devious traps. In Roman times, it was not uncommon for extensive catacombs to be built under the great cities, and it is from these that most Inconnu coteries still rule.

Certain clans, by dint of necessity or their own dark preferences, have taken up and expanded the idea of the labyrinth for their own uses. Nosferatu hide in their mazes from the hatred of their fairer brethren. Lasombra, so akin to the shadows, create private labyrinths for havens or retreats. The Cappadocians make extensive use of the catacombs beneath the Roman-founded cities, feeling more at home among the moldering dead and chilly stone. To what purpose the Tzimisce put their labyrinths few know, and those who have gotten glimpses speak of gibbering monstrosities and chambers built deep below the earth to muffle the screams of their unfortunate inhabitants.

Each labyrinth is frequently built to the specifications of its owner, and even the Roman catacombs are rarely left untouched. One Lasombra claims to have based his maze on the notes for the Labyrinth of Crete (though no one is certain if he furnished his with a Minotaur). Only the architect and the workers know the true layout of a maze, and the wise vampire Dominates or kills the workmen to ensure its secrecy.

Labyrinths can be of any size, from a modified castle dungeons to networks of hollowed-out caverns. Many mazes employ security measures like those used in the surface world: portculli, moats, iron gates and pit traps lined with wooden stakes. Certain features are exclusive to labyrinths, such as lakes of flaming oil or monstrous guardians dwelling in moats. Such security works both to slow entry of intruders and alert vampires to invaders.

Something may always be found at the center of any maze, and here the inhabitants (if any) make their havens. Some elders never leave, too paranoid to chance the surface world. So formidable are some of these labyrinths that it is sometimes easier to simply seal the Cainites inside, making their havens into tombs. Who knows what awaits the unwary vampire who attempts to reopen such a place….

Stories abound of forgotten or hidden labyrinths. A labyrinth abandoned should warn the would-be explorer — what could have driven off an elder or coterie? Relatively few Cainites ever see the insides of such places (for no elder wishes to give away her secrets), so it is impossible to say what is true and what is false about them.

Lextalionis

There is and always has been a system of punishment for those who disobey the rules set down by their elders. The system is simple: a vampire who breaks the rules is slain. Those who violate the laws of a fief and thereby anger the elders are hunted down and extinguished by all who hear the call. This credo of "just retribution" is known formally as Lextalionis, or more commonly as the Blood Hunt.

Tradition demands that the Lextalionis can only be called by the eldest Cainite in a domain, who is almost always the prince. Other elders or even ancillæ may call for a Hunt, but most vampires will not respond, for they risk the wrath of the prince in so doing. In this day and age, a prince will often call Hunts for his own purposes. So long as the majority of the others in the area support him, there is little anyone else can do.

Most princes prefer to rule with the consent and support of the fief's vampires. They do not call Hunts so much to bolster their power as to protect their subjects, and so can expect support for Hunts within their fiefs. However, too many Blood Hunts makes for draconian justice, and a few princes have been overthrown for it.

Blood Hunts

The Blood Hunt is the most extreme punishment which a vampire can suffer. Theoretically, any prince may call a Hunt against any Cainite who displeases her. In practice it is not so simple. If a prince calls a Hunt she must be certain that other Cainites will participate — for whatever reason — or declaring the Hunt has no impact and the prince loses face.

Some princes maintain a "hearth troop" of trained ghouls or vampires to act as enforcers and to pursue those against whom Hunts are called. Such retainers are given special privileges, often including money, safe havens and the best weapons. But this is a dangerous policy: what stops the hearth troop from overthrowing the prince? And if the prince's power is dependent upon the support of a small group of thugs, then who is the real ruler of the fief?

In areas where princes are weak or particular coteries are powerful — usually in towns — coteries or other groups of Cainites have been known to stage private Blood Hunts. For whatever reasons, members of a group mark one or more vampires for death and carry out the Hunt themselves. Word always reaches the prince's ears, but may be too late in coming or the prince may be too ineffectual to put a stop to the killing.

A Blood Hunt that occurs without a prince's authority is always answered with a second — this one with the prince's backing, staged against the offenders of the law. If the prince cannot punish those who stage their own Hunt, he is usually usurped or destroyed, either by those who defy his word or other elders who realize that a new, hopefully more effective figurehead must ascend.

The Ordeal

The ordeal is a method used by many princes for determining the guilt or innocence of a vampire accused of a crime. Such crimes might be as simple as violating a vassal's feeding grounds or as serious as breaking one of the ancient Six Traditions. Visiting princes and other elders who have been accused are almost always permitted to undergo an ordeal rather than face summary judgment. This is considered a matter of courtesy among princes.

The ordeal may be as easy or difficult as the prince warrants. The very difficult ones can be deadly, offering the accused little chance of survival. The possibilities for such trials are as varied as the princes who devise them, though many princes seem to have favored means of determining the truth. Many such tests exist; the following examples depict some of the most common.

• **Trial by Combat**

This ordeal is most common when the validity of the accusations is in doubt. This ordeal allows the accused to face his accuser in single combat. Princes or ranking elders are often afforded this option, even if there is little question of guilt. In such cases the accused faces a champion chosen by the prince.

Many variations of this trial exist. A duel may be fought until one combatant has been crippled or driven into torpor. A stake may be placed in the center of a circle, with both opponents at the edge of the ring, facing each another; the first one to drive the other into torpor is considered the victor. Or, two vampires may engage in a contest in which each drinks the other's blood until one falls into torpor. Some accidental diablerizations have occurred this way. There are also rumors of duels fought with mental powers, or even with magic if such is available to the contestants.

This method is often favored by princes for its entertainment value. Many vampires from surrounding counties will attend a trial by combat, especially if the accused is a Cainite of some notoriety.

• Ordeal by Fire

More often than not, this ordeal results in the death of the accused. Several variations of this trial exist, some more deadly than others. The most common requires that a number of Cainites (as many as the prince can assemble) form two lines facing each other. Each of the vampires carries a lit torch. The accused is then required to run between the vampires as they beat him with the torches. Variations on this require the accused to be covered in oil or to be completely nude. Some princes even require that the accused walk, rather than run down the lines. To run is considered an admission of guilt, which is followed by an immediate execution.

Another method of ordeal by fire involves the accused being bound to a wooden stake and surrounded by tinder. A fire is then lit beneath the feet of the accused, at which time he is allowed to attempt escape. This method almost always results in the death of the vampire, unless the prince severely underestimates the strength of the accused.

• Test of the Beast

The accused is cast into a pit or a sealed room with a ferocious wild animal, often a bear or wolf. The carnivore has usually been starved for several nights (and has often been turned into a ghoul to acquire a taste for vampiric blood) before the trial takes place.

The unarmed vampire must defeat the beast in order to prove his innocence. Obviously, Cainites who are known to have powers of influence over animals are not subjected to this test. Like trial by combat, this test often becomes a form of entertainment for the prince and any visitors he should have in attendance.

• Ordeal of Purifying Light

The Cainite suffering this ordeal is locked in a closed courtyard, minutes before dawn. He is then forced to endure the light of the sun for a period determined by the prince before being released by one of the prince's ghouls. Variations on this ordeal include chaining the accused to the eastern wall of a keep just moments before dawn. If he is able to escape, he is declared innocent.

This test is usually reserved for those deemed guilty of the most horrible crimes. Most believe that this ordeal scourges the guilt from even the most wicked soul. Some have willingly undergone this ordeal as a means of attempting to purge their own souls. It is even rumored that some few have regained their humanity through this method of purification.

Alternative Punishments

Though they are rare, there are crimes that have gone unpunished through Blood Hunts. Some princes worry about appearing too draconian, and may call Hunts only with great reluctance. However, a prince is under obligation to his subjects to punish offenders, and showing any favoritism shakes the power structure. This is of particular importance when a prince's childe has been caught in or accused of a crime, or the crime was committed with the tacit approval of the prince, such as the killing of a rival. In such cases, the prince may call for the accused to prove his or her innocence through some task, such as a quest. Frequently these tasks are of such Herculean proportions as to stagger all but the most resourceful or cunning vampires.

The accused is often watched from afar through powerful Auspex or via news from allies. Those who attempt to abandon their tasks are promptly targeted for a Blood Hunt.

The Mortal World
Society

Dark Medieval society is feudal, with power and rank dependent upon lands held and military might. In the medieval world there is no such thing as "equality of opportunity." If your family is powerful, then you will have an immediate and tangible advantage over others. If your family is peasantry, you will live in poverty and die young. A man's rank is determined by his birth. A woman's rank is determined by her husband's.

Medieval men divide themselves into those who fight, those who work and those who pray.

Nobility

The nobility are the military, landholding class. The great nobles own the land; petty nobles retain tracts of land in exchange for military service and money. Many nobles are trained from youth to fight, and are equipped with fine armor and weaponry. On a day-to-day level, however, they are administrators and civil servants — running their lands, enforcing royal law, commanding garrisons, and working as officers of the law courts or as senior servants in royal households.

Some petty nobles are hardly richer than wealthy peasants: they simply have a little land and status, and in return must agree to fight for their overlords if war threatens. The noble magnates — the kings, dukes and earls — live in opulent luxury, maintaining palatial castles and being able to call upon the military service (and taxes) of dozens or hundreds of lesser nobles.

In between the social extremes are barons and wealthy knights, who maintain strong castles or fortified manor houses, perhaps commanding the allegiance of lesser nobles, but who in turn swear homage to great magnates.

Cainites who dwell among the mortal nobility have a dual existence. They must function within the society of other nobles and lord over the lands and people of their fiefs. Just as mortal nobles have responsibilities to their overlords and underlings, so do vampire lords. Yet Cainite nobles also have responsibilities to their undead kind, whether in positions of authority or subservience.

The difficulties of observing the responsibilities of mortal gentility arise from being undead. Vampire lords cannot appear before their underlings and serfs during the day, and must arrange all affairs to occur at night. Such nocturnal behavior cannot go unnoticed for long, and that is when superstitious rumors spread among the mortals.

The best way for a Cainite lord to manage her mortal affairs might be through kine proxies or ghouls. A sheriff can be an effective tool at enforcing the laws and seeing justice done, while a reeve can arrange the affairs of the manor house. Of course, should there be a daytime emergency…

The fact is, a feudal noble holds stable power when his authority can be directly attributed to a name and a face. When many subjects fail to see the face of their master, it is easier to blame problems on him. Still, there's much to be said for the ominous silhouette of a lord standing atop his battlements, the moon casting his cold shadow across the cringing mortal souls below.

Other difficulties of feudal authority lie in reconciling mortal and immortal power. How does a duke explain his meekness before a mere baron who comes calling after sunset? If a noble's Cainite authority spreads much further than his mortal authority, how does he explain the presence of some of his ghouls in the lands of another mortal lord? And what of a group of rebellious vampires who won't answer to a mortal overlord, but will answer to a lesser lord, who also happens to be the local Cainite prince?

Peasants

The medieval masses are the peasants — the farmers who till the nobles' fields. The more fortunate are "freemen," who rent land from the nobles, working their plots in return for heavy rents, tithes and taxes. The less fortunate are "serfs," peasants who are the slaves of their noble masters, who own nothing — not even their own bodies. A serf pays heavier taxes, and may not marry or move away without his lord's permission; if a serf is assaulted, the attacker must pay a fine or compensation to the serf's lord for damaging his "property."

Although mortal social classes have little bearing on Cainite society, it is difficult for neonates and others sired since the age of Charlemagne to recognize the prominence of some vampires over others. Vampires with such limited vision have particular difficulty with Cainites who were drawn from or exist among the mortal peasantry. It is difficult for a newly sired vampire, who is a noble or clergyman in mortal society, to take orders from a vampire who is ostensibly a mortal freeman. That is the paradoxical nature of Cainite society, though, and the newcomer who cannot adapt quickly is short-lived.

Vampires who exist among kine peasants do bear a terrible burden, though. To try to remain true to her former lifestyle, a peasant Cainite must somehow account for her absence during the daytime, when everyone else in the manor or town is working. She is also expected to go to Mass with everyone else, and would be missed at the frequent festivals that manor lords often allow their serfs.

A clever Cainite who still lives as a serf could make ghouls of the right people and justify her strange behavior as part of her services "at the manor house." The local gossips could also be controlled to ensure that no ill word is spread, or that rumors are actually squelched. Ultimately, though, most vampires who are chosen from the peasantry break their mortal social bonds and seek higher lifestyles. Why be a predator of humans while living a lie as their prey?

CLERGY

The Church is the single greatest institution in the medieval world. Arguably, it is the only important institution. The Church runs the universities and cathedral schools of medieval Europe, educating the sons of the wealthy and powerful. It appoints priests to local parishes, and from every pulpit those priests tell the people to obey God and their mortal masters. Few people outside the Church can read, nor do they own books. The monasteries and cathedrals of Europe own vast amounts of land and are the most important patrons of the arts. Furthermore, every single person in Europe is supposed to pay a tithe (a tax constituting one-tenth of one's possessions) to the Church.

Churchmen — called clergy or clerics — are usually the younger sons of wealthy peasants or nobles. Important clerics (the bishops, the abbots who run great monasteries) are inevitably of noble birth. Priests of backwater parishes are always of peasant stock.

The power of the Church in the Dark Medieval world can not be understated. The lords of the Church are very wealthy and very influential. They tell people what to believe, and bribe and cajole them with the promise of eternal life. An angered bishop may "excommunicate" an unfortunate soul, cutting off a person from the Church and from God's mercy, and only a priest may absolve a person of her sins. Perhaps even more importantly, in a world in which creatures like vampires and werewolves are very real, the Church's ceremonies claim to offer protection from the creatures of darkness and the unknown.

In case that were not enough, the Church also includes several orders of knights — highly trained fighters, many of them noblemen — who live as monks but fight for Christ and the Church (or at least that's what they say). Most notorious among these are the Knights Templar, who are rumored to indulge in unsavory (and un-Christian) occult ceremonies. The Hospitalers and Teutonic Knights, as well as several lesser orders, share with them the task of defending Christianity from the heathens.

Cainites who exist among the mortal clergy have the greatest protection from vampire and mortal opponents, but that protection comes at a price. By posing as God's devout — though usually only through lip service — vampires in the clergy have the power of the Church behind them, the most influential institution in the medieval world. If an opponent ever grows too strong, Cainites in the Church can bring the mortal authority of God down upon that foe. All the vampires need do is trump up the right charges and provide the right "evidence."

Ironically, the Church also provides defenses for its cursed brethren through the power of faith. Mortal clergymen are often unfaithful, but there are some who are not, and their conviction can be enough to stave off an attacker who would hunt a Cainite in his very abbey or monastery. All the Cainite brother need know is who of faith that should be avoided among the disciples.

The dangers of hiding among the clergy are immense, though. At some point it must mean contact with True Faith. Cainite power must also be wielded subtly for fear of raising suspicion and avoiding charges of diabolism. And the duties of the clergy must be fulfilled to a point that is convincing to other brethren; an obvious lack of conviction would be as dangerous to a vampire as exposure to too much.

Vampires' failure to hide their existence properly within the Church may ultimately lead to witch hunts.

MERCHANTS AND CRAFTSMEN

Many of the merchants and artisans of the medieval world receive little respect from the nobility or Church. A trader's pursuit of profit is considered unwholesome, mildly shameful in fact. Artisans (who range from weavers and carpenters to goldsmiths and armorers) are considered very useful, but no more than that.

Merchants and craftsmen congregate in the towns and cities where they set up shops and market stalls. Some (especially greater merchants) become very wealthy, and in key trade centers like Venice can be as powerful and influential as nobles.

Cainites who hide among the merchants and craftsmen of the Dark Medieval world probably hold the greatest liberties in undead pursuits. Traveling under the aegis of trade allows a vampire access to a world to feed upon. As long as her drinking habits are kept low-key, a merchant vampire can live out a long and plentiful immortality. The freedom of travel would also allow her to set up shop and hunting grounds in a new locale, when an old one grows too competitive, in business or sustenance. A Cainite craftsperson or merchant is also afforded the luxury of always living in towns and cities — the veritable banquets for the undead.

The pitfalls of living the life of an immortal merchant lie in the relative classlessness of the profession. Merchants do not fall easily into the feudal plan of noble, peasant and clergyman. If a Cainite merchant holds sway over a Cainite noble, that power must be exercised behind closed doors. Before mortal eyes, a lesser Cainite could refuse a Cainite merchant's credit, pleading disreputable backers or foreign suppliers. According to kine ways, this insult would be justifiable. Any retribution would have to wait until only vampires were in witness.

Women in the Dark Ages

Priests, kings and warriors — these are the archetypes that come to mind when we think of the Middle Ages. But what about the other half of the population? What role do women play in the Dark Medieval world?

Women in the Middle Ages were a bundle of contradictions, with sinful Eve and saintly Mary representing the two aspects of their sex. While women were not allowed to possess property in most circumstances, they were also looked on with great respect as the focus of chivalry. Few women owned shops in their own right, but they worked alongside their fathers, husbands and sons at trades and crafts for the good of the family. Even fewer women than men were literate, but their roles in raising families were considered important nonetheless.

Eleanor of Aquitaine, Marie de France, Christine de Pisan, Hildegarde von Bingen and many other medieval women whose names time has forgotten were able to rise to positions of power. They were the exceptions and not the rule, but the fact that they achieved a large degree of personal power demonstrates that it was not impossible — even in the historical medieval world — for women to rise to positions of prominence.

Hierarchy of Blood

In comparison to the mortal world, in the world of Cainites, the roles to which people are born take on little significance. A powerful ancient vampire may Embrace an old woman, a leper, a child, a Jew or a Saracen, and woe to the neonate who attempts to enforce mortal prejudices upon his vampiric betters! In a world where Chimerstry, Obfuscate and Vicissitude can transform one's appearance in an instant, any vampire who survives for long quickly learns that judging his fellows on the basis of superficial traits like gender is not only dangerous, but often deadly. Though it often takes a century or more for some neonates to get used to the idea, female vampires are considered equals to their male counterparts, particularly among elders. Vampire society is thus comparatively progressive.

Life Among the Kine

Most people live on the land, and are slaves to the rhythms of the seasons. Spring and early summer are slow, monotonous times, with plowing, sowing, animals' births and crafts to occupy the long daylight hours. There are festivals and Christian holidays, and the long Lent fast (a month before Easter when the Church insists that people abstain from eating meat or dairy products). The damage of winter is repaired, and vegetable plots are overhauled.

Late summer and fall are fraught with constant hard work (reaping, haymaking, grape picking and threshing) and plenty of worries. (What if a high wind flattens the nearly ripe barley? What if the grapes wither from drought?) Villagers who pursue other trades through the rest of the year (miners, weavers, carpenters) are recruited to help with the harvests. Even beggars and the destitute might find work and a square meal at these times.

Winter is a time to hole up and hope, to make and mend, and to pray for mild weather. Peasants' drafty huts are often made of wattle and daub (wooden frames with mud and dung for plaster). Harsh winters kill livestock and people alike, storms demolish houses and farm buildings, rats and insects eat or spoil cured meats and grains laid up for the winter.

For the few who live in the towns and cities life is more regular, but often no easier. Many craftsmen labor from dawn to dusk each day, and it is hunger — not greed — that drives them to work even on Sundays and holy days. The poor artisan spends nearly all his income on food, or more if the harvest is poor.

Indeed, cities suffer more than anywhere else when the harvests fail, as country nobles and peasants keep the scarce food for themselves. Famines sweep Europe at least once every 10 years. Even more dangerous to the townsfolk are fire and disease, for urban settlements are cramped and squalid, with sewage running in the gutters between flammable, thatched, wooden buildings. Frequent visitors bring illnesses, and carelessness brings fires.

Plagues

Disease is one of the leading causes of death in the Dark Medieval world. The Black Plague that decimated nearly a third of Europe is many years away from the late 12th century, but smaller outbreaks of disease can still wipe out entire towns. Plague is transmitted through blood and saliva (coughing or sneezing), and its most disgusting symptoms mimic those of the Mortis power Plague.

Many of the deaths attributed to plague are in fact the work of vampires. As their victims waste away over a period of days or weeks, growing paler and weaker with each feeding, it may appear to friends and family the unfortunate are stricken with sickness.

Some groups of vampires, often those who think little of Caine's Six Traditions, actively pursue and sometimes perpetuate plague and disease. In some cases, whole mortal villages have been wiped out over the course of a single winter. Vampires are mostly unharmed by mortal ailments, and may transfer disease from one vessel to another during feeding. Certain diseases will manifest in vampires from drinking tainted blood, but these effects are nonaggravated and can be healed normally.

Shortly after signs of plague strike an area, coteries of brash Cainites arrive to feed upon the dying and the still-healthy. The truly ruthless have been known to create plagues of their own and expose whole mortal communities to the ailments, the better to hide their blood-drinking. It can only be so long before such blatant atrocities go punished.

Medical science is in its infancy, and while the nobility may be able to afford the best, even the most expensive physicians may do more harm than good. Epidemics respect neither rank nor wealth. Nobles might fall victim to the atrocities of war, or die on some journey; the wealthy travel a great deal (touring their estates, negotiating with their peers). They might find themselves beset by bandits, wrecked at sea by some storm or dying of more common misfortunes — an infected wound inflicted by a fall from a horse, or a chill brought on by being caught in a storm. Furthermore, peasant rebellions are not uncommon, and although they never really achieve anything, the mobs often kill a few of their hated overlords before they are routed.

MEDIEVAL BELIEFS

The vast majority of medieval people do not believe in liberty, equality, democracy or individualism. They do not believe in science, rational inquiry or the power of the human mind. Instead, they believe in rigid social distinctions, the rule of the elite and the organization of society according to groups. This is a world in which the nobility is believed to be appointed by God and assumed to be naturally superior as rulers. It is also a world in which "justice" dictates that a whole community may be punished for the crimes of one member (an entire village may be burned because some of its people have hunted the king's deer, for example). And it is a world in which an entire ethnic group — the Jews — are persecuted for what their forebears are said to have done a millennium before.

In place of science and inquiry, the medieval world has religion and belief. True knowledge, the Church teaches, comes only from God, and is revealed through the Bible — and through the Church.

RELIGION

The vast majority of Europe's inhabitants are at least nominally Christian. The remainder are mainly Jews, although in places isolated groups of pagans persist. The only true stronghold of paganism is the kingdom of Lithuania, although pockets of paganism endure among the Lapps of the far north, the tribes of northern Poland, the inhabitants of the Isle of Man in the Irish Sea, and in isolated mountain communities scattered throughout Eastern Europe. Elsewhere, Christianity has replaced the old religions.

The medieval Christian Church believes that it is the only true religion, worshipping the only true God. All other religions are false and are thus blasphemies against God, serving the purposes of Satan. The Church offers salvation, based on the belief that Jesus Christ physically rose from the dead and now sits in Heaven to grant eternal life to those who follow Him. Of course, the Church argues that to follow Christ a person must not only believe in Him, but must also obey the Church, avoid sin and, if possible, perform good works. "Sins" include theft, murder, assault and other crimes, but also pride, gluttony, laziness, greed, witchcraft, adultery, fornication, sodomy and usury, among other things.

Throughout Europe, Christianity has a religious monopoly. The Jews do not proselytize, and pagans are slain if they attempt to undermine the Church's teachings. The Church can tell the people whatever it wants. Many people may have unusual understandings of Christian doctrine, and sometimes they band together to form organized groups of heretics — but even these people are essentially Christians. They may disagree about the particulars of Christian doctrine (they might believe that the Church should forsake its property, that priests need not be celibate or that only the poor will be saved), but they accept the basics: there is a God, Christ was His "Son," and there is a Devil.

To the medieval mind, it is nigh-inconceivable that God does not exist. Agnosticism and atheism would seem absurd or insane — if indeed anyone suggested such a thing.

THE CAINITE HERESY

Founded in 413 by a Byzantine priest named Procopius, the Cainite heresy is one of the most insidious and terrible effects that the undead have had on mortal society. Rumored to have been pieced together from fragments of the *Book of Nod* discovered in a cave near the Dead Sea, the Cainite heresy melds together certain of the more eschatological (i.e., relating to the end of the world) traditional Biblical texts and recovered sections of the *Book of Nod* to create a worship that is both debased and glorious.

The heresy is founded on the notion that Caine was in fact God's favorite of Adam's two sons, and that the mark that was placed upon him was in fact a sign of God's favor. Had God truly been displeased with Abel's murder, He would not have hesitated to slay Caine as well. By permitting Caine to live and setting a mark upon him, God expressed tacit approval of the murder. Caine, then, and all his brood had been touched by the hand of the Lord, and were to be revered as angels.

Originally restricted to certain flagellant and monastic sects, the heresy found its way westward with the Byzantine armies that surged over the Italian peninsula during Justinian's reign. It settled in Rome even as the Arian Christians were driven out, and insinuated itself into the belly of the Western Church. And so, in the corridors of power of the Roman and Eastern Churches, the heretics quietly steered the wrath of the holy against targets other than their angels.

By A.D. 879, the Cainite worship had become formalized, and it has continued to the current day in more or less the same form. Most of the forms and figures of traditional Catholic or Eastern Orthodox Christianity are retained, with the primary difference coming in the form of the Communion offered and sought.

As might be expected, the body and blood with which the Cainites take Communion is not the symbolic wafer and wine. The question of the transubstantiation of the Host into actual flesh never raises its head in Cainite religious debates. Having come to the conclusion that the blood and the body of the brood of Caine are one and the same, Cainite priests and worshippers (for there are many Cainite heretics among the laity) take their infrequent Communion with vampiric vitæ.

Of course, true vitæ is not always available, and certain, more degraded congregations have substituted animal or even children's blood for that of vampires'. It was through the actions of one such group in Ostia that the heresy was finally uncovered and declared anathema in 754, but by then the Cainite worship was too extensive to be destroyed. Both mortals and Cainites despise these pathetic brutalities; the former for obvious reasons, the latter for the fact that they find being associated with these feeble imitators to be insulting. Furthermore, Cainite heretics of this sort do more to stir up mortal wrath against vampires than do the depredations of a dozen ravenous Gangrel on the prowl.

Many Cainites are aware of and actively encourage the activities of Cainite cells. They will happily contribute some of their vitæ to these unholy rituals, for the notion of creating cadres

of fanatical ghoul followers is an attractive one. Furthermore, this sort of arrangement usually results in Blood Oaths being formed by entire heretic congregations to the fonts of their Communion. As a result, the Cainite heresy is splintered into many small cults of personality, each devoted to one particular vampire.

This factionalism is the only thing that prevents the Cainite cult from exerting a much greater influence over the Church and Europe as a whole. Indeed, many heretic groups find themselves at each other's throats, each accusing the other of serving an inferior representative of divine grace. Doglike in their loyalty, the notion that they are merely pawns in the squabbles of two Cainites never crosses their minds.

There are Cainite heretics in the Vatican and the great abbeys as well, though these tend to be a more subtle breed of worshipper. Very few are Blood Oath-bound to a particular Cainite, as there are more than enough vampires dealing with such to ensure a fresh supply of vitæ for each Communion. These heretics use their influence to protect the rights and properties of those they worship, and twist policy and doctrine to serve Cainite ends. Each bears a silver ring inscribed with a passage from Genesis 4:15 ("Therefore whosoever slayeth Caine, vengeance shall be taken on him sevenfold") or simply the cryptic inscription "I:IV:XV." While fellowship in the heresy is not acknowledged in public, it is a real and potent force in the politics of the Curias and debates of the holy.

Geography

In the Dark Medieval world, Europe is dominated by a small number of powerful kingdoms. The Holy Roman Empire is the largest state in Europe, and covers Germany, northern Italy and part of western France. It is currently in the midst of a long civil war fought between two rival Emperors, Otto of Brunswick and Philip of Swabia. The Empire actually comprises dozens of small duchies; the dukes owe allegiance to the emperor but often rule their lands as independent monarchs, and it is the feuds between these rulers that so often divide the empire.

The English kings (currently King Richard the Lionheart) rule lands in England, Wales, northern France and (theoretically) Ireland. In 1199 Richard is killed in battle and is succeeded by his vicious brother John. The Kingdom of France under Philip II, perhaps the strongest single kingdom in Europe and certainly the best administered, is expanding by seizing lands in northern France from England. Constantinople, under the Emperor Alexius III, controls an empire including modern-day Turkey (disputed with the Moors), Serbia and Greece.

Other kingdoms rule the fringes of Europe, including the kingdoms of Hungary, Poland, Jerusalem (actually based on Cyprus, as Jerusalem itself is in Moslem hands) and Scotland; the Principalities of Russia; and the "Empire" of Bulgaria. Numerous smaller kingdoms and principalities also exist, such as the petty kingdoms of Iberia, the four principalities of Ireland, the tiny states of

Switzerland, and the kingdom of Denmark. Europe also contains one last bulwark against Christianity, the pagan kingdom of Lithuania and the lands surrounding it along the Baltic coast.

Perhaps the most powerful person in Europe is the Pope. The Pope controls his own private principality in central Italy, including the city of Rome itself, but more importantly, he is the head of the Church throughout western Europe. While the earthly kingdoms are divided among warring monarchs, all acknowledge the Pope as a higher spiritual authority beneath whose jurisdiction all mortal kingdoms fall. Some also argue that as Christ's representative on earth, the Pope should have supreme authority on all matters, and claim that all secular rulers should bow down in obedience to him. The year 1198 sees the death of the moderate Pope, Celestine III, and his replacement by the shrewd and domineering Innocent III.

Law and Order

There are no "police forces" or other professional law enforcement agencies in the medieval world. There are, however, numerous groups and individuals who share responsibility for keeping the peace.

Individual wardens or groups of soldiers are posted to each town and city gate, to ensure that lepers and known criminals do not enter, and to levy tolls on the merchants who pass through. Each town or city also has a watch. This is usually organized into groups of one to four lightly armed men, who patrol the streets with lanterns, looking for criminals, vagrants and signs of fire. Most patrol on foot, but in large cities they may have horses. Small cities have only single watches. Larger settlements are divided into wards, each with its own watch.

The ruler of each town or city (be it a mayor, magnate or royally appointed nobleman) also maintains a group of soldiers — not mindless thugs and mercenaries, but intelligent, scrupulous men who can be trusted to conduct searches for outlaws and criminals in and around the town. Most powerful nobles maintain small personal armies, which may be called upon to hunt out or pursue criminals. In the countryside, these nobles and their men are the only enforcers of order, and many noblemen abuse this power.

Any citizen who sees a crime in progress is obliged to "call a hue and cry." This means that he screams, shouts and pursues the perpetrator, alerting all around him to the criminal's misdeeds. Those standing nearby are obliged to join in the chase, unless some urgent need prevents them. Those who ignore a hue and cry may be fined.

"Crimes" in the Dark Medieval world range from petty disturbance and selling shoddy merchandise to immorality (e.g., running a brothel inside the city walls) to theft and murder. However, crimes which smack of blasphemy are investigated by the Church. Gross crimes (such as devil worship or blatant supernatural activity) sometimes attract special Inquisitors. These are well- educated, astute men, who are appointed by a local bishop to investigate crimes against God. They have no power to punish offenders, but they are so respected (or feared) by the nobility that they can easily persuade local authorities to arrest or execute blasphemers.

Personal Security

Medieval mortals may carry daggers or eating knives around with them. In most regions people are required by law to keep spears or bows, for use in defending their towns or settlements, but carrying such weapons in public is often illegal and is certainly rare. The wardens who guard town gates and the watches that patrol the streets at night may carry swords or maces, but only nobles and professional soldiers are more heavily armed.

Soldiers may carry swords or spears, shields and sometimes bows or crossbows. Nobles can own an array of weapons, usually including swords, daggers, lances and shields, plus metal armor — but they rarely go about armed, unless war or other danger threatens.

Locks are expensive and rare, and are crude by modern standards. Doors and shutters are normally just fastened from within by sturdy wooden bars. Wealthy mortals may have dull glass in their windows, but most folk just cover them with sackcloth, and fasten shutters across them at night. This means that a barred door or window cannot be opened from the outside, except by brute force, but also that a building can only be secured if there are people inside.

People routinely bar all doors and windows before going to sleep each night. Shops as well as houses are locked, since merchants and artisans live above or adjacent to their storehouses and workshops. It is very rare for folk to set guards over their houses or premises at night. Important nobles might have soldiers who patrol their castles, but the closest things that most mortals have to private security systems are guard dogs or flocks of geese. Of course, Cainites should not underestimate these animals. The dogs may be as tough as wolves (some are bred to hunt down wolves, others to bait bears or chase stags), and even geese can make a fearful noise.

Superstition in the Medieval World

The people of the Dark Medieval world know that vampires exist. They tell stories and legends of the dead who walk, of people who gain immortality but cannot bear the light of day, of semihuman monsters and fiends who eat human flesh or drink human blood. These stories are often inaccurate; some tales actually confuse vampires with other creatures. But however confused their ideas about vampires might be, these people know of vampires, and fear them.

Such stories tell of people who rise from the dead to terrorize their neighbors and relatives. These creatures are often seen as ravenous beasts (cunning vampires tend to evade notice), or are portrayed as ghosts (legends spawned by wraiths have become confused with vampire myths). Many vampire stories have no mention of blood-drinking — vampires can erase evidence of their feeding, after all — but portray the undead creatures as purposeless revenants.

Ghouls are often considered examples of people "possessed" by evil spirits, and are rarely connected with vampires. Cainites themselves are often considered to be demonic spirits inhabiting the bodies of the dead. The effects of vampires' supernatural powers, called Disciplines, reinforce the belief that they are demons or aided by evil spirits.

Many "traditional" charms against vampires are advocated by peasant wise women and priests. It is believed that garlic, acorns and hawthorn boughs can keep vampires at bay. It is said that the undead cannot cross a line of salt or holy water. A crucifix or a holy man's prayers are meant to hold them back, and vampires may not cross thresholds without an invitation. In most cases, the charms are empty superstitions.

Popular methods for destroying vampires are crude but effective. The most common method is to rip out the vampire's heart or burn the entire body. Some knowledgeable individuals, however, may have more accurate or detailed understandings of Cainites and their customs. Some pious priests, for example, have committed themselves to destroying all of "Satan's minions" (including vampires, of course), and may learn much of the Cainites during their Inquisitions.

Hunters and Hunted

Though vampires fancy themselves to be at the top of the food chain, there are many who come into conflict with these hunters of the night. These antagonists may often be dealt with through guile and subterfuge, and the vampire who attempts to kill anything that poses an obstacle to him will quickly learn that not every problem can be solved through brute strength.

- **Templars and Church Knights:** With the power of the Church supporting the might of their swords, these foes are dangerous indeed. Their ability to rally townsfolk against "the forces of Lucifer" — real or imagined — can pose a serious threat to any Cainites who cross their path.

- **Mortal Authorities:** Dismissed by some as insignificant, mortal authorities outside the Church can still make unlife decidedly unpleasant for a vampire if they are crossed.

- **Other Vampires:** Though most disagreements and power struggles are settled by intrigue, duels to the death between Cainite foes are not unheard of. Should the local prince be called upon to dispense justice, the consequences could be dire indeed.

- **Mythic Beasts:** Rarely seen, these are among the most deadly enemies a vampire can face. Fortunately they are only found in remote areas usually unfrequented by mortals, and therefore unlikely places for a vampire to be anyway.

- **Demons and Diabolists:** Those who would serve Hell are often even more of a threat to a vampire's existence than those who serve Heaven. With their reasonable requests and often sympathetic conversation, these fiends will more often than not twist the soul of a vampire. After all, which is more fearsome: the foe who attacks you with sword and crucifix, or the one who tempts you into his palace?

- **Werewolves:** These shapechanging beasts are age-old enemies of vampires. To travel through forests they claim as their domain is extremely dangerous, as their hatred of vampires verges on lunacy.

- **Magicians:** Their magicks are often potent, but many are physically weak. Still, only the most foolish neonate would scoff at the power they wield. Though the magicks that most common folk know can do little more than heal the pox or predict what the future may hold, the mightiest sorcerors are said to be able to cause the sun to shine in the dead of night, or smite their enemies with bolts of flame from leagues away.

- **Ghosts:** According to legend, these spirits of the restless dead are cursed to walk the earth until Doomsday. Though not all have power in the physical world, those that do can make even the stones and winds do their bidding. Most seek revenge for wrongs against them in life, but stories persist of mad ghosts bent on the destruction of all the living world.

- **Faeries:** Unpredictable and wild, faeries may help or harm individual Cainites at a whim. Mortals are familiar with the warnings against taking the gifts or food of faeries, but it is whispered that but a drop of their blood may bring ecstasy or fae powers…or agony beyond imagining.

Chapter Three: Clans

How art thou lost! how on a sudden lost,
Defaced, deflowered, and now to death devote!
– Milton, Paradise Lost

The clans are like most human societies in a few respects. Each clan has a certain flavor, like a rare vintage, imparted by its particular bloodline from the progeny of Caine. Just as one might speak of a mannerism or tradition as being "typically German" or "very English," the Cainites might stereotype someone as "the archetypal Toreador" or "hopelessly Malkavian."

But the clans are also in a state of constant flux. Every few generations bring great change in human society, and the parasitic Cainites change as well. Sects rise and are as quickly reabsorbed. Some clans even perish, as the fall of Saulot and the Salubri shows. Ideologies change with human philosophies, as exemplified by the adoption of the Roads. In short, the status quo for any given clan may be quite different a hundred years hence – or even in another country. Players should use the clan descriptions as guidelines, not rules. The only things that hold true for all clan members are the Clan Disciplines and Weaknesses.

The following 13 clans claim descent from the Antediluvians, and are the only known true clans in existence. Although the Baali are often mentioned, details of this bloodline can be found under Antagonists (Chapter Nine). The devil-worshipping Baali are not a full-blooded clan, and are so uniformly and unwaveringly vile that they are recommended as Storyteller characters only. Other bloodlines exist, but have little influence or respect. Players may choose from any of the 13 clans, or may be one of the rare Caitiff — the clanless.

ASSAMITE

The Crusaders brought back many tales from the Holy Land, some of which concerned a band of fanatical killers. The word the Europeans coined for these silent murderers was *assassin*. The Cainites, however, already knew of a similar but far more dangerous threat from Araby — the diabolists of Clan Assamite.

The vampires of the West had encountered the Assamites long before the Crusaders. Some say that the conquerors who set out for the East — Alexander, for example — were pawns of the Cainites who feared the Assamites. Rumors aside, the Assamites are dreaded for good reason — they seek to better themselves through the practice of diablerie.

According to Assamite teachings, one must lower his generation in order to become closer to Caine, and therefore to Heaven. The truest method is, of course, diablerie. Murder was simply part and parcel of the way, and they became skilled of necessity. They even began a practice of accepting assassination contracts, payable by blood, from other Cainites. Although honor-bound to defend their clanmates, the Assamites had no compunctions about slaying any foreign vampires.

Recently, the Crusades have stirred up a new rash of Assamite activity. Many of the clan have watched their herds and living families suffer at the hands of the marauding Westerners, and they thirst for revenge. As Islam takes root in the lands of the Middle East, and Western atrocities hover ever closer, the Assamites are now more ready than ever to drink deeply of the European vitae, whether contracted to do so or not.

Sobriquet: Saracens

Appearance: There are no known Assamites from any culture other than those of the East — Arabs, Moors and the like. Consequently, most have the distinguishing characteristics of the "Saracens": swarthy skin, aquiline features and dark hair and eyes. Unlike other Cainites, they do not grow paler in death. Instead, their skin becomes darker over the years; very elder Assamites are nearly ebony-black.

Haven: The clan elders live at Alamut, a hidden fortress atop a mountain somewhere in Asia Minor. Neonates who operate in Europe choose the most inaccessible, remote and private locations as their havens.

Background: The clan tends to watch potential neonates before allowing an Assamite to sire progeny. Although necessity sometimes demands that a new childe be sired quickly, the Assamites prefer making time for an apprenticeship. Optimally, they teach a new initiate (or *fida'i*) for seven years, but this varies with need. The one thing that no Assamite sire neglects to instill in his childe is clan loyalty.

Character Creation: Assamites do not Embrace females or Westerners, and tend to select mathematicians, poets and scientists as often as they choose warriors or thieves. Their Demeanors disguise their true selves by necessity. Any Attributes may be primary, but Skills are usually the primary Abilities. Popular Backgrounds include Mentor (the sire) and Generation (often from diablerie). Virtually every Assamite follows the Blood Road.

Clan Disciplines: Celerity, Obfuscate, Quietus

Weaknesses: All Assamites must give a 20 percent blood tithe to their sires, in accordance with clan law. In addition, the practices of the Assamites mean that any ritual or Auspex use which could detect a diabolist will pinpoint an Assamite — even if the Assamite had never even so much as tasted another vampire's blood.

Organization: The Assamites follow a hierarchy that peaks with the Old Man of the Mountain, the master of the clan. Assamites are incredibly loyal to one another, and the clan operates with a startling efficiency. If not for the clan's insistence on self-reliance, one who wrongs a *fida'i* could well feel an Assamite elder's anger.

Quote: *Hush and be still, O my enemy. It is nothing less than Fate which drives my hand, and you suffer no dishonor in falling to a superior foe.*

STEREOTYPES

• Brujah — Had they remained scholars and not taken up arms, we would have been as friends.

• Cappadocians — Such magics should not be. They defy Allah with their practices.

• Followers of Set — I fear no serpent, not even that which walks as men do.

• Gangrel — There is no honor in becoming a beast, no matter how well you kill.

• Lasombra — I have seen their hand behind the Crusades. They owe us a debt of blood.

• Malkavians — Give charity to the mad, so it is written. But remember that their minds are feeble and broken.

• Nosferatu — Is it not said that deformity is the mark of a tainted soul? To destroy one of these pitiful horrors is certainly a great service to them.

• Ravnos — Honorless dogs. Surely even their blood is tainted.

• Toreador — They have attained some primitive enlightenment, but they are ultimately weak.

• Tremere — These sorcerers are of like mind to us. They make useful pawns — and dangerous foes.

• Tzimisce — They are distorted, selfish and base. Even the Gangrel are more like men than these.

• Ventrue — They have learned of Alamut and would lay siege to the Eagle's Nest. A shame they will always fail.

• Baali — We bear them no malice and do not consider them fearsome. But the sons of the Shaitan must never reach their goal.

BRUJAH

The Brujah are the ultimate scholar-warriors, always striving toward perfection of mind and body. The elders of the clan can recall the Golden Age, and speak wistfully of lost Carthage. It is the ultimate goal of the Brujah to bring about a better place, one where vampires of all sorts can exist peacefully and prosperously.

Unfortunately, no wound stings worse than a dream denied. The death of Carthage seems to have only increased their rancor, and the other clans' refusal to move beyond the status quo leaves a bitter taste in their mouths. So they fight. They fight the Ventrue for destroying Carthage, they fight the Lasombra for encouraging the status quo, they fight the Tremere for slaying Saulot — the list seems eternal. The Brujah are nothing if not lovers of a cause.

Currently, the Brujah are becoming a clan divided. They cannot agree among themselves how best to bring about change, or indeed what goal they should pursue. Some favor creating a society where humans and Cainites peacefully coexist; others wish to remain in the shadows, egalitarian among themselves but superior to mortals. In addition, clan members are now Embracing as many men-at-arms as they are thinkers and philosophers, preparing for the battles they say are coming. The clan that believes in harmony is splintering under the weight of its own change.

Although the clan's infrastructure is suffering through a state of decay, Brujah will rally to one another's side when the need is there. Most sires treat their childer with more respect than is demonstrated in other clans. The Brujah are traditionally suspicious of outsiders, but if their favor is won, they can be the most doggedly loyal (and stubborn) friends one can have.

Sobriquet: Zealots

Appearance: For the most part, Brujah are fit and have the bearing of eagles. They prefer Embracing neonates that are near perfection in body and mind, but the current age is forcing them to lower their standards somewhat. Brujah identify strongly with mortals, and neonates prefer dressing as they did in life (or at least looking as normal as possible).

Haven: Brujah live where they choose, but most prefer to live near people. Many maintain their mortal residences (if any), and on rare occasions, two will share accommodations in a city.

Background: Brujah look for thinkers and those frequently dissatisfied with society as they know it. A craftsman may be unlettered, but will be considered if he can express his thoughts reasonably well. Martial candidates for the Embrace are considered for their thinking ability, strategy and planning, not just for how well they swing a sword. The Brujah prize egalitarianism and will choose whomever they deem worthy, whether man or woman, serf or noble.

Character Creation: Brujah tend to come from intellectual or man-at-arms concepts, but can be of practically any background. Spain is the current seat of Brujah power, and many neonates come from there. The common link is their desire to see the status quo turned into something truly important. They usually have aggressive or dynamic Natures and Demeanors. Physical or Mental Attributes are usually primary, as are Talents and Knowledges. Brujah tend to have Allies, Retainers and Herd as their Backgrounds. Most follow the Roads of Humanity or Heaven.

Clan Disciplines: Celerity, Potence, Presence

Weaknesses: Although they consistently deny it, the Brujah are far and away the clan most susceptible to frenzy. Most take no pride in this flaw of their blood, and many become hostile to the point of frenzy if the subject is raised. The difficulty for a Brujah's frenzy roll is always two higher than the listed number.

Organization: Brujah tend to their own affairs for the most part, but can call on their clanfolk in times of need. Occasionally, the Brujah of a region will gather for a council, sharing news and attempting to settle on a specific common purpose. These councils rarely end with much accomplished, save more promises of loyalty and camaraderie.

Quote: *You fools! There are greater things in existence, and they are within your reach! We can change the world if you but stand with us. Wake up before you die!*

STEREOTYPES

- Assamites — We share a common enemy in the Ventrue, but nothing else.
- Cappadocians — Morbid and deluded. Leave them to their graverobbing.
- Followers of Set — Where we build, they corrode. They are our enemies.
- Gangrel — Their breasts burn with the fire of the Beast, but they do not try to rise above it. If only they were civilized, they would make fine allies.
- Lasombra — Contemptible skulkers and puppetmasters. The first steps to a just society will have to be taken on Lasombra corpses.
- Malkavians — Alas for the children of Malkav, for they are a broken clan. Learn from them, and aid your brethren, lest we fall into chaos as deeply as they have.

- Nosferatu — Despite their curse, they have the sharpest ears of us all. Do not dismiss them.
- Ravnos — They despise truth and run from it.
- Toreador — We value art and accomplishment, as do they. But their disdain to fight for their beliefs damns them, as it would us, were we to rely on the Toreador.
- Tremere — Never believe their lies. They killed Saulot for love of power, and would kill you for the same.
- Tzimisce — Be wary when you walk with them. Close two eyes, and you will wake up with none.
- Ventrue — They have hated us since Carthage. Since Carthage, we have hated them.
- Baali — There is nothing I prize that the Baali do not seek to defile. Send them back to the pits they so long for.

CAPPADOCIANS

Known among Cainites for millennia as the "Clan of Death," the Cappadocians are shunned even by their brethren for their macabre interests. Cappadocius himself was an iconoclastic priest in life, and continued his search for the secrets of life, death and what lay beyond after his Becoming. His childer have continued his research, and through their efforts Cainites have learned much about the nature of their existence. Still, the secretive nature of the clan has caused as many people to fear them as respect them.

In vampiric society, Cappadocians often fill the role of advisors to princes. They are respected for their insight and wisdom, and largely trusted due to their lack of interest in earthly power. Because of this, the Ventrue and Cappadocians have formed an unofficial alliance, whereby the former provides a secure place to do research in exchange for the counsel of the latter. Their seat of power lies in Turkey, where they have access to remote research locations as well as centers of learning.

The clan has recently Embraced a small cabal of necromancers in order to further their studies. These new vampires are currently developing a Discipline of their own, although it is far from polished. It is the hope of the Cappadocians that this shared knowledge will help break down the final barriers, revealing the truths they have sought for millennia.

Sobriquet: Graverobbers

Appearance: Most Cappadocians spend their nights engaged in study of death, so it is not surprising that many of them affect the dress of scholars and monks. Long dark robes, simply cut and unadorned, are most common, though some also wear carved and painted masks, fashioned to look like skulls or death-throes.

Haven: Members of the Clan of Death often choose tombs and ossuaries, or the catacombs beneath cathedrals or monasteries, where one more robed figure is unlikely to attract attention. They surround themselves with reminders of mortality, often in the form of macabre works of art.

Background: Cappadocians select neonates from scholars and the priesthood, though occasionally an executioner, tomb-robber, thief or Crusader is chosen for the Becoming. A love of learning and insatiable curiosity are of the utmost importance if the neonate is to be able to carry out the clan's research.

Character Creation: Most Cappadocians are learned folk and those who are of a philosophical bent, including many of Scholar and Visionary concepts. Mental Attributes are always primary, and Knowledges tend to predominate over Talents and Skills. Though the ability to contribute to the clan's knowledge of death is paramount, this is not to say that every Graverobber is a weakling. Many prefer the Road of Heaven.

Clan Disciplines: Auspex, Fortitude, Mortis

Weaknesses: No matter how much blood a Cappadocian drinks, her skin will always remain pale and cold as a bloodless corpse. Because of this deathly pallor, the difficulty for any Social roll is increased by one, and they are more easily marked as vampires. **Note:** If you are using the optional system of Merits and Flaws, Cappadocians may not take the Merit *Sanguine Humor*.

Organization: Cappadocians are largely solitary and meet only infrequently with each other to exchange knowledge. Each winter all members of the clan who are able travel to a disused monastery, where they perform secret rituals on the winter solstice.

Quote: *In the end, we shall all end up as dust — yes, even you, my brother. But are you really foolish enough to think that will be the end of existence?*

STEREOTYPES

- Assamites — Killers who have no appreciation for the sacred act they carry out time and again.
- Brujah — They claim to fight for what they believe in, but there is rarely any spiritual depth to their crusades.
- Followers of Set — To corrupt another's soul is surely the greatest crime imaginable. Although they believe themselves to be masters of spiritual decay, they know little of the consequences of their actions.
- Gangrel — In their attempt to reconcile man and beast, they have left their higher selves behind.
- Lasombra — With all their talk of darkness, they forget that without light, there can be no shadow.
- Malkavians — To see into the realms of the spirit as they do requires true wisdom and self-knowledge. While others dismiss them as fools and madmen, we know the wisdom behind their eyes.
- Nosferatu — Always hiding, always afraid to let people see them for what they are. What kind of toll does this constant deception take on their souls?
- Ravnos — Vagabonds and beggars who debase the name *vampyr* with their childish games.
- Toreador — Their search to understand the eternal through art is admirable, but until they learn to look beyond the temporal world they are doomed to fail.
- Tremere — Upstarts who seek a power they cannot hope to understand. A little knowledge of the occult arts can be a dangerous thing indeed, as they will doubtless learn in time.
- Tzimisce — Mastery of the flesh is admirable; if they could but see beyond it….
- Ventrue — Their realm is the temporal, fleeting world of mortal power. Admirable allies, they have achieved near mastery of what they set their sights on.
- Baali — Fools. If they truly understood the meaning of the eternity beyond death, they would not talk of it so lightly.

FOLLOWERS OF SET

There are few vampires who would willingly grant hospitality to a Follower of Set, and for good reason. The Setites, as they call themselves, are servants of darkness and corruption incarnate. The clan's ultimate goal is to corrode the ethics away from humanity and Cainites alike, creating a surfeit of slaves for themselves and their dark master.

Legends name Set, or sometimes Sutekh, as the clan's founder. In ancient Egypt, or so they say, Set was a great warrior and hunter. He hounded the desert nights like a beast and became worshipped by mortals as the god of night. He welcomed such worship and enjoyed the respect of his fellow Cainites. But eventually he was cast out. Here the stories become confused; some say Osiris banished Set, while others claim Horus defeated him. In any event, Set swore to reestablish his rule, but this time from the darkness. And in his footprints walked his childer.

Set disappeared in A.D. 33, promising to return someday to his followers. The Setites therefore work to make the world a fitting place for their master's return. So far, they have enjoyed moderate success. They approve of the widespread disease and imbalance of wealth; the more unhappy someone is, the more likely she will snatch at any chance to better her lot.

Setites work in insidious ways. They believe that the best way to corrupt someone is to give that person exactly what he wants, and watch desire breed even stronger desire. They foster ecstasy and indulgence in their flocks, always encouraging excess, quietly addicting their prey to the pleasures only the Setites can provide. Pity the Thrall with a Setite Regnant, or anyone else caught in their honeyed snare. The Followers of Set do what they do from religious zeal, and thus can be even more merciless than the inhuman Tzimisce.

Sobriquet: Serpents

Appearance: Most Setites come from Middle Eastern or North African backgrounds; however, some appear in the most unexpected places. Red hair is prized as a mark of Set. Many of the Followers wear archaic neo-Egyptian robes while in the privacy of their havens. Ritual disfigurement is popular among zealous Setites, though the nature of such varies among individuals.

Haven: Setites prefer lairs deep underground; caverns, grottoes and oubliettes are all popular. They enjoy decorating the walls of these havens with Egyptian hieroglyphs detailing the story of Set. Rare cloths and incenses are also popular among those Setites who enjoy boasting of their decadence. They call their havens temples, and often place them under or near the headquarters of any cult they may be controlling.

Background: Followers of Set typically choose neonates from their own retainers. They tend to select only those of Egyptian descent, but some say that the most extensive Viking raids picked up Setites and carried them back to the north. These rumors, and those of Norse Cainites paying homage to the Midgard Serpent through debased rites, have yet to be proven.

Character Creation: Setites, particularly those in Western Europe, tend to come from outsider concepts. Possible Natures include Tyrant, Rogue or Monster; their Demeanors might be whatever seems appropriate. They lean toward primary Social Attributes and Talents. Most have the Background of Retainers, as well as some Contacts, Herd or Influence. Loyal Setites follow the Road of Typhon.

Clan Disciplines: Obfuscate, Presence, Serpentis

Weaknesses: Setites are very susceptible to sunlight. Double the dice for damage from any exposure to the sun.

Organization: Setite groups organize into temples and have a form of church hierarchy passed down from the first priests of Set. They often form small cults of mortal followers, with themselves as the dark clergy. There is some backstabbing and treachery within the ranks, but only as long as no outside force threatens the clan.

Quote: *Ah, say no more, my friend. No words are necessary. You hunger — I can sate you. You thirst — I can quench that thirst. Please, follow me.*

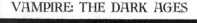

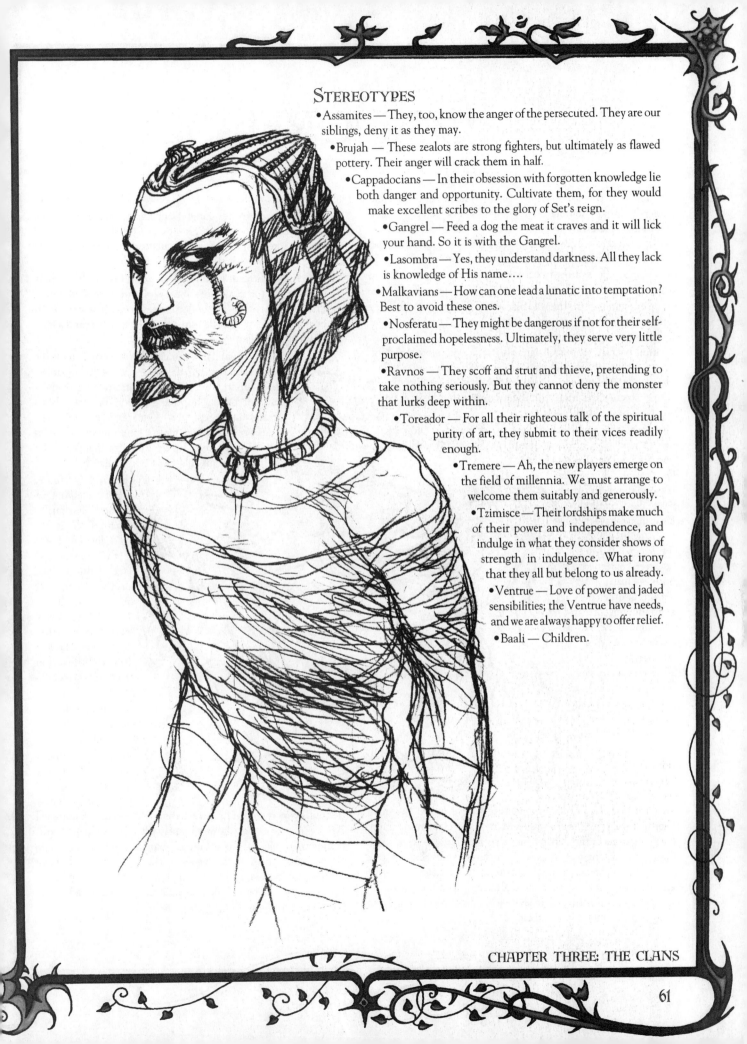

STEREOTYPES

- Assamites — They, too, know the anger of the persecuted. They are our siblings, deny it as they may.
- Brujah — These zealots are strong fighters, but ultimately as flawed pottery. Their anger will crack them in half.
- Cappadocians — In their obsession with forgotten knowledge lie both danger and opportunity. Cultivate them, for they would make excellent scribes to the glory of Set's reign.
- Gangrel — Feed a dog the meat it craves and it will lick your hand. So it is with the Gangrel.
- Lasombra — Yes, they understand darkness. All they lack is knowledge of His name....
- Malkavians — How can one lead a lunatic into temptation? Best to avoid these ones.
- Nosferatu — They might be dangerous if not for their self-proclaimed hopelessness. Ultimately, they serve very little purpose.
- Ravnos — They scoff and strut and thieve, pretending to take nothing seriously. But they cannot deny the monster that lurks deep within.
- Toreador — For all their righteous talk of the spiritual purity of art, they submit to their vices readily enough.
- Tremere — Ah, the new players emerge on the field of millennia. We must arrange to welcome them suitably and generously.
- Tzimisce — Their lordships make much of their power and independence, and indulge in what they consider shows of strength in indulgence. What irony that they all but belong to us already.
- Ventrue — Love of power and jaded sensibilities; the Ventrue have needs, and we are always happy to offer relief.
- Baali — Children.

GANGREL

Through the forest nights wander the lonely, nomadic Gangrel. Unlike their brethren, Gangrel spurn the trappings of civilization, preferring to roam the deep wilds in solitude. The Gangrel is a clan only in the loosest sense; its members tend to be rugged individualists, indifferent to the protocols of either mortal or vampire. They are the bestial ones, the closest to losing themselves to the wild.

Few beings know the wild places like the Gangrel do. They remember many of the ancient sites of elder magic, and have allied with (or at least know how to avoid) the few mythic beasts still dwelling near those sites. Gangrel also traffic with more mundane beasts, and most Gangrel can converse with the denizens of forest and field. Indeed, Gangrel tend to be more comfortable with such creatures than with the mortals they were or the vampires they have become.

Of all vampires, Gangrel have made the most progress toward establishing anything close to tolerable relations with the Lupines. Perhaps this is because Gangrel are themselves master shapeshifters; most tales of transforming vampires have their roots in the doings of the Gangrel. This talent, however, comes with a price — many older Gangrel lose their human form altogether, becoming more like the beasts they emulate. Many Gangrel also have lost any semblance of human behavior, and hunt and feast like wild animals.

Gangrel were once more common, but the decline of the ancient pagan cultures and the spread of human civilization (and its vampiric parasites) have forced the clan deeper and deeper into the wastes. Many Gangrel resent this, and battles have recently been fought between civilized "settlers" and Gangrel reluctant to leave their hunting grounds. Even those Gangrel who have accepted Christendom (if not necessarily Christianity) rarely venture into the more populous regions, instead wandering the back roads from hamlet to hamlet and farm to farm as the mood strikes them.

Sobriquet: Animals

Appearance: Many Gangrel appear as, and dress in the manner of, barbarian peoples. Furs, plaids, deerskin clothing and similar garb predominate. Some, emulating the Highland Picts, go about in woad and little else.

Of course, those unfortunate Gangrel who have fallen prey to the Beast one too many times have a look all their own. Tufted ears, horns, coats of fur, razor talons, gleaming catlike eyes, even feathers and scales adorn (deform?) these *bêtes noires*, and a feral musk wafts from them.

Haven: The Animals almost never establish a permanent haven, but instead wander the continent in an inscrutable migratory pattern. Occasionally one will mark a "hunting territory," but even this is usually quite expansive. Gangrel rarely enter the cities, preferring deep forests, lonely moors and even peat bogs and fens. Their ability to meld into the earth often means that the world is their haven.

Background: Many Gangrel come from pagan and barbarian civilizations: Celts, Vikings, Mongols, Lapps and the like. Those Gangrel drawn from "civilized" peoples tend to be chosen from foresters, yeomen and other sturdy, resourceful folk on the outer reaches of their civilization.

Character Creation: Gangrel rarely have sociable Natures or Demeanors, though Nature and Demeanor can be dissimilar (Gangrel rarely lie, but even more rarely reveal their true agendas). Physical Attributes are almost always primary, while Talents and Skills predominate among the Abilities. Gangrel often have Allies (forest tribes, magical creatures and the like), but rarely have Influence. Most Gangrel follow the Road of the Beast, though a very few from ancient bloodlines walk the Paradox Road.

Clan Disciplines: Animalism, Fortitude, Protean

Weaknesses: Gangrel are closely attuned to their inner Beasts, but this carries a drawback. As Gangrel fall prey to their ravenous urges, the Beast leaves its taint on their bodies. Each time a Gangrel frenzies, she gains an animal feature (a furry coat, a tail, hooves, horns, luminous eyes, a guttural voice, etc.). Every five such features reduce one of the Gangrel's Social Attributes (player's choice) by one. Ancient Gangrel often look (and sound, and smell) completely bestial.

Organization: The clan has no formal organization to speak of. Elder Gangrel are often respected for their might and cunning, but there are also tales of ancient, monstrous Gangrel berserkers brought down by packs of outraged younglings. A Gangrel's status, on the rare occasions it comes into play, is based on the tales of that Gangrel's deeds (even if told by the Gangrel herself — similar to the Celtic boasting contests).

Quote: *Thou art a valorous warrior, mortal, to have won through to this place. I shall give thee a death worthy of a champion and tell tales of thy heroism.*

STEREOTYPES

• **Assamites** — They are valiant, honorable and seek to stop Christendom's advance. Were they not hell-bent on hunting us down and drinking our blood, they might be boon companions.

• **Brujah** — Heh! They seek to find Heaven by locking themselves and a bunch of humans in a great walled crypt? Knowing the Brujah, their perfect city would be a blood-spattered abattoir in three nights.

• **Cappadocians** — They would learn more from the songs of a cricket than from the whispers of an ancient cadaver.

• **Followers of Set** — These tainted spawn of Jormungandr are most honest when shrieking in their death-throes.

• **Lasombra** — Treacherous churls. One worm of a Lasombra sought to ensnare me in his foul plot. For all his airs of superiority, his insides looked little different from most other vampires'.

• **Malkavians** — When a Malkavian speaks, listen. When a Malkavian acts, leave. When two Malkavians gather, run.

• **Nosferatu** — A great doom follows them. Leave these wretches to their misery.

• **Ravnos** — Vile, craven wastrels, the worst of our kind. They pander to the most contemptible vices and craft garish illusions to bolster their lies. When you meet one, rake your claws through its entrails to make sure it's real.

• **Toreador** — They have great gifts and could have been our kind's venerated bards. But instead of crafting stirring epics to exalt the valiant and praise the virtuous, the Toreador spew vilest slander and spin gaudy webs of lies.

• **Tremere** — These sorcerers must die, and may no songs be sung of their passing, but let their name be stricken from the sagas and forgotten by all worthy creatures.

• **Tzimisce** — They respect the land, and that is good. Yet they harbor no corresponding respect for the land's creatures, and for that we must kill them. Still, that night must wait until the Tremere are extinguished.

• **Ventrue** — He who seeks chieftainship over me must earn it.

• **Baali** — There is rot in these scholars' mouths and poison in their footprints.

LASOMBRA

Elegant yet predatory, the Lasombra honestly think of themselves as the apex of Cainite existence. Firm believers in Divine Right and the rule of the superior, they have little patience, though often much pity, for those Cainites who are (through no fault of their own) inferior.

The Lasombra character is a curious mix of *noblesse oblige* and healthy contempt. They actively seek power wherever it may be found, from the halls of the cloisters to the corridors of palaces, yet they do not seek the titles and glory that come along with rule. Instead of chasing command for its own sake, Lasombra take the reins of power out of a firm belief that no one can hold them better. The appearance of power is unimportant; what matters is that the decisions are being made by those most suited to make them. Indeed, most Lasombra prefer the role of kingmaker to the title of king.

Hand in hand with this determination to be the final arbiters of all decisions comes a healthy contempt for those who the Lasombra feel are inferior to them in mind, body or breeding. In essence this means the rest of Cainite society, and while some of the various clans have been accorded a modicum of respect, there are none the Lasombra will acknowledge as equals. A Lasombra will work with other Cainites, and even go so far as to consider members of other clans to be friends, but one will never, ever consider a member of another clan to be an equal.

Unfortunately, there are those Lasombra whose delight in the great game of politics blinds them to all but the game itself. Master manipulators, these Cainites view all of Europe as but a chessboard that they and their opponents play upon, the fall of kingdoms being of only abstract interest to them. It is these Lasombra whom the other clans fear most, and their talents and tastes have been attributed to the clan as a whole.

Sobriquet: Magisters

Appearance: Lasombra are generally dark-skinned, with fine-boned features that announce their Italian, Spanish or Moorish heritage. Many still look slightly tanned or weathered from their exposure to the harsh southern sun during their days as mortals. As befitting their noble station, those not bound by holy orders to wear church vestments prefer the finest silks and other expensive garments.

Haven: Many clan members dwell in the manors and guest houses of their family lands. Others seek refuge in the fortresslike monasteries of Spain and Italy.

Background: Lasombra come almost exclusively from noble bloodlines, particularly those of Spanish, Italian or Moorish extraction. Most are skilled in the arts of war and court, though a significant number have backgrounds in the Church. It is extraordinarily rare for a commoner to be Embraced by a Lasombra.

Character Creation: Nobles and clergymen are common character concepts for the Magisters. Architect and Judge are common Natures, while Mental Attributes and Talents are often primary. It is rare for a Lasombra not to have the Retainers and Resources Backgrounds, and many have Mentors in the clan as well. They tend toward the Road of Heaven, but many question its values and are experimenting with new codes of ethics.

Clan Disciplines: Dominate, Obtenebration, Potence

Weaknesses: The members of Clan Lasombra cannot be seen in mirrors or any other reflective surfaces, such as windows, bodies of water or pools of quicksilver.

Organization: The Lasombra clan structure is a very formal one, loosely based on the hierarchy of the Church. Both secular and ecclesiastical titles are used within the clan, and members are permitted to retain their arms and titles from their breathing days. During gatherings of the Lasombra, more actual work is done in the cloakroom than on the debating floor, though even their *sub rosa* dealings are performed in perfect dignity.

Quote: *An excellent decision. I applaud. Did you actually manage to reach it all by yourself?*

STEREOTYPES

- Assamites — Fury leashed by honor, the Assamites are worthy of respect and even fear. Hold tight to that leash, for if they ever slip it, they will be at your throat.
- Brujah — The Brujah are like an Arabian stallion with a broken leg; once great, and too proud to know that they are dead.
- Cappadocians — These befuddled scholars may yet stumble onto some great secret or philosopher's stone, and on the night they do, they will become dangerous. That night will come, in all probability, a week after the last trump.
- Followers of Set — Skulkers in the dark with their outdated rituals and antiquated paganism, they belong to a dead age. Even the Brujah have adapted better.
- Gangrel — Leave them to the wild and the company of the wolves they love so much. With any luck, the shapechangers will exterminate these beasts and save us the effort.
- Malkavians — When one sees a mad dog, one puts it down lest it attack and worry one's leg. The same policy should be followed here.
- Nosferatu — They crawl from the plague pits to infect our prey with fever and foulness. Seal the graves, and seal them inside.
- Ravnos — The tramps are amusing while working their jests upon others, not so amusing when oneself is the target. Better to avoid them entirely.
- Toreador — Any court worthy of its name has one Toreador. Of course, any court worthy of its name also has a dwarf and an idiot jester, so one more amusing freak means nothing.
- Tremere — The wizards are ambitious, and this is worrisome. We should have shown Tremere and his simpering progeny the beauty of the sunrise years ago.
- Tzimisce — They have won for our kind the name of "monster." Is it not enough to rule without laying waste to one's dominion?
- Ventrue — Petty little princes and self-ennobled lords, the Ventrue are pale imitations of majesty. Let them have the thrones; we rule from the shadows.
- Baali — The depth of their depravity lies not in their foul rites, but in the fact that they wish to summon demonic masters for themselves. What sane Cainite works toward slavery?

MALKAVIAN

Vampires are not easily frightened. They have already conquered death, and the weaknesses of their mortal selves are long gone. But the Cainites of Clan Malkavian worry even the boldest Brujah or most jaded Tzimisce, for wherever they walk, the stale stench of madness follows.

To the medieval mind, insanity is one of the most frightening things imaginable. Most consider madness to be some sort of curse from God (or mark of the Devil), rather than an illness. In the case of the Malkavians, Cainite lore hints that they might be right.

In the old days, or so some of the mad ones claim, Malkav was one of the favored childer of Caine. Caine sought wisdom in the dark corners of the world, and his progeny mimicked him. But it was neither Saulot, nor Brujah, nor even Cappadocius who eventually found the secrets that Caine sought. Malkav brought wisdom to his sire, and Caine blessed the childe and his line with the liberating gift of insanity.

Clan Malkavian seems to be the most incoherent bloodline of vampires. Gently deluded souls and slavering psychotics are found in equal numbers, and they are but a taste of the diversity characterizing Malkav's get. If not for the common trait of insanity, they would scarcely seem a clan at all. But the other clans have no choice but to acknowledge them. Malkavian oracles have been part of vampiric courts for generations, and even the Lasombra and Ventrue, if they seek information, will sup with the Malkavians — with a long spoon.

To this day, the Malkavians wander in and out of Cainite society. They play the fools, the jesters, the seers and idiots, ever uncovering strange new secrets buried in their madness. They play bizarre, often disturbing and sometimes dangerous pranks on ally and enemy alike. They embrace causes with all their souls, or flit among allegiances like drunken moths. In the end, no other vampire can predict just how a Malkavian will change her environment.

Sobriquet: Madmen

Appearance: Malkavians could be anyone, anywhere. For every tattered village idiot clutching at imaginary butterflies, there is a normal-seeming person whose insanity visibly manifests only at the most dangerous times.

Haven: Many Malkavians tend toward abandoned or partially destroyed buildings. Often their havens are decorated in some unsettling fashion, or with some obsessive object relating to their lunacy (a sculpture made of teeth, or a room of immaculate cleanliness, for example).

Background: The Madmen tend to Embrace those who are close to death, the hopelessly insane or the unusually enlightened. Typically, they choose neonates who would be somehow "bettered" by induction into Clan Malkavian, or who show useful and progressive insight.

Character Creation: Malkavians can have any concept whatsoever. Their Natures and Demeanors rarely coincide. Mental Attributes tend to be primary, as do Talents. Background Traits vary widely and depend more on the individual's concept than clan tradition. Obviously, Malkavians could zealously follow any Road.

Clan Disciplines: Auspex, Dementation, Obfuscate

Weaknesses: All Malkavians are insane and begin play with at least one Derangement of the player's choice. This Derangement cannot be permanently overcome, no matter how much Willpower is spent. Malkav's blood prevents his progeny from ever achieving sanity.

Organization: The Malkavians have the most variable organization of any clan. Much of their intraclan structure is regional, and small groups of Malkavians often gather in parodies of local governments and institutions. They seem anarchic, but can cooperate with eerie precision if they believe it necessary.

Quote: *Ha! You demand order, expect hierarchy? Yes. It's there, milord. In the cracks, milord. But can you look on it without tearing out your eyes?*

STEREOTYPES

- Assamites — Live by the sword, trip and fall on your sword, die by the sword.
- Brujah — Well, they have their perfection of body and they have their perfection of mind, there's no denying. Temperate and mild, every last one of them.
- Cappadocians — There's a *reason* that cadavers don't speak, my friends. And trust me, you don't want to know what they're keeping from you.
- Followers of Set — I have but one thing to say: Set was madder than Malkav. I swear it on my sire's bones.
- Gangrel — Look on these fools that dance on the Lupines' hunting grounds. Then call us mad.
- Lasombra — Half puppeteer and half puppet, the Lasombra certainly keep the children entertained.
- Nosferatu — Poor devils. Ah, but they and we have the virtue of honesty to keep us warm. We are all made in God's image.
- Ravnos — Ah, the prattling jackdaws who think if you laugh hard enough, the abyss tiptoes away. Ho ho.
- Toreador — Tch. It is truly thankless work, defending a chunk of stone or splotch of dye against the centuries. But they are wrong when they claim that nobody understands them. We do. They're mad.
- Tremere — God's wounds! These ducklings certainly livened up the Great Cainite Hierarchy, now didn't they? Oh, I think *every* town square should have one of these, just to keep us all guessing.
- Tzimisce — The dear little ones, you can see how they envy the Nosferatu in everything they do. Well, if they believe disfigurement leads to enlightenment, I have always been happy to volunteer my help. They have too many limbs, anyway....
- Ventrue — The glass throne is most comfortable when the king believes he sits on stone.
- Baali — Tcha! They want to see a pattern in everything, even their evil. If they *really* knew what rules them, their minds would break. Hmmm…

Nosferatu

Caine's childer are called "the Damned," and none embody this more than do the wretched Nosferatu. Nosferatu bear an ancient and terrible curse, for they are no longer made in God's image; the vampiric transformation warps their forms, rendering them abominations in the eyes of men and angels. Outcast from mortal and vampire society alike, these misshapen horrors haunt the catacombs, wastes and other hidden places of the Dark Medieval world.

In the nights of antiquity, Nosferatu rarely fraternized with mortals, but stalked the fringes of human society as monsters. Other vampires, dismayed by the Nosferatu's depredations on their herds, drove the creatures into the barrens. This exile, combined with the intrinsic revulsion their appearance inspired, made Nosferatu convenient scapegoats for all manner of dark deeds, real and imagined. This evil (and largely undeserved) reputation forced Nosferatu to remain ever moving, always hidden, never daring to rest for fear of extermination.

Nosferatu often avoid destruction by trafficking in information. Their dependency on stealth, rapport with beasts and constant need to travel from fiefdom to fiefdom provide them with access to data unavailable to their less venturesome brethren. Even citybound Nosferatu find that their choices of abodes and victims make them privy to all manner of information and gossip inaccessible to the loftier clans. Nosferatu have learned that the most refined Ventrue prince will often hold his gorge, cover his nose and give up a beggar or two in exchange for information about his Lasombra rival in the next duchy. (And should bargaining prove futile, Nosferatu are not above a little blackmail....)

Since the coming of Christianity, many Nosferatu have modified their behavior. Seeing themselves as cursed by God but capable of redemption through Christ (or whomever), Nosferatu stoically endure their penance on Earth in an attempt to avoid Hell. Because Nosferatu must lurk among the lowest strata of mortal society, they find much opportunity to do good works from the shadows. Nosferatu are particularly attracted to the penitent movement; superhuman toughness and vampiric healing enable a Nosferatu to endure weeks of self-flagellation.

Sobriquet: Lepers

Appearance: Each Nosferatu is unique, and each is more loathsome than the last. Nosferatu deformities are as innumerable as they are grotesque. Some wear the visages of rotting corpses, including missing noses and earlobes; others appear as tusked demons or feral rodents; still others sport bloated and distended features, like drowned sailors. Many lose their hair and sprout lumps and warts like a toad, or grow clumps of bristly spines in the manner of a hedgehog. Some are covered in pustulant sores and bursting boils; others wear a greasy, wrinkled hide; and some true horrors lack skin entirely, resembling flayed swine at market. A miasmal stench surrounds most Nosferatu, and plagues of flies and locusts often follow these vampires. On all Nosferatu the taint of uncleanliness hangs heavily. In an effort to hide their shame (and avoid witch-hunters), most Nosferatu shroud themselves in sackcloth swathings.

Haven: Nosferatu haunt abandoned, pestilent sites, preferring ruins, fens, darksome forests or, ideally, plague-infested zones. In cities, they tend to inhabit ancient catacombs, leprosaries, dungeons, ethnic ghettos and tenements outside the city walls. The huge cesspits common to medieval towns provide ample, if foul, shelter from the daytime sun (and even the most zealous witch-hunter is unlikely to go digging through a mountain of dung in search of a sleeping vampire).

Background: Nosferatu take their victims from society's pariahs: idiots and freaks, lepers, hermits, vagabonds, criminals, defrocked priests and the like. Nosferatu on the Road of Heaven often punish the prideful, hypocrites and other sinners by inducting them into the clan. Jews are favored because they are often intelligent and practical, but lack societal protection against vampiric abductors. Occasionally an outraged Nosferatu chooses a beautiful victim to make monstrous, but this practice is currently uncommon.

Character Creation: Nosferatu often have beggar or outsider concepts. Physical Attributes and Talents are usually primary, as Nosferatu must be quick, clever and hardy to survive their innumerable privations. Nosferatu rarely have any Allies, Contacts, Retainers or other Backgrounds linking them to the mortal world — though the rare mortal who befriends a Leper has a friend for life (and her children's lives, and their children's…). The Road of Heaven is most common among Nosferatu, followed closely by the Road of the Beast. Many Nosferatu spurn the Road of Humanity, considering either themselves unworthy of humanity or humanity unworthy of them. Only a few Nosferatu follow the Devil's Road, but those who do are terrors indeed, reveling in their hideousness and playing to the hilt their role of frightful monster.

Clan Disciplines: Animalism, Obfuscate, Potence

Weaknesses: All Nosferatu are monstrously deformed. Their Appearance Trait is automatically rated zero and cannot be improved. All Social rolls involving Appearance (including most first impressions) automatically fail.

Organization: Nosferatu society is informally but nonetheless tightly organized. They are perhaps the most internally cohesive clan; millennia of shared deformity, abuse and privation have forged strong bonds among Nosferatu. Elders are revered, but are expected to treat the young fairly. Nosferatu treat each other with careful respect and elaborate courtesy, and freely trade information among themselves. This makes the clan extremely well informed; important Nosferatu can accurately forecast events from Hibernia to Kiev.

Quote: *Oh, woe, my prince, that one so lowly as I hath offended thee! Flog me into torpor! Stake me and leave me for the sun! Lop off my head! Just…don't send me back to the fief of the Lasombra Contessa Isabel… What? She is your enemy, milord? Why yes, I did escape her impregnable fortress…through the secret tunnel, of course. What secret tunnel, you say? Well, milord, perhaps we should discourse in your private chambers….*

STEREOTYPES

• **Assamites** — They are savage, bloodthirsty infidels, but they adhere to their codes far more steadfastly than do most so-called "Christians."

• **Brujah** — For all their egalitarian prattle, few embrace us as equals. They will burn in Hell like the rest of us.

• **Cappadocians** — They delve into mysteries best left buried. One night they will open one tomb too many — and we know all too well what will crawl up to greet them….

• **Followers of Set** — These bastards would hiss a different tune if they had to cloak themselves in the shroud of their iniquity, as do we.

• **Gangrel** — Grant these nomads respect, and do not dispute their passage — save when they seek to establish themselves in our hunting grounds. Then battle is inevitable; strike first and swiftly.

• **Lasombra** — Are we to love those whose greatest vexation is *not* being able to see themselves? Still, they are useful; hide your hate, exploit their paranoia and provide them with the secrets they crave. The right — or properly chosen wrong — word in a Magister's ear can ensure your safety for decades.

• **Malkavians** — I like them better than most of the others. Oh, make no mistake, they're demon-ridden villains, but they make no especial attempt to single us out for their caprices.

• **Ravnos** — They laugh in the face of God's anger. I am sure that Satan has many pretty tricks awaiting them in Hell.

• **Toreador** — Fools! to have been given eternity, merely to squander it questing for something as transitory as beauty.

• **Tremere** — Grant them neither forgiveness nor forgetfulness. Remember our friend Saulot and his childer, for they alone treated us with compassion. Confront the Usurpers not, for they are strong, but haunt their shadows and carry whispers of their sins to the ends of the earth.

• **Tzimisce** — Have they learned nothing from our state, that they would degrade all of God's works in like manner? Heaven's hammer will surely smite these devils.

• **Ventrue** — They demand our fealty without offering their guardianship in return. We crawl into their courts wailing for succor and yet they turn us away into the cold and darkness. One night a doom will rise to envelop these false nobles, and we shall laugh safely amid the darkness into which they exiled us.

• **Baali** — Foulest of foul creatures, they gleefully revel in their damnation. We should help them along to Hell so they can continue their dancing in the eternal flames.

Ravnos

Tramps and thieves, the Ravnos are scattered throughout Europe like chaff on the wind. Every country hosts a few, but where they can be found varies from night to night and whim to whim. Many travel with bands of roving tinkers or other undesirables. It is rare for more than one or two to be found in the same place at the same time, for they are solitary Cainites and prefer audiences and marks to company.

All Ravnos are nomadic, as much out of necessity as taste. There is nowhere in the realms of civilized Cainites where Ravnos are welcomed, and even should one try to settle, she would be harried forth as soon as she was discovered. The Ravnos' reputation for trickery and theft precedes them everywhere they go, and even those clan members who did not initially have a taste for larceny find themselves forced into it very quickly by circumstance and expectation.

There is a reason the Ravnos have a reputation for chicanery — it's because so many of them are so very good at it. Reynard the Fox, with all of his mythical cleverness, could find himself talked out of his fur and fangs were he to deal with a Ravnos, and most Cainites and humans don't do nearly so well as that. Ravnos live by their wits, and they are constantly testing and sharpening those wits against all comers. Shell games, convoluted thefts, storytelling for coin, the selling of "holy relics" and a dozen other arts for separating fools from their possessions are all Ravnos calling cards. Most Ravnos will express professional admiration for any non-Ravnos who attempts to make a living in their field — and then rob the interloper blind.

There is nothing a Ravnos values so highly as his freedom. Wise Cainites do not seek to keep Ravnos from a place of their choosing, only to hurry them from that place once they have arrived. Once word travels that a certain location is barred to Ravnos, they will appear by the dozens to test the ban until it shatters. They then take their vengeance by descending upon the newly opened city in force and stripping it, by hook or by crook, of anything that strikes their fancy. About the only way in which an infestation of Ravnos is preferable to a military conquest is that the Ravnos sometimes leave more of the town standing.

The one thing that Ravnos prize more highly than a good trick (and a Ravnos who manages an exceptional theft will be regarded highly indeed by his clan members) is their honor. However, it is Ravnos honor, and defined differently than most Cainite honor is. A Ravnos never breaks her word — provided she has spit into her palm and shaken hands on it. Otherwise, the oath, no matter how fearsome, simply does not count and can be broken with impunity. A Ravnos will go to the ends of the earth to avenge an insult to her "good name," but it is up to each Ravnos to decide what constitutes an insult. Finally, a Ravnos will not cheat or steal from a fellow Ravnos or one whom she considers to be a friend or "brother." The rest of the world, however, is fair game.

Sobriquet: Charlatans

Appearance: Ravnos enjoy dressing in gaily colored rags and tatters, showing their tatterdemalion status off with pride. Some who have wandered far from home show the distinctive features of the Far East. Most tend to be of outsider or mongrel mortal stock.

Haven: Very few Ravnos have any sort of fixed haven. Many have wagons or carts which serve the purpose, but a good many find shelter from night to night.

Background: Wanderlust and a gift for trickery are all that's required for Embrace into Clan Ravnos. Certain mortal bloodlines (such as those that will someday be called Rom or Gypsies) are preferred, but runaways and buskers of all ethnicities have found their way into the clan.

Character Creation: Most Ravnos come from tinker, thief or drifter types, though highwaymen and musicians are also logical choices for induction. Jester is the most common Nature among Ravnos, and Social Attributes are primary. Most Ravnos concentrate on Talents and have Contacts as their most common Background. They tend to follow the clan's Road of Paradox.

Clan Disciplines: Animalism, Chimerstry, Fortitude

Weaknesses: Each Ravnos has a flair for one particular flavor of deception, such as lying, theft, gambling or cheating. This specialty must be chosen at the time of character creation, and the character must indulge it whenever possible. A Willpower roll (difficulty 6) is required to resist the temptation to indulge at each opportunity.

Organization: The structure of Clan Ravnos is best summed up by an ancient Arab proverb: "Me against my brother, my brother and I against my uncle, my uncle and I against the stranger."

Quote: *Call me a vagabond, and I'll smile. Call me a thief, and I'll laugh. Call me a liar, and I'll feed you your liver.*

STEREOTYPES

•Assamites — Their game has ended, and instead of finding a new one, they've decided to kill everyone instead. Charming people, really.

•Brujah — Another example of the perils of living in the past. Do they even taste the present, or are they ghosts with flesh?

•Cappadocians — Dusty and dry the scholars are, and easy to fool. But the best part is the way they rage when they realize they've been tricked....

•Followers of Set — They can keep their hoary mysteries of Egypt, thank you very much, and all their other tainted gifts. You can fool a Snake, but you risk getting bitten.

•Gangrel — Some of them are our cousins, and it is sad to see what they have come to. Aid them if you can, but let none know; we stand as a sign of what they've lost, and they hate us for it.

•Lasombra — So noble they make my teeth grind, so stuffy they squeak when they walk. Their arm is long, but their grasp is weak, and they own much that is worth liberating.

•Malkavians — Hey, a better show than we put on! Watch the madmen and marvel, then count your limbs after the show to make certain they're all still there.

•Nosferatu — They all seem to be so depressed that they're up and about that you want to put a stake in them just to put them out of their misery. But when you try, do they thank you? Noooooooo…

•Toreador — Useful guides to what is worth stealing, and useful places to sell what has been stolen, and that is what the Toreador are good for.

•Tremere — Evil wizards casting dastardly spells, hey? Few have yet learned how to keep a hand on their purses while waggling their fingers about.

•Tzimisce — Great will be the fame of any Ravnos who gets the better of a Tzimisce and survives. Many have the first part down; few have learned the secret of the second.

•Ventrue — Even more boring than the Lasombra, if that is possible. It's so easy, it's almost no fun involving them in our little japes. Babies are less gullible — but not as tasty.

•Baali — A little Chimerstry correctly applied and you can have a Baali following you around for years, convinced you've brought his favorite demon lord to earth. The poor idiots…

TOREADOR

From their beginning, the Toreador have always been devotees of beauty in all its forms. Beauty means so much to them, for they devote the entirety of their vampiric senses to it, immersing themselves in the aesthetic. They consider themselves the preservers and guardians of the exquisite, the bearers of the flame of inspiration. Of all the clans, the Toreador are the ones who most appreciate the accomplishments of the human race.

Throughout their history, the Toreador have always associated with mortal artists and creators. Many elders recall the splendors of the Golden Age — but they also remember the Roman Empire, when the Toreador fell into decadence and excess. Many of the Artisans fell in the sack of Rome, and now the Toreador seek temperance, the better to preserve what they love most.

Currently, the Toreador of Western Europe are strongly associated with the Church and the artwork it inspires. They oversee the building of cathedrals with great joy, and many undergo something akin to religious rapture when presented with exceptional craftsmanship or beauty. They particularly enjoy artwork that inspires those who look on it.

Unfortunately, they still retain their love for pleasure and luxury; it is an easy thing for a Toreador to succumb to sophisticated temptation. Their attraction to various forms of vice (those that can still stir the undead breast) is legendary. Their desire to find truth and meaning in the beautiful has led many a careless Toreador into ruin of some form or another. In addition, their disdain for Cainite politicking or causes has not endeared them to the other clans, who usually consider the Toreador apathetic and useless. The Artisans know this, but care little for others' opinions. They have all the proof they need that their vision is worth following.

Sobriquet: Artisans

Appearance: The Toreador often Embrace the very beautiful in order to preserve them for eternity. They are common in Spain, Italy and France, and frequently choose neonates from these regions. Toreador are rarely slovenly or unkempt, even those associated with somber monastic lifestyles.

Haven: They typically live either in the best portions of large cities or near monasteries and the like: wherever art and fine crafts are produced. Few Toreador live the life of a hermit.

Background: Toreador select only those with much to offer for initiation into their clan. Many members were artists, musicians or teachers of great ability. They are the clan most likely to Embrace mortals on impulse.

Character Creation: Many Toreador have religious or entertainer concepts. Their Natures are often passionate and inspired, while their Demeanors can be of any sort. Social Attributes are usually primary, as are Skills. Their Backgrounds often include Resources, Herd and Retainers. Toreador prefer the Road of Humanity to all others.

Clan Disciplines: Auspex, Celerity, Presence

Weaknesses: The Toreador sensitivity to the beautiful is also their greatest flaw. They may be overcome with a thing or person's beauty, standing in fascination for hours. Only a successful Willpower roll will break the reverie quickly; otherwise, the Toreador is helpless for minutes or even hours. Even sunrises can captivate them, and the Toreador are the Cainites most likely to fall in love with mortals.

Organization: Toreador maintain informal communications with one another, occasionally gathering to exchange news. They rarely unite as a clan to pursue a common goal, preferring their individual pursuits.

Quote: *We have eternity stretched out before us, while the mortals have but an eyeblink. How can we be so selfish as to spend our time fighting and despoiling? The eventual salvation of us all lies in the secrets of creative genius — you have but to look for it.*

STEREOTYPES

- **Assamites** — They are the defenders of an enlightened culture with much to offer. It is one of the world's tragedies that they hate all other clans with such ferocity.
- **Brujah** — In their rage, they destroy exactly that which they would find worth preserving. If only they knew how to use their strength…
- **Cappadocians** — The past has much to offer, but it is a death of the soul to ignore the present.
- **Followers of Set** — These basilisks offer poisoned gifts with honeyed promises. Be ever wary of these clever serpents.
- **Gangrel** — There are many wonders in the wild places, but the Animals have sacrificed too much to look on them.
- **Lasombra** — How can they be so lettered and so ignorant at once? Their souls were lost to them along with their reflections.
- **Malkavians** — I wonder at the design that granted them such wisdom but consumed their minds. I weep for them, because that is all that may be done for the Malkavians.
- **Nosferatu** — Ai! These things are all that is foul in the vampiric being. They may see much, but I cannot bear to hear their stories. It is too much to ask of me.
- **Ravnos** — These lying robbers steal without knowledge of the value of their gains. Nothing will ever be able to sate their greed, and so the hollow Ravnos dance on, until they devour themselves from spite.
- **Tremere** — They sought immortality for all the wrong reasons, and now all Cainites are cursed with their presence. Alas for Saulot and his kin, for surely they were the most enlightened of our fellow clans.
- **Tzimisce** — There is nothing the Tzimisce or their chosen do that deserves to survive into the next century. With luck, they and the Usurpers will exterminate one another, and their kine will be free to explore what it is to be alive.
- **Ventrue** — Royal blood does not nobility make, and that is something that the Ventrue must understand. Forgive me if I do not stand at attention until they do.
- **Baali** — Truly they must abhor themselves, for why else would anyone take their path? Be wary of these ones, for they seek company in their damnation.

TREMERE

Those of this clan are called "usurpers" for no small reason. They were once a cabal of mortal mages, but their leader, Tremere, became obsessed with the search for immortality, the better to provide him time enough to perfect his art for eternity. Their efforts proved fruitful; although it took the deaths of a Tzimisce elder and two of their own apprentices, the cabal achieved vampirism.

Not satisfied with this, the Tremere took steps to establish themselves as a full clan. They tracked down Saulot, the enigmatic founder of Clan Salubri, and slew him in torpor; Tremere himself drank the Antediluvian's vitæ.

Of course, the new clan immediately came under siege. The Tzimisce thirst for revenge, for the Tremere killed members of their clan and even seized part of the Fiends' ancestral lands. The Gangrel find the Tremere an obscenity, especially because the Usurpers have captured Gangrel for use in their foul experiments. Then, of course, there are the Cainites who had befriended the Salubri and even now work to protect the surviving members from the Tremere.

For now, the Tremere live a precarious existence. Their mortal magic was all but destroyed by the Embrace, the salvaged remnants forming their unique Discipline of Thaumaturgy. They have recently managed to create a servitor breed of vampire, the Gargoyles, which are the only things keeping them from the claws of the Tzimisce and Gangrel. The outrage over Saulot's diablerization continues to plague them. The clan is badly in need of allies; while a few individuals have proved themselves worthy companions, the clan as a whole is despised and distrusted.

Sobriquet: Usurpers

Appearance: This clan is almost entirely male, but more women are beginning to emerge. They tend to wear dark colors, and the more traditional prefer long robes with concealing hoods and full cloaks. They recruit from across Europe, and may be of many ethnicities.

Haven: The Tremere maintain several "chantries" in and around many of Europe's major cities, their locations known only to the Tremere who reside there. Those who choose to live outside the chantries maintain a number of residences as boltholes and to throw off potential pursuit.

Background: The Tremere normally look for students of the occult, people with intense curiosity about the world, and intellects and scholars of all varieties. Their current state of siege has forced them temporarily to Embrace for survival. Among the more recent shifts in choice: men-at-arms, officers with tactical knowledge, and diplomats to assist the Tremere in making their first overtures toward the other clans.

Character Creation: Most Tremere come from occult concepts and tend to have primary Mental Attributes and Knowledges. The odd man-at-arms neonate is equally likely to have primary Physical or Mental Attributes. Their Natures and Demeanors often reflect power, a conservative outlook and loyalty. Tremere Backgrounds often include Mentor or Resources. The Tremere, infants by clan standards, often follow the Road of Humanity, although certain evil occultists have chosen the Devil's Road.

Clan Disciplines: Auspex, Dominate, Thaumaturgy

Weaknesses: All Tremere neonates are made to drink at least twice from the blood of the seven elders when they are Embraced. This means that all are at least two steps to becoming Thrall to the entire clan. In addition, fledgling Tremere are watched very carefully by their superiors and must be wary of (even unknowingly) betraying their clan.

Organization: Tremere are tightly organized and very hierarchical, following the ideals of the old Hermetic house they once were. Younger members are expected to obey their elders without question.

Quote: *Our road is clear, and stretches toward nothing less than ultimate control over ourselves and our fellows. But we cannot reach the end alone. As a clan, and only as a clan, may we triumph.*

ARBITRIUM VINCIT OMNIA

STEREOTYPES

• Assamites — Even the most sagacious wizard may fall with a knife in his back; never give these barbarians the opportunity.

• Brujah — Philosophers and berserkers without the wits to see that their new day has already set into eternal night.

• Cappadocians — We have the most in common with them; perhaps we could learn much from each other.

• Followers of Set — True, we need allies, but I hold grave misgivings about their kind of help.

• Gangrel — Savages worthy of nothing, not even a swift death.

• Lasombra — Strong and disciplined. Their support could be vital, but likely as untrustworthy as the shadows they command.

• Malkavian — These creatures are undoubtedly possessed. Their gibberings are of no consequence to us.

• Nosferatu — Disgusting! And to think that they have survived so long. I cannot even countenance allowing one within a league of me.

• Ravnos — Tramps and thieves. Death changes nothing.

• Toreador — Faugh! They have not the spine to side with their fellows against us, and that is the only virtue I can find in the Toreador.

• Tzimisce — Do not ask, do not think — kill them without delay or mercy.

• Ventrue — Their attempts at martyrdom are laughable. Respect them only when they have earned it.

• Baali — Give the Devil his due for their tenacity in spite of such hatred. Perhaps they are a sign of things to come for us.

TZIMISCE

From time immemorial the Tzimisce have haunted Europe beyond the Elbe. Along the Oder and Danube, through the Pripet Marshes, amid the Carpathian crags stalk the Fiends, each claiming its lair and wreaking a terrible vengeance on intruders. Millennia of defending their holdings from all sides have made Tzimisce extremely vicious, and Tzimisce cruelty is infamous even among vampires. (Travelers' legends of cynocephali, *vrykolas* and other monsters can often be traced to some wretch disfigured by an annoyed Tzimisce.)

Of all clans, the Tzimisce is perhaps the least human. Tzimisce are scholarly, even brilliant beings, but their studies (and their Vicissitude Discipline) have led them to the unequivocal conclusion that vampires are superior to humans and Tzimisce are superior to other vampires. The "best" (by Tzimisce standards) humans are to be elevated; the rest are fodder. Unlike many vampires, Tzimisce do not see themselves as damned or accursed. If God has damned them, they say, then perhaps it is time for new and better gods....

During the years immediately following Rome's fall, the clan made vassals/slaves of various Eastern European hereditary chieftains, thereby creating "ghoul families" with noble lineage and inbred supernatural powers. These families provided the Tzimisce with great temporal power, and thereafter the inhabitants of the East have groaned under the yoke of their Tzimisce masters. For centuries Tzimisce dominance in the East remained unchallenged, and the clan itself was arguably the most powerful in Europe.

But recent times have proved troubling for the Fiends. A skirmish with the sorcerous Tremere (who gained immortality using stolen Tzimisce vitae) quickly blossomed into a full-scale war. At first the Tzimisce's raw power and terror tactics gave them the upper hand, but the Usurpers' superior organization and magical might have recently turned the tide. Moreover, the Fiends' distress has been balm to the hearts of rival clans. Under the cover of mortal invasions, other vampires have begun to jockey for the Tzimisce's dwindling holdings. Fearful *voivodes* increasingly send their young to fight and die in their names, and the Blood Oath-bound progeny dutifully go, though for the first time ever they have begun to grumble at their servitude....

Sobriquet: Fiends

Appearance: Few Tzimisce appear normal; most are either angelically beautiful or freakishly weird. Many Tzimisce, particularly those skilled in Vicissitude, change their shape nightly. Some displaced Tzimisce, enraged by their subjects' "betrayal," ravage their former herds as hideous monsters. Most Tzimisce dress in noble finery, though some prefer tattered shrouds or nothing whatsoever.

Haven: Tzimisce *voivodes* maintain ancestral castles, where they live amid decaying splendor with their broods. Woe to any who trespass on a Tzimisce's fief! The rare visitor (mortal, vampire or otherwise) who is invited onto Tzimisce grounds is feted like a prince — but should take care to display extreme courtesy in return. Tzimisce cherish their havens, but rarely bother with upkeep (many Tzimisce keeps are the spitting image of the classic crumbling Transylvanian castle).

Background: Tzimisce are most often chosen from the clan's "pet" noble families, and no few are ghouls prior to the Embrace. Occasionally a particularly brilliant or learned outsider is brought into the clan, and a *voivode* often takes whoever strikes his fancy (as a "bride" or the like). Particularly in the Baltics, many still worship (or are worshipped as) the pagan Slavic gods.

Character Creation: Most Tzimisce are of Eastern European origin and tend to have noble or scholarly concepts. As the war with the Tremere rages, more and more Tzimisce are chosen for their martial prowess (or sheer brutality). Mental Attributes are often primary. Many Tzimisce have Retainers in the form of monstrous, Vicissitude-sculpted ghoul servitors. Herd and Influence are also common Backgrounds. Tzimisce follow a variety of Roads, though the Road of the Beast is most common, and few openly profess allegiance to the Road of Humanity. Some Tzimisce, particularly the pagan ones, follow obscure Roads combining aspects of Devil, Beast and Blood.

Clan Disciplines: Animalism, Auspex, Vicissitude

Weaknesses: Tzimisce are very territorial and tied to the lands they knew in life. When a Tzimisce sleeps, she must surround herself with at least two handfuls of earth from a land important to her as a mortal (the land of her birth, the soil of her demesne, the earth of her grave, etc.). Failure to do this halves the Tzimisce's Dice Pools every 24 hours until all actions use only one die; this penalty is negated by eight hours' rest amid the special soil.

Organization: Tzimisce are very hierarchical but very insular creatures. The clan is subdivided into smaller units comprising one landholding vampire sire (*voivode*) and a host of progeny, many of whom have been required to submit to a Blood Oath with the sire. Progeny are expected to obey their *voivode* in all things. Relationships among *voivodes* are governed by a complex protocol and fractious at best; strife among these elders is the main reason why the clan has been unable to best the Tremere. Of late, as more and more *voivodes* have fallen, Tzimisce progeny have been forced to travel into exile in the West.

Quote: *Good evening, traveler. I bid you welcome to the demesne of my voivode, Count Vladimir Rustovitch, whose fiefdom you crossed into at the ford a league back. You are in luck — we have ample accommodations and a surfeit of choice entertainments awaiting you at our castle.*

STEREOTYPES

• **Assamites** — We have little truck with these *paynims*. They divert the Ventrue and Lasombra in Asia Minor, and that is meet by me.

• **Brujah** — Oh, a thousand pardons — a city where I can coexist harmoniously with the mortals? This is to be my earthly paradise? This is the Brujah dream? Hmmph — I thought I was a blood-drinking nocturnal marauder, but I am obviously mistaken.

• **Cappadocians** — They are interesting and enlightened, but they seek only mastery of mortality, while we seek to master the immortal state.

• **Followers of Set** — They are worms; we are dragons. They had best slither into their holes when we pass.

• **Gangrel** — Their understanding of the Beast is second only to our own; accordingly, they make useful hunting hounds against the bedamned Tremere.

• **Lasombra** — So much effort and so many nights wasted in endless chess games pitting this pawn against that. Politics is simple: tell your lessers what to do, impale those who dare disobey, and get on with business of real import.

• **Malkavians** — Their lunacy, while debilitating, can be inspirational. Craft a goblet from a Malkavian's skull and drink its blood from the vessel. The residual humors in the brain pan permeate the vitæ, providing profoundly revelatory visions.

• **Nosferatu** — They are stoic, if uncouth, and they understand the power in terror. Admire them from afar and make examples of any who dare to defile our demesnes with their noxious presence.

• **Ravnos** — Thieving trash. We will extract a thousand screams in return for every trinket they steal from us.

• **Toreador** — Mawkish, domesticated little vampires. They wish us to admire their arts, but oh, how they balk at ours! Keep them as pets until their verse begins to bore; then have them tossed in the *vozhd* pit.

• **Tremere** — We will tear their stolen gift from their flayed innards, skewer them on the Carpathian peaks they defiled, feed the Danube *vodyanoi* with their bilious humors, and leave the rest for the carrion birds. Then we will truly begin to teach them the meaning of pain.

• **Ventrue** — Teuton vipers who smile cordially as they strike at our heels. Rip out their dissembling tongues and muzzle their fangs thereby.

• **Baali** — Wasted effort. Why do we need to conjure up that which is already incarnate on earth? Of course, if they absolutely must have hideousness and grotesquerie, we would be happy to accommodate them.

VENTRUE

Striding from battlefield to battlefield and throne room to throne room, the Ventrue are the knights and kings of the Cainite chessboard. Theirs are the conquests, the wars and the Crusades; they rule from the manor houses and the throne rooms. Many were conquerors in life and have yet to shake the habit in death, while others achieved success as merchants or moneylenders. All triumphed, however, and as a reward were taken into Clan Ventrue. There are no failures among the Ventrue, only successes and the fondly remembered dead.

Tradition is very important to the Ventrue, and they place great store in both etiquette and age. The longer a Ventrue has been a Cainite, the more respect she will garner from the younger members of her clan. Indeed, many elder Ventrue enjoy "apprenticing" newer members of the clan for a decade or so, to pass on their wisdom and so they can vicariously enjoy their protégés' successes.

Mortal status does not count for much among the Ventrue, and even those titles and lands carried over into death don't bear as much weight as a single city taken *postmortem*. Many of the successes the clan garners are the result of individual action or the team building efforts of charismatic individuals; if a matter is brought to the attention of the clan as a whole, it is likely to be bogged down irretrievably in matters of precedence and credit.

However, when the Ventrue do act, they do so swiftly, effectively and decisively. A Ventrue with an ambition is a terrible thing to behold, for she will not stop until it is achieved, and woe betide any who obstruct her. Ventrue are not above allying with members of other clans, as it is their own kind they have the most trouble working with.

Sobriquet: Patricians

Appearance: Immaculately dressed, the Ventrue prefer garb appropriate to their station in life. Ventrue several centuries old will take every opportunity to wear the weeds of their days among the living. Meetings of Ventrue tend to resemble a masque of historical costuming.

Haven: Castles and fortresses, generally those controlled by their mortal descendants, are where many Ventrue slumber the day away. They are never found far from civilization.

Background: Ventrue are often Embraced from the ranks of the nobility. Those who are not tend to be successful military leaders, though there is a sizeable minority of moneylenders and merchants, and more than a few Knights Templar have joined the clan as well. The most tradition-obsessed clan members attempt to keep the clan notion literal, and will only Embrace their descendants.

Character Creation: Ventrue tend to have noble or military concepts. Mental Attributes are usually primary, as are Knowledge Abilities. Most Ventrue have Influence and Resources as Backgrounds; there are very few poor Ventrue.

Clan Disciplines: Dominate, Fortitude, Presence

Weaknesses: All Ventrue have a specific limitation on their feeding habits. They may only drink the vitae of one particular type of prey (priests, non-Christians, virgins, Englishmen, etc.), chosen at the time of character creation. Ventrue will not feed in a method that violates their prey exclusion, even if starving, wounded or deranged.

Organization: There exists a court of Ventrue, with an ever-changing king and queen. While propriety is observed during the clan's frequent gatherings, more attention is paid to garnering status within the clan than is paid to accomplishing anything, even in the enlightened self-interest of the clan. If a good idea is brought up at a Ventrue gathering, it will almost certainly be stymied by a half-dozen other Ventrue who refuse to see anything that doesn't have their name attached to it succeed.

Quote: *Your wishes may matter on your lands, Baron. This night you stand on mine, and here my word is law.*

STEREOTYPES

• Assamites — They'd not be half so frightful on the field of battle, instead of striking from the shadows and vanishing.

• Brujah — One would think they'd forget Carthage after a millennium, but it would seem not to be the case. They have an admirable talent for carrying grudges, and not much else.

• Cappadocians — Some of what they're researching may well have application; the rest seems to be pointless. Frankly, most of them are simply boring.

• Followers of Set — The next Crusade should be to the waters of the Nile, so we can wipe these vipers from the earth. Never mind the Saracens — these are the true infidels.

• Gangrel — Bestial at best, perhaps they might some night be tamed and used for sport. Like hounds, perhaps, or falcons.

• Lasombra — The lot of them is about as noble as a knife between the shoulder blades. Treachery and condescension make such a charming combination.

• Malkavians — From the mouths of madmen come revelations. Mind you Ezekiel and Amos, and then watch the Malkavians closely.

• Nosferatu — It's quite astounding that so many of these wear the faces of demons yet fall prey to their own religious manias. The sane ones, on the other hand, are impressively talented.

• Ravnos — The antithesis of all we stand for, the Ravnos ought to be banished from the continent and sent to practice their tricks on each other in the Antipodes.

• Toreador — Value their opinions on art and architecture, but not on anything else.

• Tremere — One must admire their ambition and ingenuity in seizing for themselves the mantle of Caine. Alas, there's precious little else to admire about them.

• Tzimisce — Obviously, in the lands of the East nobility means something a trifle different than it does in the West. Treat them as you would a slow-burning fire: with respect and distance.

• Baali — Why does anyone hesitate when confronted with the chance to annihilate one of these cringing diabolists?

THE WAYS OF THE CLANS

The clans themselves often lack organization. Europe is a big place in which to keep a clan united, and travel and communications prove difficult for the Cainites. Consequently, communication between clan leaders and their underlings is a slow process; it might take a year or more for a messenger to reach London from Constantinople, for example. This means that clans are rather loose-knit groups, and the most important decisions are usually made on the spot by the petty princes and local elders.

Older vampires have difficulty controlling their clan members as a group. They tend to reinforce their hierarchies with the Blood Oath, and draw on as many mortal resources as they can to help keep order. Some elders seek to control only a small group of the younger Cainites of their clan, concentrating their efforts on a small geographical area (a country like France, for example) or on a specific group of Cainites. Clans can therefore become factionalized, as different groups of members rally around different elders.

Most Cainites organize themselves around their fiefs, which may be baronies, manors or entire city-states. Many keep havens out in the surrounding villages, and some actually reside within city or castle walls. In this period, it is easy for vampires to keep track of one another, since people generally know their neighbors well. The complexities of mortal politics sometimes cause difficulties for the clans, as clan members become embroiled in their petty feuds. Europe is racked by war in the Middle Ages, and Cainites of any one clan often find their mortal allies fighting on different sides of these various struggles.

Finally the clans are spread across a large and disunited continent. The Cainites absorb and adopt local cultural variations, and poor communications prevent homogeneous traditions among the clans. Clan practices, assumptions, even beliefs can vary widely from one area to another, and archaic customs still persist in rural backwaters. The following information details more about the clans as groups, and what they do in the name of clan unity.

ASSAMITES

The Assamites trace their ancestry back to Haqim (Assam to Western ears), a noble warrior fouly Embraced by Khayyin, father of all vampires. They claim that Haqim was Khayyin's first childe, created even before those three of the Second Generation. Assamite lore tells that Haqim bade all those of his line to slay the other descendants of Khayyin, drinking their blood and thereby coming closer to their ancestor and even Heaven itself.

For time unrecorded, the Assamites have inhabited Alamut, the Eagle's Nest, a powerful, secret fortress somewhere in the mountains of the East. This fortress is inviolate; any infidel vampires found even remotely close to Alamut are quickly killed and diablerized. Assamites value their privacy beyond almost everything; the exception is the safety of the clan.

The spread of Islam has affected the Assamites, to be sure. One group of devotees, following a priest named Ismail, has settled in the mountains around Alamut. The Children of Haqim have befriended

this group and assist them against their enemies. Currently, the Assamites train the Ismailis in the arts of guile and slaying — the most promising have already earned the name *hashashiyyin*. If another Crusade comes, the East shall be ready for it.

The Assamites are likely the most strictly hierarchical clan, with the possible exception of the Tremere. They have incorporated many Islamic teachings into their personal code, strengthening the clan overall. Their greatest obstacle at this point is the animosity the Western clans bear for them, but it is nothing the Assamites had not expected.

STRENGTH AND INFLUENCE

The Assamites completely dominate large stretches of mountain land in the East, controlling their estates through impenetrable castles commanded by loyal ghouls. Their control of these areas is absolute. No Cainite may enter the lands uninvited, and all of the regions' mortals bow to them. They have leverage over monarchs as far afield as Cyprus, Jerusalem and Cairo, but as they are feared they are also hated. The Assamites have no friends, just reluctant enemies.

They have little influence among Western Cainites, and equally little desire for such. Their interactions with other clans are brief and businesslike.

ORGANIZATION

The Assamites brook no insubordination among their ranks. Fortunately, rebellious or malcontent clan members are as rare as blue rubies. Their hierarchy begins with the *fida'i*, the apprentices. After seven years of service, worthy *fida'i* may advance to full clan membership as *rafiq*. *Rafiq* are specialists and assassins, serving the clan as best they may.

Above the *rafiq* sit the *silsila*, the clan elders. They instruct *rafiq* and *fida'i* in Assamite spirituality and judge when an apprentice is ready to become *rafiq*. One is appointed to the great honor of *silsila* only by the Master and the *du'at*. The *du'at* are the three most senior clan members aside from the Master. They act as advisors on their respective fields of interest: the caliph oversees military operations; the vizier maintains the library and learning of the clan; and the amr watches over all things magical for the Assamites, including research into the Disciplines.

The Assamite hierarchy peaks with the Master of Alamut, also known as the Old Man of the Mountain. His word is law, second only to the teachings of Haqim. Any clan member may challenge the Master for his position, but the Master chooses the terms of the duel (physical, political or magical). Only the strongest and wisest Children of Haqim may rise to this post, and failures are ritually diablerized.

CURRENT PRACTICES

The Assamites recruit neonates purely from their subjects, selecting the most zealous, pious and physically impressive. Females appear only as elders, and outsiders are never Embraced. The Assamites do not tolerate infidels in their ranks. They are currently on a moderately aggressive recruiting drive. Their indoctrination process coerces neonates to serve the clan from a mix of loyalty, love, faith, fear and even brainwashing.

The clan follows the dictates of the Blood Road, actively pursuing Cainite blood in an attempt to raise themselves closer to Heaven. As a result, Assamites will offer their murderous services in exchange for vampiric vitæ. They practice diablerie without hesitation, scorning the Westerners' edicts. The only line no Assamite will cross is betraying the clan — they never accept assassination contracts against each other and do not practice diablerie on other Assamites. The goals of the Blood Road have deep spiritual meaning for the Assamites, and take precedence over most individual concerns.

PRESENT CONCERNS

The Assamites feel the need to protect their mortal holdings from attack. They believe that another Crusade will come soon, particularly as the Ventrue become more and more infuriated with Assamite activity in Europe. The clan cannot decide how much effort to take from their ultimate goal — the Blood Road — and spend on neutralizing the Crusade before it happens.

Recently, emissaries from the Followers of Set have arrived in their lands, offering assistance and special goods in exchange for unspecified favors. The Assamite elders have not yet decided what to make of these proposals, or of the Setites themselves.

Some hope that Haqim himself will awake from torpor to reunite the clan, but only a few of the elders know where he lies — if indeed he still survives.

BRUJAH

The Brujah have a dream. It is a dream of one day rebuilding Carthage, of creating a place where Cainites and kine live together in peace and prosperity. The details vary from one Brujah to another; some see it as a place where Cainites control docile mortals, while others say that the two groups will be equals. Some say that the Cainites will be free to hunt at whim, while others claim that they will feed only from animals and willing mortals. In truth, most Brujah aren't too sure what Carthage was like. They just have a hazy picture of a city where there was less poverty, misery, corruption and pain than in the cities of the 12th century. And if this Eden did once exist, it can exist again. There might be — and should be — a society without exploitation and greed, where opulent nobles do not gorge themselves while paupers starve outside.

Each Brujah has her own image of Carthage and a better world. It is this hope that they might somehow bring serenity to the world that allows them to cope with their monstrous existences, and the history of the Brujah has largely been the history of this dream.

Now the Brujah strive to reestablish cities, to reintroduce learning and art, and to quell the petty feuds that tear Europe apart. Regrettably, they have no common idea how the world might be improved. Some support certain rulers in the hopes that under their enlightened tyrannies a new world order might be established. A strong rule, or so they say, will encourage learning, bring peace and foster the towns and trade.

But for every Brujah that joins the rulers, another stands against them. These Cainites argue that the mortal rulers are selfish and greedy, pointing to the strictness of the emerging feudal system, the poverty of the serfs, the harshness of local "justice." They allow that there must be government, but they refuse to accept that any of these tyrants are fit to rule. And so they stir up the peasants, start riots and rebellions, support barons against kings, knights against barons, anyone and everyone against their cruel superiors.

Now a schism splits the Brujah, and their fellow clans laugh at the Zealots' efforts to better the world around them. As more obstacles spring up in their path, the Brujah grow increasingly frustrated, and no Cainite wants to be around when the berserkers snap....

STRENGTH AND INFLUENCE

The Brujah's greatest social strength lies with their affinity for mortals. The average Brujah can more readily empathize with a lowly peasant or soldier than might a Gangrel or Ventrue. Although the clan's influence doesn't sweep across Europe, charismatic Brujah can readily influence local affairs, inspiring a loyalty they consider more valuable than that of any Lasombra dupe or Assamite thrall, because it is voluntarily given. Spain is their chief area of influence, and they are a jagged thorn in the side of the Spanish Lasombra nobility.

The Brujah garner respect from other Cainites not for their vision, but for their fighting ability. The Zealots are akin to bears, some say, fighting on when any sane being would flee or drop. Once a Brujah makes a personal enemy (not an overly difficult task), she will doggedly destroy everything that enemy is trying to accomplish. (If the enemy shares a common goal with the Brujah, then the Brujah will simply try to kill him.) The clan's scholarly background also means that the Brujah have no small number of thinkers and tacticians in their ranks. As clans go, the Brujah control little, but are valuable allies in almost any conflict.

ORGANIZATION

The Brujah are loosely organized. Most pursue their individual dreams, either alone or in small packs. Their strong sense of clan loyalty ensures good communication, though, and it does not take long for one member to rally his brothers and sisters against a common threat. Many countries house small Brujah councils, which settle on their communal direction. The clan elders act as a sort of republic, occasionally meeting to rule on some clan affair or another. Many of these take their childer's desires under consideration; the Brujah remember the democracies of the past and still carry a fondness for such practices.

CURRENT PRACTICES

The Brujah, as ever, wander among the mortals, attempting to inspire certain enlightened individuals into clever ways of bettering their community's lot. Some take this a step further and seek out their fellow Cainites. Although these "missionaries" usually tend to meet with failure (sometimes even derision), they remain convinced that nobody can achieve true harmony until members of different clans can cooperate toward a greater purpose.

The Brujah also experiment with social structures. Any upheaval in a government tends to attract Zealots like carrion birds, as they gather to look over the situation and perhaps learn secrets to a more just society.

PRESENT CONCERNS

The Brujah currently find their dreams of reestablishing a new Carthage blocked by their rival clans. They are most enraged by the Lasombra, whose pointless power-games frustrate their own plans; and the Tremere, who exterminated the serene Salubri.

Some Brujah are concerned about the Crusades, and the possibility of another one beginning. They believe that another Crusade will simply stir up the Assamites, who will in turn kill whatever Cainites strike their fancy, reducing vampire society to total strife. Some anticipate this impending chaos as an opportunity; others dread it as dooming any likelihood of trust among clans.

CAPPADOCIANS

Clan Cappadocian is seldom seen acting as a clan proper. The members rarely socialize among themselves and have no particular love for dealing with other clans. Most other clans see the Graverobbers as a morbid, unhealthy collection of vampires who drink from the dead and parlay with the spirits of the unshriven. The Cappadocians are too busy pursuing their forbidden knowledge to correct this opinion.

They are secretive in the extreme, but do not disdain the company of fellow scholars. If a Cainite of another clan offers to share wisdom with them, they can make gracious hosts. Of course, they are one of the most single-minded clans, and the hospitality of their somber feasts can wear rather thin if one does not have a consuming interest in death. There are of course exceptions to this solemnity, but clan gatherings are never lively or whimsical.

Some Cappadocians worry that the clan's narrow vision will cause trouble at some point, and strive to Embrace neonates with a strong sense of life and practicality. These neonates often find the clan structure stifling, and set off on their own, to continue whatever journey the Embrace interrupted. They are rarely missed. After all, their sires reason, they have eternity to reach a proper view of death and whatever lies beyond. The prodigals will return someday, they chuckle dryly, and the clan will be richer for their experiences.

STRENGTH AND INFLUENCE

The havens of Cappadocians are secure and hidden, often defended with peculiar ghouls and the occasional animated corpse. They feel no need for any sort of military strength, and keep to themselves. Most of their pull in Cainite society stems from their reservoirs of lore, no matter how ancient. It is commonly held that a thing once known to any clan is known to the Cappadocians today, so long as it was written down. Few consider it worth the trouble to slay a Graverobber, particularly as all their memorized knowledge would be lost.

ORGANIZATION

Cappadocian hierarchy hinges on knowledge. The more ancient lore a Graverobber has at his fingertips, the higher his rank among his peers. This is rarely brought into play, however.

Although individuals often meet to share learning, the only large clan gatherings take place on the winter solstice, in a forgotten temple high in the mountains of Turkey. At these meetings, the elders make any policy changes they deem appropriate, and all those who did not attend the solstice rite are expected to learn the changes quickly and abide by them.

CURRENT PRACTICES

All Cappadocian neonates undergo an initiation rite at the time of their Embrace. The exact details vary from sire to sire, but usually involve burying the initiate alive for an extended period of time, as a sort of "dark night of the soul" where the initiate stares into the face of mortality. Those who emerge with their minds broken are deemed unfit and are mercifully extinguished.

Interestingly, the Cappadocians are also involved in advancing the medical sciences. They often conduct autopsies and observe the more talented physicks at work, the better to understand how and why the cycle of life ends. To this end, they have brought a number of herbalists and barbers under their wing, observing both the healers' successes and failures.

PRESENT CONCERNS

The rise of the Tremere has led to some rifts in Clan Cappadocian. Some believe that the Usurpers' success with their magical Discipline, Thaumaturgy, represents a new breakthrough in vampiric learning. Others highly disapprove of the extermination of Saulot, who was considered one of the most enlightened Cainites. In typically scattered manner, the clan has yet to agree on what to do about the Tremere.

The recent Embrace of a cabal of Venetian necromancers is advancing the clan's knowledge of death, but the neonates have yet to share any great discoveries. They have made some progress toward developing a new Discipline, one that will enable contact with the dead. However, many clan traditionalists disapprove of the upstarts and claim no good will come of their unusually aggressive methods.

FOLLOWERS OF SET

The Followers of Set are a scattered clan. They do not congregrate in large groups, yet their fingers brush all of Europe, even beyond to Africa and the East. And for all their scarcity, they are a threat to any careless Cainite.

The Setites' clan loyalty mirrors that of the Assamites and Brujah, but is different in form. They stand by one another for religious reasons; each Follower of Set knows herself to be a disciple of the God of Darkness, lord among the Antediluvians. The clan is a cult, with all the ritual and fanaticism one would expect, and yet is also much more. Because the Setites follow a mythic figure rather than a visible charismatic leader, they can reach farther than a mere cult.

For all their influence, no other clan trusts the Followers of Set, an attitude the Serpents repay in full. They regard all other clans as hopelessly lost, not even worthy of the title "heretic." They hold the Baali bloodline in particular contempt, considering them weak relics adhering to a miserable philosophy. However, they refuse to go to war with any other lines, preferring instead to snare gently whom they can. The reptilian ones are patient and willing to wait out the centuries between now and the eventual return of Set. On that day, they promise, their foes will be cast into the underworld forever, and even the hated sun will be blotted from the sky. It is no less than Set's will.

STRENGTH AND INFLUENCE

The Followers of Set rule those mortals who have fallen to vice and temptation. Avaricious merchants, lusty false monks, fallen Templars and desperate vassals — all can be found as a Setite's pawns. Thusly, the clan has a surprising amount of mortal influence. Their innate sense of corruption also permits them to prey on Cainite weaknesses, and more than one local elder has ended up Thrall to a Serpent.

The clan has little military strength, however. Setites draw their power from subtle means, and the average Follower of Set would likely lose to the average Brujah, Gangrel or Assamite in personal combat. They prefer to let powerful ghouls do their fighting for them, often knights or strong laborers under Blood Oath to their masters.

ORGANIZATION

Setites actually tend to prefer the company of their worshipful disciples to that of their vampiric peers. They will gather in small groups or temples from time to time, but hold no real love for one another. Still, the Followers of Set trust one another and only one another — they avoid situations where they would have to rely on another clan.

Setites on the Road of Typhon hold all higher positions in the clan — no other philosophy is permitted to gain a foothold. These dark priests encourage and abet their underlings, fostering many small cults across Europe. Clan leaders gather every so often, on the night preceding any total solar eclipse. These meetings take place at the Grand Temple of Set, currently located somewhere below Alexandria. It is here that the Setites devise their plans of corruption and conquest.

CURRENT PRACTICES

Setites try to addict mortals and vampires alike to whatever pleasures they can. They fully endorse blackmail, extortion, bribery, prostitution and murder, and particularly enjoy catching "holy men" in their coils. They are currently encouraging the burgeoning practice of small criminal organizations, although the results have been varied. In every major European city, there is likely to be at least one Setite. In addition, some Followers of Set have been provoking obvious acts of cruelty to agitate mortals against vampires. They hope to start a wave of witch-hunting that will sweep away their rivals, leaving the Setites the undisputed lords of the night.

PRESENT CONCERNS

Some Setite cults have been exposed to mortal attention, and the religious backlash in Christian Europe has proved unsettling. Whispers of debased witches are now traveling the continent, and several hunters have set after the Serpents. Although physically stronger than human trackers, the Setites are concerned that other Cainites might follow on their heels.

The Followers considered the Crusades an excellent opportunity and are attempting to begin another. To date, they seem to be meeting with some success. They are also considering ending their rivalry with the Baali once and for all, and are pursuing friendly relations with the Assamites to this end.

Gangrel

The Gangrel are individualists, wandering where they will, and as such have fewer hoary traditions and cobwebby protocols than other clans do. Still, what customs they do follow are deeply revered, as eternal and inviolate as the changing of the seasons or the migrations of birds and beasts.

Other clans have learned the hard way not to curtail Gangrel's freedom or hinder their travels; even the most territorial Tzimisce generally lets a Gangrel pass so long as some acknowledgment of domain is granted. For their part, Gangrel are indifferent to the doings of other vampires, save when those vampires attempt to use Gangrel as pawns in their schemes. A Gangrel tricked into a course of action becomes as savage as a wounded leopard and will do anything to extract revenge on the deceiver. This could be the reason that Gangrel so dislike the Ravnos....

Some Gangrel establish semipermanent territories, but even these prefer to stay deep in the wilderness, where Europe's few remaining mystic sites are. Enchanted springs, magical glens and toadstool rings often have Gangrel guardians. Gangrel know their territories intimately and often befriend the faeries, nymphs and monsters indigenous to the land. It saddens them that the Lupines are less receptive to their overtures.

Strength and Influence

The Gangrel have always walked apart from mortals, and thus hold little influence over their lives. Gangrel drift from village to village, rarely staying in one place long enough to befriend or control anyone. In any case, the Animals' bestial taint makes such interaction difficult.

It is said that in the north roam bands of nocturnal brigands led by bloodthirsty Gangrel. Occasionally stories surface of Gangrel who "protect" an isolated farm community or hamlet: sometimes altruistically, more often in exchange for tribute, with savage retribution awaiting those who do not pay up. Mainly, however, Gangrel impact humanity only as predators. Indeed, Gangrel see the power-games of the other clans as silly. Why manipulate a duke or mayor into enacting political change when you can just eviscerate the fool and end his meddling then and there?

Gangrel are strongest in those areas isolated from human habitation: the Black Forest, the Scandinavian peninsula, the Scottish Highlands and similar places. Here Gangrel often assume a sinister demeanor, becoming night-fiends and bogeymen in a desperate attempt to stop mortal incursion into the wilds.

Other vampires tread lightly around Gangrel, and for good reason: the Animals are as cunning and savage in combat as the beasts they emulate. Gangrel are equally adept at a full-tilt charge and a sudden strike from the undergrowth. Elder Gangrel are particularly deadly, for they can shapeshift into wolf and bat forms to harry prey, vanish in a wisp of smoke and resume the battle at their convenience. Gangrel also commonly make pacts with faeries, magical beasts and other wilderness denizens, and can call on these allies *in extremis*.

ORGANIZATION

Gangrel do as they will and brook no elders or princes telling them what to do. Still, Gangrel have a modicum of honor, and those Gangrel who prove themselves oathbreakers or scarelings are often culled from the clan.

Status among the Gangrel is loose and based mainly on the number and quality of tales told concerning a given Gangrel's deeds. A Gangrel renowned for protecting a mystic site, slaying a lake-wyrm or navigating a trackless waste will be accorded a wider space at the talefire than will an anonymous newcomer.

PRESENT CONCERNS

Unlike other vampires, who benefit from civilization's spread, the Gangrel suffer from it. As the wilderlands shrink and city walls enclose more land, the Gangrel find their hunting grounds dwindling and themselves thrust into territorial conflicts with the Lupines. The fact that the werewolves refuse to heed the Gangrel's entreaties for an alliance frustrates the Animals even more. More and more Gangrel flee Europe for the Siberian wilds or the sub-Saharan expanses; those who stay find themselves increasingly bestial, lashing out frenziedly in all directions, like caged rats.

In Eastern Europe, the rise of the Tremere greatly disturbs the Gangrel; the fact that the Usurpers routinely leech the land's magical essence for their foul spells physically sickens the nature-loving clan. Gangrel have even allied with the Tzimisce (for whom they bear little love) in an attempt to put down the Tremere once and for all.

CURRENT PRACTICES

Gangrel occasionally congregate at certain designated wilderness sites, there to celebrate the changing of the seasons. At these gatherings, the normally stoic Animals throw off all vestiges of decorum — leaping, running and howling under the moon and stars. The festivals generally culminate in a frenzied hunt and the drinking of blood tainted with distillations from hallucinogenic mushrooms and narcotic berries. Woe to the unfortunate who disturbs such a gathering!

Gangrel also hold more sedate meetings, where stories are exchanged. The laconic Gangrel can become surprisingly garrulous when presented with an audience, and all manner of elaborations and embellishments work their way into tales told at these gatherings.

LASOMBRA

Wherever kingdoms rise and fall, wherever a throne can be controlled from the shadows, there flit the Lasombra. Puppetmasters without compare, the Magisters choose the highest of social circles to frequent, fully convinced that their innate nobility gives them the right to do as they please in the pursuit of personal power.

Lasombra have manipulated rival Phoenician merchants and the rival demagogues of ancient Greek city-states. They battled for control of the ancient courts of Persia and Egypt, plotted in the labyrinths of Knossos, and fought to control the wine trade through Marseilles to the northern Celts. As the Roman Empire grew, the Senate was both battleground and playground. They have manipulated rival warlords and princes after the Empire's fall, and have now found pawns for their power-games all around the Mediterranean. Today, many delight in the intricate politicking of the emergent Church.

But many Lasombra have never dabbled in mortal politics. They find taming a savage animal or manipulating the feuds of a group of peasants to be just as challenging and intriguing as the chessboards of kine society. Some have restricted themselves to gaining power within undead society, and others have even experimented with Infernalism, tried to master the Lupines or had truck with the Fair Folk. Regrettably, the other denizens of the Dark Medieval world have proved very resistant to such attempts.

STRENGTH AND INFLUENCE

The Lasombra are spread around the Mediterranean, particularly enjoying the convoluted politics of the warring Italian cities. Lasombra princes rule most of the great cities of Italy and Sicily (Venice, Rome, Pisa, Naples, Palermo), and most of the clan elders can be found around this area. Younger members, eager to win power away from overbearing elders, have moved further afield — to the growing ports of Spain, to Cyprus and the Holy Land, to northern France and into the Alps toward Germany.

Wherever the Lasombra settle, they quickly accumulate influence both in local governments and in the Church. They use this influence, their typically considerable wealth and hand-picked Retainers to defend themselves from physical assault. It is a rare Lasombra who can be forced into a corner, and even there they are dangerous. The weakness in their defenses is their reputation — few Cainites will freely aid one of the manipulative Magisters without hefty coercion.

ORGANIZATION

The Lasombra actually have two levels of organization. Their first, more obvious hierarchy is patterned after that of the Church. Each member seems completely subservient to her betters. However, the real stratification lies with interpersonal influence politicking, and it is entirely possible for a mere "bishop" to garner more respect and obedience than the Lasombra "pontiff." Although each Lasombra knows his place in this invisible web, all constantly scheme to better their station.

Lasombra elders control their juniors through trickery and deceit, threats, blackmail, promises and disinformation. Gifted neonates sometimes gain some converse influence over elders the same way. (And yet, some neonates believe that they have influence, but are actually under the thumb of their "supporter"....)

CURRENT PRACTICES

Many Lasombra traditions would draw a shudder from outsiders. The Lasombra, in their own "noble" way, are fond of many courtly pastimes. Hunts are a favorite; some hunt game at night, some hunt humans, and some foolhardy Magisters even try to bring down Lupines. Some also enjoy "human chess," played on life-size boards with living pieces. What happens to a piece that is "taken" depends entirely on the Lasombra's whim.

Even more unsettling (to Cainites) is the Lasombra approach to diablerie. If a Lasombra can prove, in a court of her elders, that an elder is incompetent and unfit to rule, then she is

granted right to his blood. The defendant need not be present for such a hearing, or indeed even aware that his competence is in question. If the court finds fault with the accuser's points, she may be dismissed without a word — or the court may send word of her claim to the elder in question. It all depends on how the game could best be played....

PRESENT CONCERNS

The Lasombra's power-games have made them many enemies. Their interference at the Pope's court in Rome has come to the attention of some mortal churchmen and is stirring up investigations. Some perceptive witches and magi have been angered by the Lasombra's attempts to manipulate them. Rumors of their dealings with demons have caused widespread concern and distrust amongst the other Cainites — and attracted the attention of the Baali. The Lasombra are also encountering some mixed Malkavian and Ravnos attention, which they find quite unsettling.

The Brujah and Ventrue are currently the two clans with the most malice for the Lasombra, and the Magisters spend much of their time fending off their plots. And as the Assamites settle into the Iberian Peninsula, the Lasombra now have a new threat near their Castillean strongholds....

MALKAVIAN

The history of Clan Malkavian is practically undocumented by outsiders and preserved only by a strange sort of communal "clan memory." However, most suspect that the mad Cainites have been involved in numerous strange happenings in the last few thousand years. They seem drawn to heresies and weird religions, experiments in social control, daft mysticism and magic.

Had they been manipulators and autocrats, like the Lasombra or Ventrue, then they would have tried to control all of the innovations, which would have been disastrous. The Malkavians prefer to hang on the edges of mortal groups, absorbing, twisting and exaggerating the mortals' ideas and theories, or transplanting them from one culture to another. Sometimes they are credited with some of the most insane practices of the mortals; sometimes they claim responsibility for some of the most incongruous things. For example, one Malkavian claims the clan pulled off one of its greatest practical jokes twelve hundred years ago — a bit of graverobbing in Jerusalem. Of course, this selfsame Malkavian claimed friendship with an entire tribe of Lupines, so he has been proclaimed even more deranged than most.

Mystery religions, crazed philosophers and other strangeness abounded in the Roman Empire, and the Malkavians loved the Empire's decadent cities. The current age has been less fruitful, with most mortals too busy trying to survive to break out and try anything really new. As a clan, they seem to have no overall agenda or purpose in the Dark Medieval times. Their fellow Cainites hope that such is the case.

STRENGTH AND INFLUENCE

Nobody can fathom the concept of Malkavians having influence. The other clans despise them or despair of ever manipulating them, and generally leave them be. And this is just what the Malkavians prefer.

The least coherent can often secretly be the most skilled manipulators. Many Malkavians are quite ancient, and individually very powerful. Precisely because they shun politics and conflict, these elders have grown to a considerable age and quietly accumulated quite the power base. This may seem cold comfort to the clan's younger members, but the elders are usually swift to aid any younger member who is being persecuted by an outsider. In times of crisis, the Malkavians of each region inevitably pull together. The hidden hand is no weaker than that which wears the iron gauntlet, or so they say....

ORGANIZATION

The clan has no formal organization and no apparent hierarchy. Still, the younger members have great respect for their elders and expect guidance from them if any threat looms.

The clan has adopted several key centers, around which members often cluster. There are important sites in their own rights, and most Malkavians accept the need to protect them. These meeting grounds include the underground Library of Valentinus in Marseilles (a repository of vast amounts of inspired prophesy and mad ranting), the "Great and Magnificent Court of Carthage" (a randomly chosen ruin on the North African coast), the Church of Saint Herod the Bloody in Palestine, and the Well of Mirth (a spring that spews forth hallucinogenic waters) in northern Germany.

Outsiders sometimes suspect that the Malkavians do in fact have a secret hierarchy. True, most of Dark Medieval society is very stratified, and the Malkavians need not be an exception. Some Malkavians encourage this belief, answering to arcane or surreal titles and ranks. Only the Madmen can say whether these supposed titles hold any weight with the rest of the clan or not.

CURRENT PRACTICES

Clan Malkavian has vested interest in Europe's recent growth. The Church, the expanding economy and the growing cities have created more scholars and books, more privileged people with time on their hands, more room for weird beliefs and popular movements to spread. The clan tends to take advantage of whatever opportunities it can to encourage "liberal thinking" and play sick jokes on whomever it feels like.

But the clan as a whole has no real lasting traditions, save for a few exceptions. Once in a great while, many Malkavians from across the continent suddenly set their affairs aside and make a great pilgrimage. The destination varies each time, but always seems to have great significance for the lunatics. Once there, a bizarre scene takes place. Sometimes it is a mock court, sometimes a pseudo-religious ceremony, sometimes a huge brawl. No sane Cainite knows why they do it, or how they all know where to go. In addition, some Malkavians have recently adopted the tendency to mimic important figures of other clans. These impersonations can sometimes be confusing, as the Obfuscated duplicate goes about giving contradictory orders to the target's underlings.

PRESENT CONCERNS

The Malkavians openly display little concern for anything in particular, and this disparate clan has no apparent unifying agenda. As the Malkavians scatter, meddling with religions, governments, learning and whatever else takes their fancy, other Cainites take reassurance that the mad ones will never act toward a common goal. Or so they hope.

NOSFERATU

Amazingly enough, the horrid Nosferatu have a strong sense of clan unity. Perhaps this is somewhat unavoidable; after all, who but a monster can tolerate the company of other monsters? For whatever reason, Nosferatu readily cooperate with others of their kind and have a strong sense of *esprit de corps* — or perhaps just a mutual hatred for their fairer brethren....

Unlike most clans, which exalt their Antediluvian founders as mythic heroes and the source of all things good in the vampiric paradigm, the Nosferatu dread and despise their progenitor. Indeed, the Nosferatu go so far as to speak of a mystic pogrom carried out against them by their torpid founder. The agents of this pogrom, creatures deemed even more monstrous than the Nosferatu themselves, have a variety of appellations: Nictuku, Nephilim and Echidnae, among others.

STRENGTH AND INFLUENCE

Obviously Nosferatu are severely handicapped with regard to obtaining positions of influence in the mortal world. Not only does their deformity render them incapable of directly commanding mortals, but Nosferatu often find it difficult even to convince a mortal to remain in their presence long enough to listen to a proposition of vassalage.

Nevertheless, there are more Nosferatu ghouls than one might imagine. The Dark Medieval world is a harsh place, and many worthies will traffic with the Devil — or a similarly grotesque proxy — in exchange for an edge in life. Even the subtle deformity induced by ingestion of Nosferatu vitae means little if the added physical vigor enables one to farm additional crops or survive the year's epidemic.

Nosferatu have, through temperament and design, made inroads into the burgeoning Masonic movements, and no few Masonic orders have a Nosferatu in the upper echelons. Not only does Freemasonry's secretive structure allow a Nosferatu to cloak his deformity more readily (the Hidden Master in the Waxen Mask, etc.), but Masonic movements also allow the Nosferatu access to new constructions and building techniques. Masons who, on the orders of their superiors, build a construction with some "occult" significance may in fact simply be erecting a structure to the specifications of the Nosferatu.

Nosferatu rarely resort to open warfare, but are masters of ambush; their aptitude for Obfuscate makes them formidable skirmishers. They are adept at using their sheer hideousness to paralyze a victim with fright, and at using their superhuman strength to rip apart said paralyzed victim before he can recover. Nosferatu also use menageries of gigantic, grotesque animal ghouls as both spies and support troops.

ORGANIZATION

Nosferatu are often solitary through force of circumstance; a village of 100 is hard pressed to conceal one monster, let alone a dozen. Still, given the choice, Nosferatu prefer the company of

their own loathsome peers. Larger cities, particularly those boasting ancient catacombs from the days of Rome, may house entire broods of Nosferatu.

Nosferatu broods are surprisingly egalitarian. Elders are revered (as examples of the discipline and cunning necessary to survive centuries of existence as monsters), but are expected to treat the young fairly. Occasionally rumors surface of a Nosferatu tyrant, a "monster king" ruling its subterranean brood through terror and violence, but these rumors are few and far between.

The Nosferatu also display a surprising amount of interbrood unity. Broods in different baronies, duchies or even countries readily cooperate. Nosferatu have largely divorced themselves from the trivial squabbles over status and prestige that mar the cooperative ventures of the other clans.

PRESENT CONCERNS

The clan is presently concerned with the same thing it always has been: survival.

Nosferatu strongly support the rise of cities and towns, particularly those erected on old Roman sites (the accompanying ruins and catacombs provide excellent hidey-holes). Nosferatu tend to support the rise of the bourgeoisie, seeing them as more meritorious and less pretentious than the old feudal dynasties. Town councilmen have occasionally been able to wring concessions or even independence from their feudal lieges, using illicit information clandestinely given them by a skulking Nosferatu.

CURRENT PRACTICES

Things actually seem to be looking up for the Nosferatu — although perhaps this is because the clan has nowhere else to look. As people congregate into cities and towns, Nosferatu find more and more places to hide by day and hunt by night. The phenomenal number of taverns clustered within most settlements means that many Nosferatu attacks are written off as wine-induced delirium.

Nosferatu often gather on solstices and equinoxes to perform various elaborate rituals emulating (or mocking) human and vampire festivals. One such festival, the Dance of the Dead or Danse Macabre, is performed every 10 years in a secret location; this location changes every time. As many of the clan as can safely travel attend the Danse Macabre, which (in contrast to most things Nosferatu) is an orgy of pageantry and spectacle. Here, Nosferatu celebrate their own grotesquerie, and the catacombs run red with the blood of their human "guests."

RAVNOS

The Ravnos are not present in Europe in significant numbers. Their people, the Gypsies, are currently slowly moving west, spreading across Europe. For now most are found around the cities of the East, through the Arab lands and northern India and as far away as China. There are a few groups of Ravnos vampires around the eastern Mediterranean. They have a prince in the Crusaders' city of Acre, where dark Cainites (Setites, Assamites, Lasombra, *et al.*) often meet to trade goods and information, hatch plots and strike alliances, and they have a community in the Setite-

controlled port of Alexandria. From here, small bands of scoundrels visit Constantinople, Venice and other European ports to steal or extort from the Cainites or mortals.

Many Cainites resent the offhand way that Ravnos trick, rob or swindle other clans. The Ravnos believe they have a sacred duty to keep others from becoming too attached to impermanent things (possessions, beliefs and really just about everything). However, they also see the dim view the outsiders take of their activities. So for now, the Ravnos are a tatterdemalion collection of wanderers and loners, nothing like the hierarchical clans of Europe. It is not their place for such stuffiness, the Ravnos maintain, and so it is the open road and the back alley for them, from now until the final trump.

STRENGTH AND INFLUENCE

The Ravnos have very little military strength in Europe. If threatened with violence, the typical Charlatan will simply laugh and go away (quickly, if need be). If one needs to do harm to an enemy, she will try to trick her foe into a deadly feud with another Cainite (preferably another enemy). If all goes well, the two will be at each other's throats long enough to let the Ravnos go her own way. If not, the Ravnos tries to make as clean a getaway as possible.

The Ravnos are master storytellers and serve as messengers when few others are able. They bring news from far places, and if need be are willing to shape the news to their own advantage. A clever Ravnos can begin a slander that sounds perfectly true, feed it to all the reliable sources and watch his enemy's power base crumble like old clay. Of course, one must be very good to make this stratagem work, but the Ravnos elders have had quite some time to perfect their little fabrications.

ORGANIZATION

Ravnos deliberately shy away from organization, as that would require entirely too much trust and too little independence. It is generally acknowledged that the oldest of the clan are somewhere in the East and have little interest in their childer's doings. However, there is always a grudging respect between Ravnos, and they will usually leap to each other's defense when an outsider starts making threats. "Only I am allowed to insult my brother," or so they would say.

CURRENT PRACTICES

Although outsiders see no real method to the Ravnos' ways, the Charlatans are actually carefully examining Europe. Those elder Ravnos who walk European lands are scouts after a fashion, ascertaining the best time for the majority of their clan (and their mortal people) to return.

The nomadic lifestyle is the most important facet of any Ravnos' unlife; if shackled to one place for too long, they would likely grow mad as a Malkavian. To some extent, the Ravnos have pursued friendly relations with the Gangrel, whom they call cousins, the better to survive the long wild roads. The Gangrel do not welcome such efforts and hold the deceitful Ravnos in contempt. This does not deter the Ravnos, whose sense of humor keeps them good-natured even when confronted with a snarling, bestial Cainite and his menagerie.

PRESENT CONCERNS

Many locals call the meandering Ravnos plague-bearers and stormcrows. The outsider is often mistrusted in times of war, and so the Ravnos steer as clear as they can of the petty battles and feuds across Europe. They avoid the Tremere war when possible, but are not averse to striking deals (or cons) with combatants or suppliers on either side. Those clans concerned with "courtly decorum" run the Ravnos out of their domains on whatever grounds they can find.

Ravnos wagons have also been threatened by Lupine attacks in recent years. As the bloody excesses of many vampires stir up other supernatural activity, the lonely Charlatans have found the long roads growing more dangerous.

TOREADOR

When the Roman Empire collapsed six centuries ago, the Toreador were in dire straits. Many elders slipped into torpor, hoping to awaken in another time of debauchery and excess. Some traveled eastward, seeking refuge in Constantinople or settling in the cities of the East. Those who stayed, however, found strength in temperance and virtue in restraint. As time passed, they were able to nurture art once more from their kine.

As some Toreador became increasingly involved with the Arabs and Moors, others found a beauty in the solemn but unusually impassioned art and architecture of Western Europe. It has been a slow process to nurture the fledgling artistic creativity of the Christians, but as the foundations for the great cathedrals are set, the Toreador consider their time well spent.

Many clans are surprised by the change that came over the Toreador. Where once they joined Nero's revelry and Caligula's perversions, now they keep to sober monasteries and chill stone castles. Even the clan's sobriquet has changed to reflect their attitudes; where once they were scorned as "Dionysians," now they are labeled "Artisans."

And so, while some Toreador make perilous journeys to the North to seek out worthy skalds, and some wander Byzantine halls to Eastern music, most stay where they are, quietly encouraging human achievement. When humanity is ready for a second Golden Age, the Toreador will teach them of ancient art and literature. Until then, *patience* is the Artisans' watchword. Time will tell if they can hold to it.

STRENGTH AND INFLUENCE

The Toreador are not an overly influential clan. They abstain from the dickerings of petty princes and Cainite fishmongers, preferring to follow their calling. Still, they are one of the most perceptive of clans. Many elders and princes who dislike trusting Malkavian or Cappadocian seers will instead keep a Toreador advisor on hand. Constantinople is one place which has benefited from a constant Toreador presence.

The Toreador's military strength is not overwhelmingly impressive. Apart from a few Retainers or Dominated kine, they have few people to call on to fight for them. Some Toreador are excellent fighters, but not all. For this reason, some tend to keep a loose alliance with local Brujah, who also see the need to preserve learning. However, not that many Toreador are openly

attacked. Because they seem harmless, few vampires actually seek their destruction. Because they seem useless, they are not targets to be controlled.

ORGANIZATION

The Toreador do not involve themselves heavily in Cainite politics, and so their organization is reasonably loose. Sires tend to create childer they can trust, and so most Toreador are relatively free to pursue their own ends (which often coincidentally match those of their elders). They gather in Iberia, Alexandria, Constantinople and even in Rome.

Some Toreador gather in groups akin to craft guilds, exchanging information and insight concerning their particular field of interest. These "guilds" are extremely secretive, full of ritual and mysticism. Occasionally they adopt a mortal member into their fold, but only those they deem worthy of receiving the secrets of the ages. These lucky few often return to their work inspired but troubled by what they have seen.

CURRENT PRACTICES

The Toreador are currently working hard to preserve the arts and culture of the lands where they have settled. Most European Toreador have worked themselves into Church affairs, realizing that the majority of modern art and sculpture serves a religious purpose. Some travel to Eastern lands to bring back cultural advancements, but this is a tenuous practice, particularly considering the Easterners' hostility brought on by the Crusades. They tend to arrange benefactors and work for the finer artisans, and encourage creative people to follow their visions. Some French Toreador oversee the construction of cathedrals; tragically, they will never know the buildings in their full glory, with sunlight streaming through the stained glass.

PRESENT CONCERNS

Distasteful though it is, the Toreador find themselves entangled in mortal politics and locked in fierce conflicts with other clans. They are among the strongest defenders of Constantinople and its culture, vocally arguing that the Cainites should play an active role in defending it from the "barbarians" who slowly steal away its territories. They also disapprove of recent Lasombra forays into the Church, believing that the Magisters will turn more and more churchmen away from art and education, emphasizing instead control, intolerance and politics.

The clan also respects Moslem art and achievements and tries to persuade the Brujah and Lasombra to help nurture the Moslem kingdoms on the Iberian Peninsula. Unfortunately, rumors of Assamite footholds are hindering this pact.

TREMERE

The Tremere only recently appeared among the Cainites. It was not until 1022 that the first Tremere vampires were created (or rather, created themselves) through trickery and magic. They slew a Tzimisce elder and vivisected two apprentice magi whom they had caused to be Embraced. The experiments eventually created a potion which allowed the *magus* Tremere to convert himself and his seven closest followers into undead.

Once it had been discovered what their new immortality had cost them, the new Tremere sought to recreate the powers that they had known in life. The result was the magical Discipline they called Thaumaturgy. However, Tremere was not satisfied. He was well aware that the fledgling vampires were in still in great danger, and he wanted to strengthen their place in the vampire hierarchy. After long research and seeking, he learned how the other clans had gained their permanency — by way of an ancient founder. He discovered the location of the sleeping Salubri founder, Saulot, and decided that the peaceful vampire would make the best target for his designs. He tracked Saulot to his resting-place and diablerized him. All accounts say that Saulot died peacefully and without resistance, although the Tremere were terrified by the sight of his third eye opening and gazing on them.

The resulting war has continued now for nearly two centuries. The Tzimisce and Gangrel — the strongest clans in Hungary — have led the battle against the upstarts, but have been unable to defeat them. The Tremere have called upon the aid of the Order of Hermes, a circle of mortal magicians of which they are still a part, and have both their sorceries and mortal armies to protect them.

Over this period, the power of the Tremere has expanded. Now around half of the mages once loyal to Tremere have been Embraced, a few of them remaining in contact with their fellows in the Order of Hermes. Other mages have been Embraced, too, and brought into the clan. Perhaps most importantly, the Tremere have recently created new foot soldiers — the monstrous Gargoyles.

Strength and Influence

The Tremere's main strongholds are great fortresses in the mountains of Transylvania and Hungary, although they have fortified chantries (magical "guild houses") throughout Europe. Recently they have achieved a major victory against the older Cainites of Hungary, slaughtering several noble families upon whom the Tzimisce depended and thereby cementing their power within the country.

Their old links with the Order of Hermes bolster their power, as they can sometimes embroil these magicians in their plots. They also retain several of their mortal contacts and have the resources to employ many mortal messengers and spies.

Organization

Clan Tremere has the tightest organization of all clans. The war for survival demands nothing but absolute precision, and consequently neonates are often put under the Blood Oath. The founder now sleeps for years on end and shows little of his old fire when he wakes. The leadership of the clan has thus passed to the deeply divided Council of Seven, the seven mages who were first transformed into vampires with Tremere himself. Recently, the Council divided the known world between themselves to avoid fractious arguments.

The unofficial leader of the Council is Goratrix, the loyal but scheming man who in life masterminded Tremere's plot to gain immortality. The Council has recently sent him to oversee the House's business in western Europe. The defensive, humane Etrius remains in the clan's stronghold of Ceoris in Hungary, coordinating the defense of their holdings and attempting to make peace with the Tzimisce and Gangrel. Meerlinda moderates disputes among the Council and governs the British Isles. The remaining members are still establishing their authority and do not contact their disciples with any frequency. Neonate Tremere under their authority might not even know the Councilors' names, answering instead to their chosen lieutenants.

The Council of Seven are in regular magical contact, but all seven only meet together each seven years to discuss important matters. Their next meeting is scheduled for 1199.

Current Practices

The Tremere are researching as much occult lore as possible, as they have always done, the better to survive the current war and earn a place among the other clans. To this end, they attempt communications with those Cainites which do not appear immediately hostile (which are few). They also pursue the legends of the Lupines, but not so aggressively.

Some members know a ritual that allows them to communicate with their sire across great distances. This, plus their access to several mortal messengers, allows the clan to collect information and coordinate its plans far better than any other clan.

Finally, the Tremere are encouraging the spread of their freakish creations, the Gargoyles. These brutish vampires were developed from Gangrel and Tzimisce "materials," but are now able to sire their own progeny.

Present Concerns

The bulk of the clan's elders are preoccupied with the battle against the Tzimisce and Gangrel. These older clans have recently launched a counterattack against the Hungarian Tremere, unleashing neonates, ghouls and mortal pawns in a final bid to curb the Usurpers' expansions. The violence has not been obvious to the mortals — just a few assassinations, brigands' raids and nobles' feuds — but Cainite casualties have been high. Vampires who had previously managed to remain neutral are being forced to choose sides or else flee from Hungary. However, the Tremere have been able to repel the worst of these attacks, particularly with the aid of the Gargoyles.

The Tremere are now making bids to extend their powers beyond their isolated chantries and settle in the towns and cities. Many younger members have been ordered to make havens or establish small chantries in western Europe's cities, where their Tzimisce and Gangrel enemies are weak.

The Tremere are also concerned with their reputation in the Order of Hermes. The Order has so far been unaware that the Tremere's leaders have become vampires. As the Seven have sought to extend their influence, however, they have Embraced an increasing number of mages, and the Order is coming to realize what creatures lurk within their ranks. The Tremere fear that they must soon either split from the Order or make a bid to control it.

Tzimisce

Clan Tzimisce is a venerable clan, steeped in tradition and lore. The clan has long clung to its Baltic roosts and until recently was deemed unconquerable. This, of course, makes the current nights of upheaval all the more intolerable.

The Tzimisce have long been among the most knowledgeable and erudite Cainites. For millennia other vampires have made the perilous trek to the Carpathians in search of Tzimisce wisdom (the fact that many such vampires do not return deters them little). Until the Tremere's rise, the Tzimisce were the master sorcerers among vampires, practicing a bizarre amalgam of alchemical rituals, Slavic charms and demonology. Indeed, erudition and sorcerous skill rank second only to land held when determining a given Fiend's status.

Tzimisce lore rarely juxtaposes with human concerns, and only intermittently with vampiric ones. The clan has its own agenda, one little concerned with the petty doings of others. Whereas other vampires see themselves as damned, the Tzimisce believe themselves masters of their destiny, subservient to neither God nor Devil. Of all the clans, the Tzimisce takes an approach most similar to what will one day be called humanistic thought.

Not that the clan is by any means humanistic, humanitarian or even human. Tzimisce, indeed, affect a cold contempt for the lesser creatures who provide them with food and fodder, and even other vampires are at best second-rate beings. Tzimisce believe that with sufficient mastery of their Vicissitude Discipline, they can literally sculpt themselves into the image of God — or into an even superior form.

This continuous refinement of Vicissitude has reaped many practical rewards. No clan is so skilled in the use and creation of ghouls. Tzimisce, though free use of their flesh-shaping bent, are fiendishly skilled at warcraft. Though other vampires may be more personally formidable in battle, none are so terrifying. A Tzimisce assault typically takes the form of a nightmarish swarm of twisted monster-ghouls. Such onslaughts are even more frightening when led by the Tzimisce themselves, often in the gigantic, nearly invulnerable Zulo Form. Moreover, stories of what the Tzimisce do to their foes often lead enemies to flee rather than risk capture. There are reasons why the Balkans have spawned so many tales of terror.

The Tzimisce have used their powers to sculpt ghoul servitors to their specifications, creating legions of terrifying minions. Monstrous, shark-mawed Tzimisce hellhounds, some nearly as large as ponies, prowl the clan's demesnes. Squadrons of formerly human ghouls, their very bones and tissues warped into weapons of war, descend on the villages by night to collect Tzimisce tribute. The worst are the *vozhd*, or war ghouls: elephantine horrors created by the fusion of a dozen or more ghouls (human or animal) into a multilimbed composite monster.

STRENGTH AND INFLUENCE

Clan Tzimisce, despite its current woes, clings tenaciously to the Eastern European homeland it has haunted since its earliest nights. Tzimisce maintain strongholds and control puppets in Hungary, Poland, Bulgaria, Wallachia, Bavaria, Austria, Serbia and Kievan Russia. The Tzimisce is particularly strong in pagan Lithuania, where certain powerful elders still maintain the worship of the ancient Slavic gods. Here the clan struggles against the Teutonic Knights, who have begun to unearth evidence of the clan's (and its servitors') practices.

Tzimisce maintain their temporal power through their "revenants": ghouls with hereditary supernatural powers. Through marriage, intimidation and outright violence, revenant lines

have riddled most noble Eastern European (and many Byzantine) families. The clan has also infiltrated the Eastern Orthodox church, although not nearly to the extent that their Lasombra brethren have riddled the Roman Catholic church.

ORGANIZATION

Voivodes rule "families" of childer; these childer are required to submit to a Blood Oath binding them to their sire. Alas, the childer are rarely bound to each other; centuries of brutal jockeying for the *voivode's* favor, in a grotesque parody of familial interaction, remain the norm among Tzimisce broods. Occasionally a *voivode* will impart a favored childe some measure of responsibility — overseeing the ghouls, interacting with the serfs, maintaining the ancestral castle — but this is uncommon.

The clan was much more unified in the elder nights, but complacence and decadence have set in. The fragmented political landscape of the Balkans bears mute testimony to the disharmony rending the clan. Each *voivode* advances her own goals with little concern for the well-being of the clan as a whole. While such self-centeredness is ubiquitous to the Cainite race, Tzimisce arrogance and territoriality ensure that two feuding *voivodes* are less likely to compromise (or be forced to compromise) than, say, two Ventrue elders.

As more and more *voivodes* fall to pyre, stake or spell, increasing numbers of dispossessed childer roam the world. These childer set up squatter demesnes as best they can or simply wander into the unknown realms beyond the Danube. A few such childer, taking possession of their sire's artifacts and Tremere spoils, have done rather well for themselves in the West.

PRESENT CONCERNS

Obviously, the war with the Tremere eclipses current Tzimisce thought. From their aeries the Fiends rage against the Tremere sorcerers and hurl legions of childer and ghouls at their chantries. Unfortunately, with the rise of the Tremere's own servitor creatures, such tactics prove increasingly ineffective. The clan's internal strife only compounds the problem.

As if this weren't enough, many Tzimisce holdings are crumbling from within. The Fiends' human subjects, weary after centuries of abuse, welcome invaders and the like; even the Germans, they figure, must make better masters than the rapacious *voivode* on the mountain above the village. This attitude shocks the Tzimisce, who often view their subjects as unthinking extensions of the ancestral land. Many younger Tzimisce, angered by their subjects' "betrayal," have begun to adopt an actively hostile stance toward humanity.

CURRENT PRACTICES

The war with the Tremere has not only disrupted the traditional Tzimisce unlifestyle, but has made it plain that Tzimisce elders are quite out of touch with the needs of their progeny. In an effort to maintain their identity and purpose, many younger Tzimisce congregate among themselves. These Tzimisce celebrate the ancient rites of their land (Kupala's Night, the equinoxes, etc.) with grand communal festivities (an outside observer might call them massacres). At these fetes, Tzimisce reaffirm their loyalty to each other in the face of adversity by actually drinking each other's blood. Some Tzimisce whisper that those who have participated in these blood-drinking festivals for years or decades actually become less submissive to the will of their *voivodes*.

VENTRUE

Since the days of the Roman Empire, the Ventrue have lived hidden within the castles of the great nobles, guiding these magnates and sharing their luxuries. Even when barbarians swept through their lands, few Ventrue had to live among the common folk or drink anything but the noblest blood. If one family was destroyed by an invader, the Ventrue could easily adopt another magnate.

As Europe's economy developed and trade became more profitable, the Ventrue began to adopt merchant families as well. And as the Franks and then the Normans began to conquer lands outside of France, the Ventrue often followed the victorious mortals, to Germany, to northern England and Ireland, northern Italy and Sicily, Cyprus and the Holy Land.

Now old ghosts are returning to haunt the Ventrue. Few neonates have learned of the long-ago war with the Brujah, or the city that fell to Roman swords. All they know is that the Brujah loathe them for some ancient slight and seek to block their every goal. The Assamites are emerging out of the East, and the Lasombra are challenging their authority; all in all, the Ventrue have some trying times ahead of them.

STRENGTH AND INFLUENCE

The Ventrue are the dominant Cainites of France and England and have influence in many other countries. Their center of power is Paris, and they maintain a firm grip on the fairs and markets of the surrounding regions. Many Ventrue have developed a sentimental attachment to the French noble families. The University of Paris, the splendor of the French royal court and the success of local merchants are all sources of great Ventrue pride.

Most of the Ventrue's might comes from their mortal resources. Through Presence and Dominate, they control some of the most powerful nobles and merchants of Europe. Some build private armies, others attempt to sway local governments, but they are for the most part content to change little. It is only when a Ventrue's authority is challenged that he becomes truly aggressive, and then woe unto the offender.…

ORGANIZATION

Ventrue organize along courtly standards, both locally and clanwide. The oldest Ventrue of each region is accepted as that region's monarch. Monarchs entertain visitors and supplicants, and local Ventrue are expected to heed their proclamations. Cainites of other clans are accepted into court structure if they wish to make suitable supplications.

The Grand Court is set above all other courts. Ventrue gather there for the opportunity to sum up business, strike deals and make plans for forthcoming years. It is also a place for the presiding Ventrue to commend or criticize younger Cainites, who might thereby win or lose much prestige.

Many Ventrue consider the Grand Court an excellent opportunity to flaunt wealth and influence; they often attend with a train of lavishly dressed retainers and ghouls. Others compete to bring the most attractive, sophisticated or highborn companions. The Grand Court is currently seated in Paris, where the venerable fourth-generation prince Alexander presides as king. The queen is Saviarre, an elder of great beauty who does most of the actual clan governing. Many lesser princes and elders send ambassadors to the Grand Court to beg aid, to present fine gifts or to announce their triumphs.

CURRENT PRACTICES

The Ventrue, strong among both the merchants and noble classes, cling to the trappings of the nobility upon whom they have fed for so long. Many maintain sumptuous robes to wear to their courts, often having a new robe each visit. Ventrue are fond of all manner of courtly practices, and Ventrue princes have been known to "knight" particularly loyal subjects, a ceremony that often involves the Blood Oath. A Ventrue will often be quite generous when awarding privileges, even to members of other clans.

In order to display their wealth and influence, older Ventrue often become patrons to younger clan members, supporting and encouraging them. They also make ostentatious gifts to one another and are always ready to offer assistance. This is in part a matter of pride (demonstrating their superior power and generosity), but also pragmatically reinforces the clan's power.

PRESENT CONCERNS

The Ventrue continue to engage in various power-games, attempting to gain some measure of control over Cainite society. They are often stymied in this, particularly by the Lasombra, their rivals. In addition, other clans stubbornly resist any form of Ventrue overseers, especially the Brujah, who have robbed them of their influence in Spain.

However, the Ventrue have much to look forward to. Their influence is growing in France and England, and the recent threat of the Tremere seems to be galvanizing many clans into a sort of understanding. With luck, the conflict will forge a new unity in vampire society, and the Ventrue will be the ones to lead the Cainites into the new century.

CAITIFF

There are few Caitiff in Europe, or indeed anywhere else. The blood of Caine still runs strong in his descendants, and the clan affinities and flaws are still very pronounced. However, princes are largely powerless to prevent Cainites from creating neonates. Consequently, some lineages have thinned to the 13th generation and beyond. Many of the more careless and prolific sires make little effort to educate or watch over their creations, and some of these neonates remain forever ignorant of their clan.

In many instances, elders attempt to bring such neonates into the fold (they may be useful pawns, after all), but sometimes lack the power to compel obedience. Many clans simply lack the inclination to force their Caitiff members to rejoin.

In such cases, where the vampire is allowed to remain apart from her clan, her childer and their childer may have neither a sense of belonging nor any direct link to their precursors' clan, and become truly Caitiff.

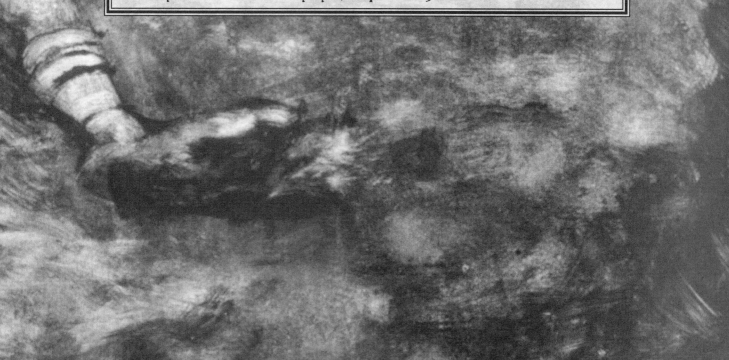

BOOK TWO: DESCENT

Owls call, somewhere beyond these tired walls. I can move, a little. I can lurch across the packed dirt to the barn's mouth, and perhaps farther. But I cannot run. I am far too faint and weary for that.

At a wayside inn, I had thought to spend a pleasant night with a drink and a cheap woman. I was welcomed there, as I swaggered in, one hand on my sword as if I'd rather fight than drink. A band of strangers not so far from the fire called me over, laughed with me, kept filling my tankard. I gladly left with them, clutching the cold hand of one of their women.

They threw me against the alley wall. They took my sword and snapped it in ten places. They laughed as my alcohol-slurred muscles tossed me unevenly at them, and then they tore the flesh away from my veins. I tried to scream I should have died, but as the devils drifted back into the shadows, the hands of one among them lifted me up. I found pity at the whim of a monster, and God help me, I am glad.

She has hidden me in a leveled barn, miles from town. I am too weak to travel — my helplessness reflects in her eyes when she visits. She touches me as one would touch a simple-minded child, and tells me dark things about myself. Sometimes she brings me a hare, or a few quail. Enough to keep me alive, though I do not hunger. But God! My thirst, my thirst...

My blood falls from my eyes, seeps into the dust.

Chapter Four: Character

Know thyself.
— Inscription at the Delphic Oracle

Before you begin to play Vampire: The Dark Ages, you must create a character. Vampire: The Dark Ages, however, is not like make-believe; you don't just make up a character as you go along (though the Storyteller is regularly faced with that challenge). A certain amount of work is involved; a character concept is born, but a character proper is built. Building a compelling yet genuine character is a creative struggle.

This chapter describes how to create a unique character, beginning with a general concept and translating this concept into numbers that can be used in the game. This process is very simple; players can easily figure it out for themselves. The Storyteller should have a good grasp of the process in order to answer the players' questions accurately.

The numbers on the character sheet may not seem particularly evocative. It is hard to imagine a novelist describing a character by saying, "She has a Charisma of 4." However, these ratings make it simple to describe the strengths and weaknesses of a character. More importantly, these numbers allow the random factor created by dice to be employed in relation to the character's Traits. A strong vampire has a better chance to move a heavy boulder than a weak vampire does.

Character creation usually follows a pattern from the general to the specific. First you develop a general concept of who and what your character is — is she more socially or mentally developed? Then you select the specific ratings of your Traits — how effective are your Charisma, Manipulation and Appearance? Do not use this process to create the "best" possible character; that defeats the purpose of making up a genuinely interesting individual. These numbers are intended to enhance roleplaying, not to open an avenue to some mythical character Hall of Fame.

Start by deciding what kind of character you want. Are you going to play a wretched beggar-child or a wealthy and educated noble? Are you a pagan from the remote valleys of Scotland, or did you enter a monastery to become closer to God? The background and personality of your character are the essential ingredients of his persona. Once you have formulated your basic concepts, the details of Attributes and choosing Traits from a variety of lists, you decide who your character is. You will receive extra points called "freebies" at the end of the process, and you can use these to add dots to any Trait, so do not agonize over all your choices.

• Most Traits are rated numerically from 1 to 5. This system is similar to the star system used to rate movies, restaurants and hotels. One dot in a Trait indicates poor or novice ability in that Trait. Two dots indicate an average Trait, while a rating of 5 indicates that you are among the best in the world. Traits are based on an average human range.

• You need to consider how well your character will interact with the group. The Dark Medieval world is dangerous enough as is; a group undergoing internal strife will have a much harder time surviving. If your character doesn't fit in and disrupts the story as a result, almost nobody will enjoy the game. The Storyteller may ask you to create a new character.

ROLE OF THE STORYTELLER

As the Storyteller, your role is to guide the players through the character generation process. After your players arrive for the game session, you need to introduce them to the basic premise of the game and describe the rules system. Your main goal should be to make character creation as easy as possible.

Pass out the character sheets and give the players a minute to look them over and ask questions. Then go through the character creation process step by step, filling in all the details of the characters' Traits.

It is sometimes advisable to spend an entire game session creating characters. This ensures that the players don't feel rushed and that they take the time to create believable characters, not paper-thin stooges. In fact, you may encourage your players to come to the character generation session with fairly developed character concepts.

Once you are done with the practical details, you can spend the rest of the session running preludes for the characters. A prelude is a form of abbreviated storytelling in which you tell the story of a character's mortal life and Embrace. Preludes are the players' introductions to the chronicle as well as their characters, so make them memorable. Preludes are described at the end of this chapter.

STEP ONE: CHARACTER CONCEPT

You begin by formulating a basic concept for your character. This concept need only be a general idea of what your character will be like, something unique and interesting that will be enjoyable to play over the long term. For example, to describe your character concept you could say, "I'm a rural priest who strives to hold onto his beliefs. I play the game of vampirism in order to survive, but am constantly looking for some way to avoid damnation."

CONCEPT

Many Kindred find it difficult to abandon their concepts of themselves as humans and cling tenaciously to the trappings of their former lives. Thus the first thing you need to do is to come up with an overall concept of who the character was before he was Embraced: what he did, how he lived and what was unique about him. This concept may describe his profession, how he saw himself or what others felt about him.

A character concept such as a gladiator might indicate an Embrace hundreds of years ago, while others, like a knight or lady-in-waiting, indicate that the character is a product of the current era. Regardless of when the character was Embraced, he has spent only 50 years or less as a vampire. All years of unlife beyond that are assumed to have been spent in torpor, sleeping the long sleep of the Damned. The table on (page 102) lists a few possible concepts; feel free to invent your own.

THE CLAN

The next step, and arguably the most important element of character conception, is to choose your character's clan. The clan describes the essential lineage of the character — you are always of the same clan as your sire. 13 clans are available; there are also various minor bloodlines, but they do not have as dramatic an effect on the Dark Medieval world.

A player does not necessarily need to choose a clan, for some younger vampires are of such diluted blood that the characteristics of any single clan have not been imprinted upon them. These clanless vampires, known as Caitiff, are very rare outcasts among the Cainites — accepted by none, scorned by all. If you wish to play such a character, simply list "Caitiff" as the character's clan.

NATURE AND DEMEANOR

At this point you can, if you wish, choose personality archetypes that fit your conception of both the internal nature and outward disposition of your character.

Your Nature is the most dominant aspect of your character's true personality, but not necessarily the only archetype that may apply. The archetype you choose for your character's Nature describes the character's most deep-rooted feelings and beliefs about herself and the world; it also provides the primary way in which she can regain Willpower into her Willpower pool. Choosing a Nature helps you describe who your character really is, on the inside.

You should also choose a Demeanor to describe the personality your character pretends to possess. This is the role she plays to the world, the façade she presents. It should probably be different from the archetype you have already chosen as the character's Nature, but not necessarily. Whatever you choose is only the character's typical pose; people can change Demeanor as quickly as they change mood. You may change your character's Demeanor at any time, allowing her to adapt to different people and different situations. Demeanor has no practical effect on the rules.

ROADS

The Cainites of the Dark Ages share different views on morality. You select a Road (essentially a vampiric philosophy and code of behavior) based on what you believe your character's morality to be. Each Road determines the ethics you must hold to or else lose yourself to the Beast. It also determines which Virtues you begin with.

Bear in mind that your character's Road will influence practically every aspect of his vampiric existence. Although some Roads are quite close to common human morality of the time, others hold rather inhuman values as sacred. Keep your character's clan, Nature and Demeanor in mind. It is highly doubtful that he would choose a code of ethics lightly, particularly with so much at stake.

STEP TWO: CHOOSING ATTRIBUTES

A character's Attributes define his intrinsic makeup. How fast are his reflexes? How attractive is he? How long does it take him to understand new ideas?

First, you must prioritize the three categories of Attributes — Physical, Mental and Social. Choose in which of these categories your character is good (primary), in which he is average (secondary) and in which he is poor (tertiary). Is your character more physical than social — is he more brawny than gregarious?

• Physical Attributes — The Physical Attributes describe how strong, nimble and sturdy your character is. They are the primary Attributes of an action-oriented character, defining the strengths and weaknesses of the body. Strength measures a character's lifting power and how much damage she can inflict in basic hand-to-hand combat. Dexterity rates a vampire's speed and agility. Stamina measures a character's constitution and resilience.

• Social Attributes — Your character's Social Attributes measure her ability to relate to, motivate and manipulate others. Charisma indicates personal magnetism and charm. Manipulation measures a character's ability to talk her way into and out of situations. Appearance describes how the character looks and carries herself.

• Mental Attributes — These Traits represent your character's thought capacity, including such things as memory, perception, learning potential and the ability to think quickly. Perception describes the character's observation skills. Intelligence represents memory, reasoning and learning potential. Wits measures a character's reaction time and ability to think on her feet.

Your character concept may help suggest Attribute priorities, even slightly unusual ones. Choose what will best fit the concept you have in mind. For now, your character should be very general — paint a broad, sweeping outline instead of concentrating on little details.

All characters start with one dot in each Attribute. Your priority selection determines how many dots you get to spend in each category. You may divide seven dots among your character's primary Attributes, five dots among her secondary Attributes and three among her tertiary Attributes. Thus, you may choose to add seven dots to your vampire's Physical Attributes and five to her Mental Attributes, which leaves three dots for her Social Attributes. Divide the dots among individual Attributes as you see fit — you may, for example, decide to assign all three of your tertiary Social Attribute dots to Charisma, one dot to each of the three Social Attributes or two dots to one and one dot to another.

You may increase some of these ratings later, so don't worry too much about your choices now. Let your intuition guide you.

Note: The space after each Attribute (and Ability) is for you to fill in a specialty, a subcategory of the Trait in which the character excels. Specialties are fully explained on (page 117); for now, concentrate on choosing your ratings.

STEP THREE: CHOOSING ABILITIES

Abilities delineate what your character knows rather than what he is; they describe the things he has learned as opposed to the things he can naturally do. Each Ability your character possesses is assigned a numerical rating representing the character's aptitude in that particular area. The number is used to determine how many dice you roll when your character attempts to use an Ability.

Abilities are divided into three different categories: Talents, Skills and Knowledges. Each type has different characteristics.

• Talents describe intuitive Abilities. Talents do not need to be practiced per se and cannot be studied or learned from a book; they are most often gained through direct experience.

• Skills are Abilities learned through training of any sort. This category includes any Ability that must be learned step by step through actual practice, but that can be taught or studied (unlike Talents).

• Knowledges include all the Abilities requiring the rigorous application of the mind. These Abilities are generally learned through education, books and tutors, but can also occasionally be picked up through experience.

You prioritize these Abilities just like you prioritized the Attributes. You decide how to rank your Talents, Skills and Knowledges, choosing in which category your character will be above average (primary), in which she will be average (secondary), and in which she will be below average (tertiary).

You get 13 dots to spend on your character's primary category, nine for the secondary category and only five dots for the tertiary category.

There is one additional restriction: you cannot give your character more than three dots in any one Ability (later, however, you can use your freebie points to gain up to five dots in an Ability).

STEP FOUR: ADVANTAGES

You do not prioritize or rank the different categories of Advantages. Instead you have a designated number of dots to assign within each one. Though this number is fixed, you can purchase additional dots later with freebie points.

DISCIPLINES

After characters first become vampires, they learn various Disciplines, which are the basis of vampires' legendary powers. You have only four points to spend and may only choose Disciplines with which your character's clan is especially proficient (Clan Disciplines). See the Clans chapter to find out what your character's Clan Disciplines are. If you are a Caitiff and have no clan, you can spend your four points on any Disciplines you would like.

Players are urged to be cautious when they choose Disciplines, for these powers are central to a vampire character. Four points aren't a lot, but characters should start out weak, and Disciplines can be raised (or new ones added) during the chronicle.

BACKGROUNDS

Every character also gets five points to allocate among the various Background Traits. In some chronicles your choice may be restricted to certain Backgrounds; the Storyteller will let you know the ground rules. Your Background Traits should fit into the general scheme of the concept originally chosen.

VIRTUES

Virtues are fundamental to a **Vampire: The Dark Ages** character, for they describe the moral strengths and weakness that play such an essential role in the vampire myth. Each of the Virtues is rolled in different circumstances to determine the emotional reactions of the character (at times when her vampiric nature might overcome her human leanings). Two of the Virtues are of dual nature, which may seem a little complex at first. Simply put, depending on a vampire's Road, she will roll Conscience or Conviction to see if she loses ground along her Road after an inhumane act. Similarly, she would roll Self-Control or Instinct to see if she can resist the urge to frenzy. Courage is essential to all vampires (and therefore has no counterpart); it determines if the character can avoid panic at the sight of open flames or the sun.

Every character automatically starts with one dot in each of her three Virtue Traits (which vary according to Road), and you may then assign seven additional dots as you see fit. The Virtues are a primary factor in determining your character's Via and Willpower ratings, so you will want to be careful with your choices. Remember, you may use freebie points to boost your character's ratings.

STEP FIVE: FINISHING TOUCHES

In this step you gain 15 freebie points, enabling you to add more dots to any of the Traits on the character sheet. Before you spend these points, however, you must record the base scores for your character's Willpower, Via rating and Blood Pool.

WILLPOWER

Your character's beginning Willpower is equal to his Courage rating, and will thus range from 1 to 5. You should probably raise it even higher by using freebie points. Willpower is essential for controlling the actions of your character, especially in times of stress when your more predatory instincts emerge. Willpower is also vital for resisting Dominate and employing the Discipline of Thaumaturgy.

VIA RATING

Your character's initial Via rating is equal to her Conscience/Conviction + Self-Control/Instinct ratings, ranging from 2 to 10. However, it is generally a good idea to purchase a higher Via score by spending freebie points. The Road is critical for determining how far your character has degenerated into bestiality. A character without a Via rating has completely succumbed to the Beast and can no longer be used as a player character.

BLOOD POOL

The crowning touch of character generation is determining how large a Blood Pool the character has at the beginning of the game. The Blood Pool indicates how much "energy" the character has — blood is the life-force of a vampire. Simply roll a 10-sided die to determine the number of Blood Points possessed. This is the only die roll that will be made during the character creation process. The irony of a vampire's existence should not be confined to the story alone.

FREEBIE POINTS

You now get 15 points to build and buy Traits anywhere on the character sheet. However, it's not as straightforward as it sounds. If you want to add a dot to an Attribute, each one costs five freebie points, while a Background dot only costs one point. Costs are listed in the chart on (page 103). You can buy any Discipline (even ones that are not listed as Clan Disciplines). You may not buy a Trait to six dots during character creation.

SPARK OF LIFE

The following details will help make your character a complete and unique person. You do not necessarily need to write these things down, but you should certainly think about them—not only now but throughout the career of your character.

APPEARANCE

Your character's appearance makes her Traits visible to other characters. You should turn the concept and relevant Traits of your character into aspects of her appearance. For example, a high Self-Control might appear as a constantly composed expression. Instead of saying, "She's got an Appearance of 4," describe what others are going to see when they look at her: "She stands about five foot four, with a slender frame and fine bone structure. Her long black hair cascades down her back like water, framing her high cheekbones and setting off her porcelain skin. Her green eyes are like gems, sparkling with intellect and interest, and she always seems to be smiling, perhaps at her own private joke."

SPECIALTIES

Each Trait with a rating of 4 or higher can be given a specialty. Though most players select specialties for their Traits during play, you can pick them immediately. A specialty describes your area of expertise with a given Ability. Simply fill in the space next to the Trait with an appropriate specialty; suggestions are made with each Trait later on in the chapter.

EQUIPMENT

If there are any possessions or pieces of equipment you want your character to have, you should work out the details now. Otherwise, you will have to acquire the equipment during the game. This can take time and is not automatically successful. Almost any piece of mundane equipment that fits your concept can be obtained, provided your character has sufficient dots in the Resources Background.

QUIRKS

By giving your character quirks, interesting personal details and anecdotes, you can add a great deal of depth and interest to him. Write a few sentences describing the strange and interesting things that define your character. A quirk could be a twisted sense of humor, a gentleness toward animals or a clumsy attempt at imitating courtly etiquette. An important thing to consider at this time is your character's nationality, particularly how it relates to the chronicle setting. How is a Russian boyar going to react when an English tavern-wench, the top of her bosom largely bared, leans over to ask him what he wants to drink? Such anecdotes can be of great help in defining personality and give the Storyteller things to play with.

MOTIVATIONS

What drives your character? What makes her laugh, makes her cry or makes her angry? What does she want from life (and unlife)? What does she fear? What gives her hope? In what does she believe? Once you know these things about your character, you can get more deeply under her skin and into this new role.

MORTAL IDENTITY

A final thing you should consider about your character is his identity in normal society, if any. A double life can be exceedingly difficult to maintain, particularly for the nocturnal Cainites. But if you can manage it, the rewards are evident. What path do you walk now, and how will you continue to do so?

CHARACTER CREATION PROCESS

- **Step One: Character Concept**
  Choose Concept, Clan, Nature, Demeanor and Road
- **Step Two: Select Attributes**
  Prioritize the three categories: Physical, Social, Mental (7/5/3)
  Choose Physical Traits: Strength, Stamina, Dexterity
  Choose Social Traits: Charisma, Manipulation, Appearance
  Choose Mental Traits: Perception, Intelligence, Wits
- **Step Three: Select Abilities (see character sheet for options)**
  Prioritize the three categories: Talents, Skills, Knowledges
  Choose Talents, Skills, Knowledges (13/9/5)
  No Ability higher than 3 at this stage
- **Step Four: Select Advantages (see Options, below)**
  Choose Disciplines (4), Backgrounds (5), Virtues (7)
- **Step Five: Finishing Touches**
  Record Via rating, Willpower, Blood Pool
  Spend Freebie Points (15)

ARCHETYPES (NATURE AND DEMEANOR)

(See page 109)

Autocrat: Stability requires order. Bring it about.

Barbarian: Civilization is a joke; honor is everything.

Caretaker: Suffering is everywhere; you must temper it with love.

Celebrant: Something fills you with joy, and you cannot hide that pleasure.

Child: You're young, or at least appear to be so.

Defender: The meek must be protected from the wicked by the strong.

Fanatic: Your cause is everything to you.

Gallant: Grace is all that counts; romance is your ideal, and God's (or the Devil's) will your pleasure.

Innovator: There is always a better way to do something. Your task is to bring it about.

Jester: There is too much pain in the world to endure without laughter. You make a mockery of sadness.

Judge: You seek justice for everyone.

Loner: You've never fit in and never will.

Monster: God has demanded that you play the beast; who are you to argue?

Penitent: Your sins can only be forgiven after you prove your true worth.

Rebel: You're sick of being ordered around! Hide your feelings well and work for the time of change.

Rogue: To hell with rules, to hell with everyone! Life (or unlife) is yours to plunder.

Survivor: No matter what storms sweep through, you will always prevail.

Tyrant: The only way to get things done is to do them your way! All other paths are folly.

SAMPLE CONCEPTS

- **Artisan** — limner, musician, embroiderer, weaponmaster
- **Beggar** — cripple, escaped slave, debtor, mutilated felon, veteran
- **Clergy** — monk, priest, bishop, nun, laity, servant, student, mystic
- **Craftsman** — smith, tailor/seamstress, stonecutter, armorer
- **Dispossessed** — refugee, Jew, Moor, foreigner, Celt, disinherited noble, slave
- **Heretic** — pagan, unorthodox Christian, Infernalist, witch, occultist, sorcerer
- **Knight** — squire, errant, courtier, poor knight
- **Lowlife** — drunkard, prostitute, moneylender, traveling player, brawler, defrocked clergyman
- **Nobility** — baron(ess), royal heir, crusader, bastard, rake
- **Outlander** — barbarian, Oriental, traveler, Moslem, spy, slave, caravaner
- **Peasant** — servant, farmer, shepherd, stablehand, tavern girl, serf
- **Pilgrim** — crusader, penitent, mad monk, palmer
- **Retainer** — huntsman, ranger, seneschal, bard, sergeant-at-arms, torturer, lady-in-waiting, steward, diplomat
- **Scholar** — student, scribe, physician, alchemist, sage, theologian
- **Soldier** — man-at-arms, mercenary, grizzled vet, guard, assassin
- **Tradesman** — bard, innkeeper, traveling trader, animal trainer
- **Wanderer** — vagabond, thief, bard, exile, camp follower
- **Youth** — runaway, child, apprentice, heir, squire, urchin

ROADS

(See page 113)

- **Road of the Beast:** Feed the Beast, that it will not break its chains.
- **Road of Blood:** Vampiric blood grants the power for revenge.
- **Road of Chivalry:** Treat your equals with honor and your betters with respect.
- **Road of the Devil:** We are created evil and must play our part.
- **Road of Heaven:** God made us vampires to exact His wrath.
- **Road of Humanity:** The struggle to maintain one's humanity.
- **Road of Paradox:** Existence is a lie; change reality for the better.
- **Road of Typhon:** Sin and corruption are the keys to understanding.

The Clans

(Complete descriptions can be found in Chapter Three: The Clans)

- **Assamites:** The mysterious "Saracens" of the Middle East have perfected the art of the silent kill.
- **Brujah:** Philosophers, scholars and athletes, the fractious "zealots" pursue their dream of a perfect society.
- **Cappadocians:** Seeking the wisdom of the grave, the "graverobbers" call on the spirits of the dead for enlightenment.
- **Followers of Set:** Originally hailing from Egypt, the "serpents" spread corruption and vice in their path.
- **Gangrel:** Wanderers and rustics, the "animals" are closer to the beasts of the forests than to any of their Cainite kin.
- **Lasombra:** Masters of darkness and shadows, the "magisters" seek to control mortal and vampiric society alike.
- **Malkavians:** Cursed with insanity, the "madmen" enjoy a surreal and disturbing insight.
- **Nosferatu:** Hideous beyond words, the ostracized "lepers" are spies and informants without equal.
- **Ravnos:** Wandering vagabonds and hucksters, the "charlatans" gleefully practice their arts of deception and theft.
- **Toreador:** Lovers of art and beauty, the "artisans" freely indulge their tastes for the aesthetic.
- **Tremere:** A recent and insular clan, the sorcerous "usurpers" are struggling to establish themselves.
- **Tzimisce:** Terrible Slavic fleshcrafters, the "fiends" mercilessly rule over their mortal subjects.
- **Ventrue:** Imperious and commanding, the "patricians" consider it their duty to lead vampiric society.
- **Caitiff:** The rare and luckless Cainites with no clan are outcasts and disgraced.

Backgrounds

Complete descriptions can be found on page 128.

- **Allies:** Human confederates, usually family or friends.
- **Contacts:** The number of information sources the character possesses.
- **Generation:** How far removed from Caine the character is.
- **Herd:** The vessels to which the character has free and safe access.
- **Influence:** The character's political power within mortal society.
- **Mentor:** The Cainite patron who advises and supports the character.
- **Resources:** Wealth, belongings and monthly income.
- **Retainers:** Followers, guards and servants.
- **Status:** The character's standing in undead society.

Disciplines

(See also Chapter Five)

- **Animalism:** Supernatural affinity with and control of animals.
- **Auspex:** Extrasensory perception, awareness and premonitions.
- **Celerity:** Supernatural quickness and reflexes.
- **Chimerstry:** The ability to create illusions and hallucinations.
- **Dementation:** The ability to pass madness on to a victim.
- **Dominate:** Mind control practiced through the piercing gaze.
- **Fortitude:** Unearthly toughness, even to the point of resisting fire and sunlight.
- **Mortis:** The supernatural power to control the process of death.
- **Obfuscate:** The ability to remain obscure and unseen, even in crowds.
- **Obtenebration:** The unearthly control over shadows.
- **Potence:** The Discipline of physical vigor and strength.
- **Presence:** The ability to attract, sway and control crowds.
- **Protean:** Shapechanging — from growing claws to melding with the earth.
- **Quietus:** The Assamites' arts of the silent kill.
- **Serpentis:** The reptilian, corruptive Discipline of the Followers of Set.
- **Thaumaturgy:** The study and practice of sorcery.
- **Vicissitude:** The Tzimisce art of flesh-shaping.

Freebie Points

Trait	Cost
Attributes	5 per dot
Abilities	2 per dot
Backgrounds	1 per dot
Willpower	1 per dot
Disciplines	7 per dot
Virtues	2 per dot
Roads	1 per dot

Experience Costs

Trait	Cost
New Ability	3
New Thaumaturgy Path	7
New Discipline	10
Willpower	current rating
Road	current rating x 2
Ability	current rating x 2
Attribute	current rating x 4
Thaumaturgy Path (primary)	current rating x 4
Thaumaturgy Path (secondary)	current rating x 5
Clan Discipline	current rating x 5
Other Discipline	current rating x 7

Example of Character Creation

Justin is starting in Ethan's new **Vampire: The Dark Ages** chronicle. He turns to the character creation outline, makes a copy of the character sheet and sits down to generate his character.

Step One: Concept

Justin pages through the Clans chapter, thinking about the various social roles of the time. The Malkavian clan catches his eye at roughly the same time the word "zealot" pops into his head. It must be fate, and he mulls it over. He conceives the idea for a mad pilgrim, one who makes war on the "unclean." The Malkavian clan seems made to order for the concept. Justin decides to make the character French and chooses the name Anatole.

Next, Justin considers Nature and Demeanor. He likes the idea of Anatole going on at length about how unworthy he is, so Justin settles on the Demeanor of Penitent. However, under the façade of self-mortification, Anatole is a determined warrior for his cause. Anatole is driven more by a desire to protect his "flock," so Justin chooses the Nature of Defender.

Finally, Justin needs to pick a Road, one that accurately depicts Anatole's code of ethics in the face of the Beast. Although tempted by the Road of Humanity, Justin finally decides that the Road of Heaven suits Anatole best.

Step Two: Attributes

Next, Justin must prioritize Anatole's Attributes. Since Justin sees Anatole as a good fighter, one who will probably have to shed blood to defend his flock, he decides to give Anatole primary Physical Attributes. (In the back of his mind, it occurs to him that Anatole used to be a guardsman.) Since Anatole is fairly sharp and perceptive, Justin makes Mental his secondary category, leaving Social as the tertiary.

Justin places three of the seven primary dots in Dexterity, liking the image of a ragged pilgrim with surprising speed. He then adds three more to Anatole's Stamina, and places the final dot in Strength. Anatole now has Strength 2, Dexterity 4 and Stamina 4.

Two of Anatole's five secondary dots go into Wits; he may be mad, but he's not an idiot. Two more go into Perception, and Justin adds the final dot to Intelligence. Anatole is going to have to rely on his first reactions; he's only so-so at extended judgment calls.

Finally, Justin has only three dots to divide among Anatole's Social Attributes. He places two in Charisma and one in Appearance; Anatole can be inspiring when he has to. This means that Anatole has a Manipulation of 1, but that's fine with Justin. He never meant for Anatole to be incredibly subtle, anyway.

Step Three: Abilities

The next step is prioritizing and selecting Abilities. Justin first looks over the character sheet, marking all the Abilities that seem most appropriate. Most seem to fall into Talents, so Justin gives that category primary consideration. Then he assigns Talents as secondary and Knowledges as tertiary.

Justin has 13 dots to divide among Anatole's Talents. He immediately puts two dots in Dodge and three in Alertness, reflecting Anatole's speed and reactions. To reflect the mad zealot's ability to deal with people, he assigns three dots to Intimidation and one to Empathy. Two more dots go into Leadership; Justin wants Anatole to be able to sway people. He puts the final two dots in Brawl; Anatole saw a fistfight or two as a guardsman.

Skills, as Anatole's secondary category, has nine dots. Justin puts three into Stealth, wanting his Malkavian to excel at skulking. Two more go into Melee, about appropriate for a guardsman. Finally, Justin reasons that Anatole had a fairly rustic background. He puts one dot each into Animal Ken, Archery, Ride and Survival.

Justin now has five dots for the tertiary Knowledges. He decides that Anatole is somewhat lettered and places one dot each into Academics and Linguistics. Two more dots are divided between Investigation and Law, reflecting Anatole's guardsman past. The final dot goes into Occult, enough knowledge to worry a superstitious vampire without revealing any real secrets. Still, it will keep things interesting....

Step Four: Advantages

Now Justin comes to the vampiric aspect. First, he picks Anatole's Disciplines — the powers of the unliving. Justin has four dots to spend and must select from his Clan Disciplines. In the Malkavians' case, they are Auspex, Dementation and Obfuscate. Justin really likes the stealthy focus of Obfuscate, and puts two dots into that Discipline. The remaining two go into Auspex; Anatole's ability to look into other people's souls serves the concept of a religious sentinel very well.

Since madmen rarely have much influence with mortals, Justin opts to put Anatole's Background dots into vampiric Traits. Two go into Generation. Anatole is now of the 10th generation, and accordingly powerful. Justin puts two more dots into Herd, representing a small flock that follows the dynamic Malkavian. The remaining dot goes into a point of Status: the other Cainites of the city recognize that Anatole has some potential, or perhaps they just defer to his sire.

Finally, Justin must assign his seven Virtue dots. Since Anatole is on the Road of Heaven, he begins with the Virtues of Conscience, Self-Control and Courage. Three dots go into Courage: Anatole is too dedicated to flee danger. Three more go into Conscience, making Anatole rather charitable. The last dot falls into Self-Control. Anatole will have some difficulty restraining his temper, but Justin likes the roleplaying opportunities this will afford.

Step Five: Finishing Touches

Most of the work has been done; all that's left is the polishing. Justin records Anatole's starting Willpower, Via rating and Blood Pool. His Willpower is equal to his Courage score, in this case 4. His Road rating is equal to his Conscience + Self-Control — here, 4 + 2, or 6. Finally, his starting Blood Pool is determined by a die roll. Luckily, Justin's die comes up 9. Anatole won't have to start his first story hungry. Justin consults the Generation chart (page 137) and notes that a 10th-generation Cainite has a maximum Blood Pool of 13.

Next, Justin has 15 freebie points to spend. To make Anatole a little more unnervingly swift, he spends seven on acquiring a point of Celerity. He also wants Anatole to be distinctive and impressive, so he puts five more into purchasing an extra point of Charisma, raising it to 4. He has three left, two of which he puts into Courage, raising it to a 5 (and his Willpower to a 5 by default). He spends the last freebie point to buy another dot of Willpower.

Lastly, Justin must choose a Derangement (the Malkavians' clan weakness). He decides that Anatole randomly hallucinates from time to time, perceiving threats as fantastic beings or beasts. Ethan, as Storyteller, heartily approves this, seeing many interesting sessions of roleplaying down the road.

Justin has all the rules for Anatole's character in place, but still wants to fill in a few details to flesh out the zealot fully. Although these details may change during the prelude, they give him and Ethan a good basis to start.

Anatole used to be a guardsman, but was driven out of his job when he started showing the first signs of madness. He was Embraced soon after, driven over the edge, given a quick education in vampiric society and left on his own (for some ulterior reason). His haven is a small crypt on the edge of his home city. He has established a small flock of believers in the city slums; he feeds from them and from any of the "Devil's servants" he runs across. Because of his Road, he can only drink from his flock if they give permission. To Anatole, the Road of Heaven was an extension of his mortal beliefs, not his sire's teachings.

He still carries a sword and has stolen a mail shirt, both of which he conceals under his tattered clothes. Neither is in the best of repair, but they are still quite serviceable. Anatole isn't bad-looking, but he is often dirty and dresses like a pauper. Despite all this, he has a powerful voice and a piercing gaze; those who listen to his impromptu sermons often remember his words.

Anatole is primarily concerned with improving and guarding the welfare of his friends and neighbors. To this aim, he has already assassinated one murderer in the slums, and will likely kill again. He doesn't trust other vampires unless their "souls seem pure" (he checks with Auspex). Justin leaves Anatole's sire to Ethan to flesh out. A Malkavian could have almost any reason for creating progeny....

That's it. Justin could choose specialties for Anatole's Traits with four dots (Dexterity, Stamina and Charisma), but he opts to wait until his prelude is finished. Anatole is more than ready to take his first few steps in the World of Darkness.

The Prelude

A prelude is a way to create character biographies before the chronicle actually begins. The purpose of a prelude is to give each character a past, thus allowing the future to be told. It is, in fact, a form of one-on-one storytelling in which the story of a character's life is told.

A prelude is quite similar to normal play, except that many years are compressed into a series of rapid-fire decisions. The personal biography a player creates in the prelude will be relevant throughout the chronicle, and you may well refer to it frequently.

Techniques

Each player undergoes the prelude alone. It is one-on-one unless two or more characters were friends or spent a lot of time together before the Embrace. While the Storyteller spends time

VAMPIRE
THE DARK AGES

NAME: Anatole
PLAYER: Justin
CHRONICLE:

NATURE: Defender
DEMEANOR: Penitent
CLAN: Malkavian

GENERATION: 10th
HAVEN: Small Crypt
CONCEPT: Mad Zealot

ATTRIBUTES

PHYSICAL
Strength ●●○○○○
Dexterity ●●●●○○
Stamina ●●●●○○

SOCIAL
Charisma ●●●●○○
Manipulation ●○○○○○
Appearance ●●○○○○

MENTAL
Perception ●●●○○○
Intelligence ●●○○○○
Wits ●●●○○○

ABILITIES

TALENTS
Acting ○○○○○○
Alertness ●●●○○○
Athletics ○○○○○○
Brawl ●●○○○○
Dodge ●●○○○○
Empathy ●○○○○○
Intimidation ●●●○○○
Larceny ○○○○○○
Leadership ●●○○○○
Subterfuge ○○○○○○

SKILLS
Animal Ken ●○○○○○
Archery ●○○○○○
Crafts ○○○○○○
Etiquette ○○○○○○
Herbalism ○○○○○○
Melee ●●○○○○
Music ○○○○○○
Ride ●○○○○○
Stealth ●●●○○○
Survival ●○○○○○

KNOWLEDGES
Academics ●○○○○○
Hearth Wisdom ○○○○○○
Investigation ●○○○○○
Law ●○○○○○
Linguistics ●○○○○○
Medicine ○○○○○○
Occult ●○○○○○
Politics ○○○○○○
Science ○○○○○○
Seneschal ○○○○○○

ADVANTAGES

DISCIPLINES
Auspex ●●○○○○
Celerity ●○○○○○
Obfuscate ●●○○○○
_____ ○○○○○○
_____ ○○○○○○

BACKGROUNDS
Generation ●●○○○
Herd ●●○○○
Status ●○○○○
_____ ○○○○○
_____ ○○○○○

VIRTUES
Conscience/~~Conviction~~ ●●●●○
Self-Control/~~Instinct~~ ●●○○○
Courage ●●●●●

OTHER TRAITS
_____ ○○○○○○
_____ ○○○○○○
_____ ○○○○○○
_____ ○○○○○○
_____ ○○○○○○

COMBAT

Weapon	Difficulty	Damage

ROAD
Heaven
●●●●●○○○○

WILLPOWER
●●●●●●○○○○
□□□□□□□□□□

BLOOD POOL
□□□□□□□□□□
□□□■■■■□□□

HEALTH
Bruised		□
Hurt	-1	□
Injured	-1	□
Wounded	-2	□
Mauled	-2	□
Crippled	-5	□
Incapacitated		□

EXPERIENCE

VAMPIRE: THE DARK AGES

with each player separately, the rest of the troupe can socialize and start to get excited about what lies ahead. Anticipation can make a story blossom.

During the prelude, the Storyteller should direct the player much more than usual. Give him lots of decisions to make, but rush everything and don't give him much time to think. You need to play through things quickly unless you are willing and able to spend more time (which can enable the creation of very detailed characters). Characters almost never engage in combat during a prelude. If they do, simply describe the results of any fights; you can't have the character die before the game even begins!

During the prelude, the player should have a chance to interact with both the setting and the rules. Perhaps he finds that some of his Trait choices weren't quite right when he actually puts the character into play. A Storyteller may grant permission for minor changes, provided they're not designed to upgrade the character to superhero status.

There are many ways to progress through a character's life; any way that helps mold a complete character is fine. During the prelude you will want to explain the full background of the character. The player should thoroughly understand the details of her Background Traits.

You should play through one or more typical scenes from the character's life to give both player and Storyteller a sense of how the character lived. The player may enjoy her role as a vampire all the more after dealing with the drudgery of the character's prior existence. Remember, it is the mundane that gives scope to the magnificent.

A prelude can proceed with something like this: "You're stepping out of church on Sunday morning. Suddenly, a hand catches at your clothing. A leper crouched by the doorway extends a scabrous hand and asks for alms. He coughs terribly. What do you do?"

The response would help determine whether the character values charity over a risk to his own health. As the Storyteller describes things, the player can interrupt with her own ideas and details. You are telling a story together, and should act as partners. You can also include details that provoke the player into feeling the emotions of the character — "Your eldest son has been slowly weakening for months." If the character now acts only at night, he can't freely visit his family anymore. His son may recover, or he may die…. Will the character be there?

QUESTIONS AND ANSWERS

Described below are some questions that should be answered by the end of the prelude. If there is no time for a full prelude, you should at least make an effort to answer these questions. It often helps to write out the answers, even if you have undergone the full prelude.

With each question we list things the player should ask herself, as well as some advice on how to shape the prelude in relationship to the question.

· HOW OLD ARE YOU?

More specifically, when were you born, and when were you Embraced? How old do you look? A good history book can do wonders for giving you appropriate or interesting dates for your character's life.

· WHAT WAS YOUR MORTAL LIFE LIKE?

Think about your childhood and how quickly you had to grow out of it. Could you remain innocent, or were you forced into adulthood even earlier than usual? Who were your parents, and how did you fit into your social class? Did you stay in one place all your life, or did you travel? Were you patriotic or apathetic? Although humans in the Dark Ages had few opportunities to change their lot, the complications of your human life are worth considering. Rare is the vampire who forgets or ignores everything before her Embrace.

· WHEN DID YOU FIRST MEET A VAMPIRE?

When did the superstition become reality for you? Was your sire the first vampire you met, or was there another? Were you expecting the Embrace? (If so, you need to explain why.) Vampires usually spend considerable time stalking their prey before they attack. The suspense of the hunt, the tension of being watched — these scenes should evoke great dread in a character (and player as well, hopefully).

· WHO WAS YOUR SIRE?

Your sire, usually the first vampire you ever meet, strongly colors your perceptions of vampires. What was your relationship like? Did you part on good or bad terms? Was he prejudiced? Did he describe certain clans according to his personal belief? Did he abandon you, or were you released when he felt you ready? Roleplaying a scene or two with a character's sire is an excellent way to establish the feel of how vampires deal with one another.

· HOW DO YOU FEEL ABOUT MORTALS?

Some Cainites consider themselves superior to mortals, citing their undead powers as evidence. Do you still think of yourself as a person, as the same person you once were? Very few vampires of the time see themselves in such a light. Are you protective of your former fellows, or do you intend to use your new powers to avenge yourself upon them? Do you think of them as only a food source, or do you love a mortal? Although not as individually powerful as Cainites, humans are still the major force shaping the World of Darkness. How you interact with them says a great deal about yourself.

· HOW DID YOU BEGIN TO LOOK AT YOURSELF?

Do you believe yourself to be damned, or do you think vampirism is an improvement? Why did you choose to fight the Beast? Do you believe the myths of vampiric society, or do you have your own theories? Obviously, no Cainite can deny her new nature for long. Even the maddest Malkavians have a gut knowledge that something has changed. Your self-image is central to understanding your character and how you will relate to other vampires.

· HOW DID YOU MEET THE REST OF YOUR COTERIE?

Were you brought together by chance or design? Do you get along with the others? Do you have common enemies, allies or purpose? How long have you been together in the city? If you don't trust each other, the stories will be doomed to failure. During the prelude, you should work out how each of you met the others. Each meeting should be somehow unique, to better cement your interpersonal relationships before the pressure starts to build.

· Where is your territory?

What are your feeding grounds, and how often do you visit them? What is a typical hunt like for you? Where is your haven for the day? You need to detail what sort of vampiric existence you have carved out for yourself. A well-conceived territory has several bonuses, including possible lowered difficulties on hunt rolls. If you have a particularly well-organized territory, you can feed without roleplaying or making rolls. Your territory is one of your most important resources — give it some thought.

· What drives you?

Do you have any outstanding enemies? What are your goals? How do you intend to spend the rest of your long existence? No real person lives without motivations. Your goals, hopes and fears are essential to your character. By fleshing out your ambitions and priorities, you understand better exactly who you are. Look to your Nature, Demeanor and Road for ideas, but feel free to add appropriate motivations that transcend those guidelines.

TRAITS

In **Vampire: The Dark Ages**, Traits are the basis of a character — they describe, conjure and delineate who and what a character really is. They enable you to detail your character's strengths and weaknesses, allow you to translate the character into game reality by using dice and, most importantly, help you focus and understand your character.

A character's Traits describe only the general parameters of her abilities. The essence of the character is created through roleplaying and imagination. Traits in **Vampire: The Dark Ages** are intentionally left sketchy — at least the number-crunching part — so you will not concentrate on the character sheet too much. What is only crudely established during character creation becomes fleshed out through play.

NATURE AND DEMEANOR

If Cowardice lends me its heart
And I follow its command
I'll never attain what I pursue.
Indeed, I am greatly shamed
Even to have considered holding back —
My heart is black with sadness.

— Chrétien De Troyes, *Lancelot*

We tend to think of "false faces" as a strictly modern innovation. The old days, some would claim, were more honest. What you saw was what you got, right?

Wrong. If nothing else, court intrigues demanded more subterfuge than we modern people ever learn, and even the average peasant had to be careful what he said and around whom. After all, in the Middle Ages, your life might depend on how well you could fool someone — harsh penalties awaited those who seemed too forward with the "wrong" feelings.

In game terms, personality archetypes reflect the everyday subterfuges people count on. A character's Nature represents her inner personality — her "true self." Her Demeanor, on the other hand, reflects the aspects that other people see — her "public face." Both Traits might be the same, of course, but most people act differently in public than they do in private. A straightforward person's Traits will be the same — or at least similar — while a devious one may have a radically different Demeanor, or possibly even more than one.

Vampires (and other characters) also refresh their Willpower Pool through actions that suit their Nature. If a Caretaker Ventrue sheds her blood to protect one of her coterie (especially if the comrade hails from a different clan), she regains a point or two of the Willpower she may have spent earlier in the story. Obviously, this only occurs when that character performs some really notable act within the story — you can't just say, "I give a penny to the beggar in the street," and get your Willpower back. By acting within our moral codes, however, we reaffirm ourselves. Thus, a game character refreshes her Willpower Trait the same way.

If a character does something really appropriate, her player may ask the Storyteller if she can regain Willpower through that act. Depending on what happened, the Storyteller may grant that character three points (for a really significant or costly action), two points (for some important task or sacrifice), one (for a small feat) or even none (for something insignificant or an action the player did just to get Willpower back).

It's important to remember that Natures and Demeanors are not rigid "character classes"; rather, they act as roleplaying hints, offering you some guidance about how your character might act under given circumstances. These archetypes also help Storytellers get a handle on your character and might influence a nonplayer character's opinion of her. A duke's reaction to a lady with a Rebel Demeanor will be, shall we say, a bit more harsh than if that same lady seemed like a Caretaker instead.

The archetypes below are only suggestions; if you want to add to this list or incorporate archetypes from other Storyteller games, feel free.

AUTOCRAT

Chaos is anathema to you; you despise disorder and tend to take control and organize things. You like to be in charge, live to organize and habitually strive to make things work smoothly. Perhaps you were once a lady or a knight, a theologian or a sheriff. Maybe you're just an especially organized peasant. In any case, you trust your own judgment and tend to think of things in black-and-white terms: "This won't work," "You're either for me or against me," "There are two ways to do this — my way and the wrong way." Tradition is important as well — after all, the best ways to do things are the proven ones.

— Regain Willpower when you lead a group and accomplish some significant task.

BARBARIAN

Civilization is for weaklings. Intrigue is for cowards. You know that the only things that matter are personal strength, honor and bravery, and you live your life by an unshakable code. No one earns your respect unless he's powerful enough to hold his own in a straightforward contest. The weak are fit only to serve the strong.

Not to say that you only respect physical violence; you may be very intelligent, caring and merciful. You cannot, however, abide weaklings or craven bastards who hide behind pretty words or others' bodies. A title means nothing unless it is earned through personal valor or wisdom, and an oath means nothing unless the maker will die to uphold it. As for the trappings of civilization, you find them a waste of time. What was good enough for your forefathers is good enough for you. After all, the measure of a man (or a woman) is endurance to hardship and honor in the face of adversity.

— Regain Willpower whenever you or your code of honor clearly triumphs over some overtly "civilized" opponent or situation.

CARETAKER

We are indeed our brothers' keepers. No matter what kind of a beast you may have become, the charge to "Love one another as I have loved you" rings in your ears. Not that you cannot kill — God kills freely, and often commands us to do the same — but if you see someone in need, you consider it a sacred charge to do what you can to help.

A Caretaker's need isn't rooted only in religion. After all, taking care of your own is only common sense in a harsh world. Even if you have turned your back upon the ways of the Church (or were not Christian to begin with), you will do whatever you can to alleviate another's suffering. Occasionally, people take advantage of you, but such is the price of nurturing. Perhaps, for you, it is the only way to atone for your sins.

— Whenever you help another person in need or sacrifice something for another's well-being, you may refresh some Willpower. This assistance can be as simple as a pat on the back at the right moment, or as drastic as a last-minute intervention before a torch-bearing mob.

CELEBRANT

You know a joy others can only imagine. Perhaps it's religious devotion or a *joie de vivre* that few can match. Maybe you appreciate the thrill of battle, or delight in the works of the ancient masters of some great art. Whatever your passion is, you gain the strength to face adversity so long as that passion is close at hand. Whenever some opportunity to praise or indulge your chosen passion arises, you will seize it with glee. This may annoy some folk, but you know it's only a matter of time before they discover your joy as well.

— Regain Willpower whenever you either celebrate the passion of your choice or convert another character to your way of thinking. Conversely, you suffer greatly (and perhaps even lose a point of Willpower if the event is traumatic enough) if your passion is denied or badly lost to you.

CHILD

You're young, either in years or in spirit, and others feel compelled to nurture you. This can be both good and bad; most people love the enthusiasm of youth, but it often leaves you open to exploitation or hardship. You're cute and frolicsome, but also tend to get in trouble. Youth, it is said, lacks wisdom, and so do you.

It bears noting that adulthood comes quickly in the Middle Ages; boys and girls as young as eight or 10 were expected to begin productive lives in trades or fighter's training. Children are rarely granted the indulgences we modern folk are used to — pampering is a luxury few can afford. A willful child will be scolded, and a pathetic adult will be shamed. A youth or a simpleton will temporarily be given more slack than an adult would be but if you cannot eventually grow up and take responsibility, you'll face a hard unlife.

— Regain Willpower whenever you get someone to nurture you, or when you achieve some great success through your childlike ways.

DEFENDER

Not everyone can be a warrior. You can, however, and whatever your chosen field of combat may be — warfare, law, medicine, religion, whatever — you bend your efforts toward defending those who deserve a fighting chance. Perhaps you are (or once were) a guardian on the road to Damascus, a city watchman or a healer. Maybe you achieved whatever title you hold (or held) by protecting your vassals, not by favoring a lord; or turned your sword-arm to God's will. Whatever history you may have, your task in life is to defend some patron. Some protect the weak, others protect the throne.

— Regain Willpower whenever you successfully ward your protectorate or patron from some hostile threat.

FANATIC

You are consumed by a cause; it is the primary force in your life, for good or ill. Every ounce of blood and passion you possess is directed toward your cause. In fact, you may feel very guilty about spending time on anything else. Nothing can stand in your way — nothing that you cannot overcome, in any case. You and those around you may suffer, but your cause is everything — the end justifies the means.

Dedication sets you apart from the Celebrant; after all, such folk are loyal only to their own pleasures. You might despise your cause, or fear it, but you still give it everything you have. Who said that life was all fun and games? Before the chronicle begins, make sure you describe your character's cause and define how it may affect her behavior.

— Regain Willpower whenever you accomplish an act that furthers your cause, or when you sacrifice yourself to the cause in some way.

GALLANT

Life is nothing without style. Let others wallow in the mud of misery — your existence will be a graceful thing, remembered by the poets and heralded by the tales of your exquisite élan.

Romance is your bread and butter; you are the troubadour, the jongleur, the mistress-in-waiting or the dashing highwayman. Reality may not live up to your expectations, but you strive to meet your ideal with as much gusto as you can muster. Others may not appreciate your carefree manner — you leave broken hearts in your wake and seem more frivolous than people prefer — but you cannot be bothered by others' misfortunes. If they cannot take the risks that come with a life well lived, to hell with them. When you meet the Devil (and you're told you will), you'll do it with a flourish and shake his hand.

— Regain Willpower when you accomplish some great victory — a seduction, a commission, a successful battle — with style and grace, or when you hear your exploits recounted with the flair that is your due.

INNOVATOR

There are always better ways to achieve a goal; you will find those better ways. Inventors, traders, philosophers and strategists are examples of your kind. You are the path-blazer; the visionary; the critic who is never satisfied, even with seeming perfection. Tradition, to you, is a snare which binds imagination. Whatever you do, strive to improve upon what went before.

— Regain Willpower whenever your quest to create some new way of doing something succeeds. Dramatic breakthroughs are worth more confidence (and thus more Willpower) than simple improvements.

JESTER

The world is a painful place, but it's not without its lighter side. People go crazy without something to laugh at. You are that someone — the fool, clown or comic, forever seeking the humor in any situation. You hate sorrow and pain, and constantly try to take others' minds off the dark side of life. Most consider you an idiot for it, but you know your ways are best. Sometimes you'll do nearly anything to forget that pain exists — as one of the Damned, there's plenty to be miserable about. Your particular brand of humor might range from witty satire to low physical humor, but it beats moping around, doesn't it? On the down side, you get on others' nerves sometimes, but laughter usually makes you feel better, anyway…if only for a while.

— Regain Willpower when you raise the spirits of those around you through the device of humor, especially when you're able to escape your own pain in the process.

JUDGE

As a facilitator, moderator, arbitrator, conciliator and peace-maker, you always seek to make things better. You pride yourself on your rationality, judgment and deductive ability when given the facts. Truth is your ideal, but you understand how difficult it is to ascertain. Thus, you favor justice, for through justice, truth will reign.

In your view, people are resources, albeit difficult ones. You hate dissension and arguments, and shy away from dogmatism. Fairness, wisdom and logic are your hallmarks, and others respect your opinion. Some Judges make good leaders, though a lack of vision can sometimes cause them to maintain the status quo instead of searching for a better way.

— Regain Willpower when you are able to separate the truth from a web of lies, or when you convince disputing individuals to agree with your judgments.

LONER

You always stand alone, even in the midst of a crowd. You are the wanderer, hunter and lone wolf; perhaps you wander from town to town as a hired sword or traveling player, or perhaps you hide away until outside events become too important to ignore.

Solitude is not your fate, it's your pleasure. Though others might think of you as lonely, forsaken or remote, you simply prefer your own company to that of others. There are many different reasons why this might be so: you don't understand people, you understand people too well, people dislike you, people like you too much, or perhaps your own thoughts mean more to you than people. Your reasons are your own.

— When you manage to accomplish some significant task on your own, without the aid of others, but still help the group in some way, you regain Willpower based on the significance of the achievement.

MONSTER

For every light, there must be darkness. You are that shadow, chosen by God to be the beast that tempts the wicked. Your Embrace has sundered any connection you once had to your humanity (or so you believe), so why bother acting human? In later days you might be called Sabbat, but now you're merely what you have become — a fiend in the night.

Darkness comes in many forms. Your evil might be as subtle as poisoned gossip or as powerful as Goliath's hammer. Whenever your better instincts — and they do still exist — surge to the top, fight them down lest others exploit your weakness. The certainty of hellfire at the end of your unlife spurs you to occasional fits of terror, but in the eyes of your peers, you are the monster that destroys, the tempter who betrays, the servant of the Devil and thus the agent of God's will.

— Dark deeds refresh your Willpower, so long as they work within God's plans for you. If you see yourself as the Tempter, then you regain Willpower if you lure a weak person into wickedness. Are you a destroyer of dreams? Then regain Willpower when you challenge another person's faith. Pick some destiny, then act within that role.

PENITENT

You know that you have sinned; every clergyman accuses you, and every dream reveals the depths of depravity you feel inside. No matter how innocent or blameless your actions may be, you know that Man is an affront to God, and Cainites even moreso. Knowing this, you try to atone for your sins as often as you can.

A vampire with this Nature is an interesting case; she knows her place in Fate, but regrets her actions, especially the choices she makes herself. Predestination and free will are hot topics for debate in this era; on one hand, humanity was seen as innately sinful and unclean, damned without God's grace. On the other hand, God was said to base His final judgment on the choices each person made during his or her existence. As a Penitent, you know that both sides hold true, and you choose to atone for your fated unlife through charity, self-denial or even aiding the Church.

— Regain Willpower whenever you feel that you have atoned for your most recent sins. Whatever acts you perform, however, must measure up to the magnitude of the crime — the worse the sin, the bigger the atonement must be. Naturally, as a vampire, you'll have plenty of opportunities to sin again, and this is a constant source of torment for you.

REBEL

The established order is a lie. Fashion is tainted, the Church is corrupt, and the lords grow fat on the people's labor. Maybe your only son was killed by a drunken nobleman, or perhaps your wife was raped by some prince's lackey. Perhaps you're just tired of toeing the line or giving everything you own over to those who haven't earned it. In any case, you hate authority and will go out of your way to undermine it.

This is a dangerous Nature to have; even the loosest groups have harsh ways of dealing with nonconformity. Nevertheless, you understand the hatred which guides the Rebel. Your actions may be subtle and your sentiments held silent, but your hatred for the established order guides your passions and your deeds.

— Regain Willpower whenever something you do harms the order you despise. This "order" could be the Church, a local lord, the current fashion or Cainite society.

Rogue

You are all that matters. Every man must fend for himself, and if your actions get in others' way, well, too bad! If they were stronger, perhaps they could enjoy their (un)lives as well as you do. Not that you're a bully, mind you — just self-centered and aggressively selfish. You need not be a dominator; you'll just be damned if you're the dominated!

Rogues pride themselves on self-sufficiency. You may be a thief, an errant knight, a vagabond or a prostitute. In any case, others look down upon you for refusing to live by their rules. In the end, however, you keep your own best interests at heart. Never let another lead you.

— Regain Willpower whenever your selfishness leads to some kind of gain, especially if you can earn it without exposing yourself to risk or following another's orders.

Survivor

No matter what happens, you always survive. You can endure, pull through, recover from, outlast and outlive nearly any circumstance. Whether you travel in a group or walk alone, self-preservation is your prime motivation. When the going gets tough, you get going. Never say die, and never give up — ever. Nothing angers you as much as a person who doesn't struggle to make things better or who surrenders to Fate or mishap. It's your way to persevere. No matter what the odds may be, you'll come out standing, if not winning. How many warriors can say the same?

— Regain Willpower whenever you survive a difficult situation through your own cunning and perseverance or successfully teach another to do the same.

Tyrant

No one can do anything right except you. Whenever you leave something in someone else's care, that person fouls it up. Therefore, you must watch over those you care for, and take matters into your own hands whenever possible. You may have been an innkeeper before your Embrace, or a knight whose squires simply couldn't achieve the chivalric ideal. Perhaps you oversee your ghouls the way you once commanded your household servants. Whatever you do, make sure that no one makes a mess of it. People may not like you for it, but at least things will be done right, this time.

— Your leadership refreshes your Willpower whenever you succeed through stubbornness, forcefulness and attention to detail.

Roads

The easy, gentle, and sloping path…is not the path of true virtue. It demands a rough and thorny road.

— Michel de Montaigne, *Essays*

The Beast is a harsh master. No matter how compassionate and virtuous the mortal, the Embrace floods her very being with urges and instincts far beyond anything a human feels. Consequently, the childer of Caine must hold to some form of discipline, some code that allows them to keep the Beast in rein. The Roads represent paths of morality, ones which maintain a Cainite's control over herself. Some, like the Human Road, are unspoken reflections of a vampire's mortal nature. Others, such as the Assamites' Road of Blood, are codes of morality developed long ago by elders of a certain mindset. No matter the origin, a Road is the only connection a vampire has to his sentient nature. If he falters along this path, he may fall utterly to the Beast.

Many vampires do not even think of themselves as on a "Road" or path to some sort of enlightenment. Their ethics can only be coincidentally classified under one of the eight recognized Roads. These eight are detailed below. There are almost certainly more, but these are the ones that the majority of European Cainites represent. We recommend that players choose from these eight rather than devising their own, at least for now. These are the Roads proved to be most effective at preventing the spiral into monstrosity. Of course, Storytellers should feel free to allow a new Road that fills an appropriate gap in their chronicles. Just be certain that the new Road is rigid enough to keep the Beast at bay. A chronicle where the players never need to worry about making Virtue rolls will be staler than one where degeneration is still a very real possibility.

Road of the Beast

Also called the Via Bestiae, the Beast Road is an instinctive path more than anything else. Those who walk the Beast's path behave like animals, but not in excess. As the ancient Gangrel Kilok noted, "a hound on a long leash is less likely to snap it." Some of Clan Gangrel teach this Road to their childer, as do a few of other clans, but most Cainites on this path adopt it without prompting.

The greatest danger that those on the Beast Road face is the wilderness. The Lupines hunt any childer of Caine that wander from the cities, and few vampires can elude or outfight a pack of werewolves. The Cainites of the Beast Road, compelled to shun the cities, constantly run the risk of encountering Lupines or worse.

The vampire on this Road must be clever and instinctive. She must act without hesitation, but not foolishly endanger her existence and territory. She never kills for sport or needlessly tortures enemies, but will tear the throat out of anyone who threatens her unlife. She avoids too much contact with the cities and devices of humanity. Her control over her frenzies and fear stems from her desire for survival. By becoming an animal, she avoids devolving into a monster.

Curiously, the Cainites of the Via Bestiae can be quite urbane and civil if the need is truly present. Most of them, though, prefer their simple code to any of the "civilized" manipulations of their fellow undead.

The Beast Road practices the Virtues of Conviction and Instinct.

ROAD OF BLOOD

The mysterious Assamites of the East practice their own moral code, one handed down from their clan's founder. This code translates into Latin as the Via Sanguinius, or the Blood Road. If the vampires of the West knew the secrets of this well-guarded Road, they would surely make war on the Assamites in order to destroy them all.

The Road of Blood is taught only to those Assamites who are deemed most loyal to their clan and kin. It teaches that the childer of Khayyin (Caine) are corrupt, one and all, save for the descendants of Haqim (whom the Westerners named Assam). Haqim bade his progeny to make war on the Cainites, to fight their taint. Therefore, the truest Assamites are those who slay vampires of other clans and feed on their blood. By following the teaches of the Blood Road, one may achieve enlightenment.

Assamites on the Road of Blood (and no other clan is permitted to learn this Road) have a strict code. They must follow the teachings of Haqim and seek all knowledge that would aid their struggle. They must take as much vampire blood as possible, to strengthen their clan. They must also keep apart from the get of Khayyin unless duty requires otherwise, and keep their spirits pure of the Cainites' corruption. Finally, the vampires of the Via Sanguinius believe strongly in honor and self-restraint. They must resist the Beast at any cost, and deal fairly and honorably with mortals.

Recently, many Assamites were infuriated by the Western armies marching on Jerusalem. Consequently, more and more of the "Saracens" have been set on the Blood Road just after their Embrace. These holy warriors believe that their ancestral enemies have shown their true colors at last. Now, the true war begins.

Assamites must not shrink from spilling blood if such becomes necessary, but must hold onto their honor at all times. Thus, the Blood Road teaches the Virtues of Conviction and Self-Control.

ROAD OF CHIVALRY

While the age of chivalry does not reach its peak in mortal society for some time yet, Cainites of this period practice a similar chivalric code of their own creation. The Road of Chivalry is more formal than most other Via, with the same principles holding true and being passed from sire to childe or prince to vassal, regardless of the geographic area.

Followers of this Road believe themselves to be of a closer association to Caine and thereby must adhere to stricter standards than those around them. The Embrace carries great power, but equally heavy responsibilities, which are outlined in this code of conduct. They hope that their example will encourage right behavior in other Cainites, thereby elevating all in the sight of God and Caine.

The values of the Via Equitum are very much like those that will be practiced in later times. Honor and nobility of character are held above all, and the Cainite with neither is a sad thing indeed. One must respect one's lord and superiors, and duty to them is a solemn matter. Pleasure and one's own desire are secondary. Should they conflict with the Via, there is no argument — the Via comes first. Oaths are not made to be broken; any oath made must be kept, and woe to the Cainite who does not. Those weaker or unable to protect themselves are to be aided when in need. Kine are viewed as noble beasts, like deer in the forest. As such, they are to be treated fairly, aided if they are in need, but in the end they are still lesser beings. One does not feel compelled to treat a hunting hound with honor, and so it is with mortals.

The Road of Chivalry teaches the Virtues of Conscience and Self-Control.

ROAD OF THE DEVIL

Many Cainites believe that the Embrace irredeemably damns them. Some of these reason further that they have been turned into servants of the Devil (or whatever power of ultimate evil they believe in). It would logically follow, they add, that they have become vampires so that they should work evil on the Earth. If they refrain from acting like devils, they will no doubt be ultimately punished for shirking their duties. These debased Cainites follow the Via Diabolis — the Devil's Road.

The very nature of a vampire's form can actually be taken as proof that the Cainites were created to do evil. After all, there's nothing intrinsically virtuous about preying on innocents. Therefore, evil must be innate to the undead, who are denied the fruits of Heaven. Interestingly enough, the followers of the Devil's Road often have no real contempt for the good and holy. They simply believe that they, as vampires, must oppose the forces of virtue to the best of their ability.

Of course, those of the Road of the Devil have difficulty dealing with vampires on other Roads. Any vampire who professes a philosophy other than theirs is clearly deluded or lying. Either way, the Devil's childer cannot trust the other Cainites. And, of course, no sane vampire on another Road would return the trust. The Via Diabolis is a lonely road. Fortunately (or perhaps not), others walk it with you....

Those on the Via Diabolis try to make their unlives as pleasurable as possible, at the expense of those who oppose them. They refrain from traits such as mercy and gentleness, finding them opposed to their role. They kill when necessary or "appropriate," and create new vampires whenever they like. (After all, they need to increase the evil in the world. Duty is duty.) They trust only those other vampires who openly agree with their philosophy. Above all, they avoid associating with priests and the like, their eternal foes.

Warning: player characters on this Road can be very destructive to a chronicle by their very nature. The player who wishes to run a vampire on this Road should discuss it with the Storyteller and the rest of the troupe. If everyone agrees, the resulting roleplaying can be very intense; just keep your friends' sensibilities in mind.

Cainites on the Devil's Road idealize callousness and excess. They practice the Virtues of Conviction and Instinct.

ROAD OF HEAVEN

Struggling to come to terms with their undead condition, wondering why God would create such creatures as themselves, some vampires come to one of two conclusions. Either they owe their existence to the Devil and should serve him, or they are a part of God's plan and must serve Him.

Many of the latter group, searching for some good purpose for their bestial powers, follow the Via Caeli. They believe that vampires are intended by God to be His avenging angels. Sinners, murderers, foul witches and inhuman beasts: all must be ready to die at the hands of the childer of Caine.

Interestingly, not all of these believe in the vampire mythology of Caine and his descendants. Many on this road are not even Christian. The only requirement is faith in some sort of purpose or plan to the universe, a purpose which includes supernatural beings designed to destroy the corrupt and sadistic. Christians, Jews, pagans and even Moslems have been known to share the Road of Heaven. Alas, they do not always accept one another....

The Cainites of the Via Caeli kill without the slightest sense of irony or concern. Murderers are common prey, and indeed they sometimes kill those whose sins are quite petty (theft, heresy, lechery), but they are convinced that they are justified. God has given them the task of destroying sinners and criminals by whatever means necessary. They are damned for their actions — but their actions are for the good of all people. They regard themselves as the ultimate martyrs, called to sacrifice not only their bodies but also their souls to protect the virtuous.

These vampires punish sinners and criminals, especially those who elude mortal justice. They know the innocent must be protected from sinners and criminals, from those who would tempt them into sin and from themselves if necessary. Every sinner should have the opportunity to mend her ways, or if she refuses, should die. They only feed from pious or righteous persons if given permission. There is enough food to avoid preying on God's beloved. They especially loathe the Setites and Baali and will go to almost any length to bring one of these monsters the Final Death.

Those on Heaven's Road uphold the Virtues of Conscience and Self-Control.

ROAD OF HUMANITY

This Road has been both taught by elders and instinctively taken by the newly Embraced. Those who follow the Via Humanitatis, whether they call it that or not, try to hold onto their mortal scruples. These Cainites still think of themselves as people, not alien monsters. They recognize that they too can succumb to the Beast, but they will fight such a thing with the ethics of their human lives.

The Road of Humanity assumes a certain amount of morality. It does not focus on acting "human" as a murderer is "human." Instead, it recognizes that people have a certain potential for goodness and charity, and encourages such behavior. Cainites who are well advanced along the Via Humanitatis tend to be just, merciful and fair. Still, there are those on this Road who have become fierce warriors among the childer of Caine. The balance of necessity and virtue is a hard path to walk.

The Via Humanitatis has no formal code of ethics. Generally speaking, its followers must refrain from cruelty and perversion. They must not kill unless absolutely necessary, and they must respect the rights of others. They should feel concern for the welfare of mortals, as well as that of their own kind. The easiest summation is one espoused by many religions and philosophies: Treat your neighbor as you would want him to treat you.

This Road is open to some interpretation; after all, the values of the common people were different in the Dark Ages. Storytellers and players often reflect their own morality by the way they interpret this Road. This is perfectly all right; it gives you a chance to explore your own value systems in a harmless environment.

The Human Road, rooted as it is in charity and temperance, urges the Virtues of Conscience and Self-Control.

ROAD OF PARADOX

Few truly understand the games of the Ravnos, the charlatans and tricksters among the vampires. Outsiders are not taught the ways of the Via Paradocis — the Road of Paradox. Those possessing its secrets, however, realize that unlife is indeed but a dream, and living creatures the merest phantasms.

The Road of Paradox teaches that all existence is fluid and malleable. Nothing is permanent or real, but is composed of variable amounts of ethereal matter. The Ravnos refer to this matter as "weig." In its natural state, weig flows willy-nilly from being to being, object to object, creating and destroying without care. A given object can be filled with weig one moment and nearly empty the next; such is change, such is existence.

According to the Ravnos, the Antediluvians are beings who were momentarily filled with great amounts of weig and never released it. They strove to sculpt reality into a fixed shape that would enable them to retain their new power. To aid their cause, they passed on small amounts of their weig, molding them into their own images. Thus were other vampires created.

Of course, the Antediluvians plan to reabsorb their weig in due time. On this night — the night of Gehenna, or the Flux — the 12 Antediluvians, acting in concert and devouring the power of their children, plan to shape the universe permanently into the gray and stagnant mausoleum-realm that is their ideal. Only the childer of the 13th weig-being, the Ravnos, know of this plan. The Ravnos' clan founder decided to fight the newly created Antediluvians on their own terms, creating a clan to assist it. Those on the Paradox Road believe that their founder came into being only to foil its brethren.

Ravnos on this Road strive to unravel the reality of the Antediluvians. To effect this, they learn to harness their internal weig for the production of reality-altering effects. These effects are mere illusions at low levels of power, but as the Ravnos becomes more powerful, the effects gradually increase in potency. They also actively attempt to alter others' perceptions of reality, usually through trickery and theft.

Ultimately, the weig must be released into the vortex. Ravnos who are far along this Road actively seek to do so. They seek out items that retain weig — "magic" items, Lupine fetishes and the like — and destroy them. The most powerful of this Via seek out vampires with great amounts of weig — of low generation — and do likewise.

Those of the Via Paradocis understand that reality is what one makes it. They seek to change their surroundings for the better, realizing that only chaos and change are truly natural. The more reality can be altered between now and the night when reality will be reshaped, the more confused the Antediluvians will be and the more likely it is that the universe will turn out for the

better. Therefore, they seek to trick, confuse and humiliate other Cainites, particularly those high in the Antediluvians' esteem. This disconcerts the ancients and is great fun in the meantime.

The vampires of Paradox strive for Conviction and Self-Control.

ROAD OF TYPHON

The Followers of Set teach a moral code that has been handed down from sire to childe from the time of great Set himself. Although some Setites choose different philosophies to maintain, the most sinister are those who follow the shadowy Road of Typhon. To those on this Path, corruption, pain, lies and sin are things to be cherished and spread throughout existence. Misery is not a means to an end, but an end in and of itself.

As far as the followers of Typhon are concerned, everyone is missing the point. They reject self-control as a way of purging oneself of the world's horrors. The Typhonites instead espouse the opposite: a complete immersion in one's weaknesses and an active embrace of the world's misery. Only through such can evil be understood, and only through understanding can it truly be purged or assimilated. True happiness — fleeting as it is — is only gained through succumbing to one's carnal desires. One had best understand and accept where one is before attempting to move on to some vaguely conceived afterlife.

The Road of Typhon is actually more like a religion than a philosophy. Its practitioners are rumored to worship various entities — perhaps personifications of various sins, perhaps otherwise — through blood libations and sacrifice. Through such worship, the Typhonites believe, mystic understanding may be gleaned.

The followers of this Road continually seek to spread war, plague, poverty, filth, stagnation and fear through the world. Through the creation and study of such phenomena, the Typhonites hope to discover the truths about, and behind, earthly existence. In the Dark Medieval world, it is obvious that they are doing quite well indeed.

The followers of the Path first practice their tenets upon others. As they advance in mystic understanding, they begin to practice their principles upon themselves; flagellation, self-mutilation and other masochistic depredations are commonplace among the enlightened. Only through a complete mortification of their flesh may they transcend their earthly limitations, and dead flesh is difficult indeed to mortify.

There are rumors that those Setites who progress to the highest (lowest?) levels of the Path of Typhon become far too riddled with external and internal foulness to continue among the mortal world. They divorce themselves from any connection to the natural world whatsoever, devolving into quasi-organic embodiments of corruption. These stinking, bloated masses are housed in the depths of the most secret Setite temples, where they perpetually rot and wail blasphemies in the dark.

Those on the Via Typhonis reject the ideals of purity and spiritual progress espoused by mortals. Only in corruption — by succumbing to all that is considered impure, vile and weak — may true enlightenment be found. In weakness lies the greatest strength of all. They refuse to struggle against their inevitable decay. They must force others to see themselves as they are, and to accept what they see. They experiment on mortals to advance the arts of depravity and deformity whenever possible. Finally, they attempt to keep redemption from as many as possible, lying and destroying to keep others from bettering themselves.

The Serpent's Road prizes misery and excess; therefore, Typhonites hold to the Virtues of Conviction and Instinct.

ATTRIBUTES

SPECIALTIES

For each Attribute or Ability Trait rated 4 or higher, a player can select a specialty. A specialty is a particular subcategory that a character is capable of performing with additional proficiency — a character may be able to appreciate music and carry a tune well, but her particular forte is playing the lute.

A specialty allows the player to reroll "10s" scored on actions directly involving the specialty. The player gets to keep the success indicated by the "10," and may subsequently try again for another success, rolling another die for each "10" obtained.

PHYSICAL ATTRIBUTES

These Traits describe how strong, dexterous and sturdy a character is; they are the primary Traits of an action-oriented character. Physical Traits concern only the strengths and weaknesses of the body.

STRENGTH

This Trait measures your mean physical strength — your ability to lift, carry loads and cause physical harm. A person with a high Strength rating is usually larger than someone with a lower rating. Of course, there are always exceptions.

Strength is used when you attempt to lift, carry, push, heave or break something. In melee combat, your Strength Trait is added to your damage Dice Pool. Strength is also used when you attempt to make any sort of jump or leap.

Specialties: Strong Grip, Broad Shoulders, Bulging Biceps, Wiry, Rocklike Fists

- •   Poor: You can lift 40 lbs.
- • •   Average: You can lift 100 lbs.
- • • •   Good: You can lift 250 lbs.
- • • • •   Exceptional: You can lift 400 lbs.
- • • • • •   Outstanding: You can lift 650 lbs.
- • • • • • •   Inhuman: You can lift 800 lbs.

DEXTERITY

This Trait measures your general physical prowess — speed, quickness and agility. It indicates the capacity for moving precisely and manipulating objects with accuracy and grace. Dexterity includes hand-eye coordination, fine motor manipulation, reaction speed, reflexes and bodily grace.

Specialties: Catlike Reflexes, Swift, Sure-Footed, Light Touch

- •   Poor: You are clumsy and avoid sharp tools.
- • •   Average: You can mend your own boots.
- • • •   Good: You have excellent raw athletic potential.
- • • • •   Exceptional: You can juggle five knives.
- • • • • •   Outstanding: You can juggle five knives while blindfolded.
- • • • • • •   Inhuman: Your hands are like striking serpents.

STAMINA

Stamina measures general health and resistance to pain; it indicates how long you can exert yourself and how much physical punishment you can sustain. Stamina is your staying power, both physically and mentally, and one of its most important elements is the will to live.

Specialties: Tireless, Enduring, Tough, Determined, Stubborn

- •   Poor: You are frail in constitution and may be sickly.
- • •   Average: You are moderately healthy.
- • • •   Good: You are in good shape and are probably a hard worker.
- • • • •   Exceptional: You could fight for hours.
- • • • • •   Outstanding: You could swim the English Channel.
- • • • • • •   Inhuman: Your endurance is that of the wild animal.

SOCIAL ATTRIBUTES

Your Social Traits describe your appearance, charm and familiarity with the human mind. Your Social Traits are vital in determining first impressions, leadership ability and the nature of your interactions with others.

CHARISMA

Charisma measures your aptitude for enticing and fascinating others. You use Charisma to win others over to you emotionally and get them to trust you. This Trait reflects a charismatic personality more than it does an overt manipulation of others. It is a sum of your presence, charm and power of influence. Charisma reflects your power to convince others to put faith in you.

Specialties: Charming, Eloquent, Outgoing, Captivating, Commanding, Inspiring

- •   Poor: Others avoid being around you.
- • •   Average: You are likable.
- • • •   Good: People trust and confide in you.
- • • • •   Exceptional: Something draws people to you.
- • • • • •   Outstanding: You could lead a nation.
- • • • • • •   Inhuman: Complete strangers would live and die for you.

MANIPULATION

This Trait measures your aptitude for active self-expression, such as when you want to get someone else to do something. It is important when you attempt to influence or manipulate another

person directly. You use Manipulation to trick, fool, bluff, outmaneuver and out-talk another. While you may be effective at manipulating people whom you have just met, those who know you are rarely fooled.

Manipulation is used in all attempts to influence or convince another person overtly. Whether the person likes you or not is of no consequence (though it can affect the difficulty of what you are trying).

If you fail a Manipulation action, and the target realizes what you were trying to do (you botch, for instance), she may well be angered. People are manipulated all the time, and usually ignore it. If the fact is brought to their attention, however, it can be very disturbing. Manipulation can net great results, but is risky to perform openly. Characters with high Manipulation ratings are not overly trusted by those who know them best.

Specialties: Glib, Expressive, Cunning, Persuasive, Smooth

- •   Poor: You express yourself in as few words as possible.
- ••   Average: Others might believe you.
- •••   Good: You can get a good price out of most merchants.
- ••••   Exceptional: Your talents belong in the king's court.
- •••••   Outstanding: You'd make an excellent power behind the throne.
- ••••••   Inhuman: Your silver tongue rivals that of the Devil himself.

Appearance

This Trait describes your attractiveness and force of presence. You do not necessarily need beauty to have a high Appearance; you only need looks that somehow attract others to you. Appearance encompasses not just actual physical looks, but poise, animation and expressiveness. It is a measure of how interesting and attractive you seem to others.

Appearance is vital in any social situation where words are not exchanged. It is more important than you might think; your impressions of another are heavily affected by that person's looks, no matter how open-minded you are.

Appearance is often used by the Storyteller to judge roughly how others react to you upon a first meeting. Thus, it can affect all other Social rolls you make involving that person (in some cases, your rating determines the maximum number of successes from a Social action that can actually be applied, making it impossible for an ugly person to achieve anything beyond minimal success).

Specialties: Bold Demeanor, Alluring, Striking Looks, Sexy

- • Poor: You tend to attract the hostility of others.
- •• Average: You are easily ignored, for you fit in so well with the crowd.
- ••• Good: You have a pleasing appearance, and people treat you well.
- •••• Exceptional: Your beauty sets you apart from your surroundings and commands respect from others.
- ••••• Outstanding: Others' first reaction to you is either awe, intense jealousy or complete solicitude.
- •••••• Inhuman: Beauty such as yours has no natural origin.

Mental Attributes

The Mental Attributes represent your character's total mental capacity, including such things as memory, perception and the ability to learn and think.

Perception

This Trait indicates your awareness of the environment around you. While Perception is sometimes used consciously, such as when you search for something, it more often works intuitively — you simply notice something. At base, Perception is a sensitivity to the world, an open-eyed quality common among children (for whom the world is a boundless and mysterious place), and seldom present among the most jaded.

Perception is used to see if you have the insight to understand or realize a certain fact or concept. It can help indicate your degree of alertness to ambushes, the subtext of a noble's speech or the subtleties of color in a painting.

Specialties: Insightful, Attentive, Paranoid, Keen-Eyed

- • Poor: You are blind to anything but the obvious.
- •• Average: You are unaware of the subtle interactions that occur around you.
- ••• Good: You are aware of moods and textures.
- •••• Exceptional: You are constantly alert to the nuances of life.
- ••••• Outstanding: You can see a needle in a haystack.
- •••••• Inhuman: You note things invisible to the human eye.

Intelligence

Intelligence represents both your memory and your ability to learn and think. It is important when using Abilities that require complex thought processes. Some people describe Intelligence as a person's quickness of mind or judgment, but it is more than that

— it is the facility for understanding and the capacity for reasoning and evaluation. Intelligence rates an individual's depth and flexibility of thought.

Common sense, street savvy and wisdom are not components of the Intelligence Attribute; these facets of the character are portrayed by the player. However, low Intelligence can indicate a character who lacks the capacity to understand complicated thoughts and learns very slowly — he might see things only in black-and-white terms and can't understand that things are really shades of gray.

Characters with high Intelligence, on the other hand, are sophisticated thinkers capable of evaluating many different levels of an argument or problem. They have discerning judgment and are well able to separate truth from lies, at least when they have time to think things over. Intelligence caters to carefully reasoned judgments rather than snap decisions (which are the purview of Wits).

Specialties: Discerning, Creative, Sharp Memory, Knowledgeable, Clear Thinker

- • Poor: Bumpkin.
- •• Average: You can learn the ins and outs of your profession.
- ••• Good: You could attain moderate skill in several trades.
- •••• Exceptional: You could master a field of knowledge and pioneer its growth.
- ••••• Outstanding: Your reasoning and ideas are far ahead of your time.
- •••••• Inhuman: The intricacies of your thought processes cannot even be explained to lessers.

Wits

The Wits Attribute describes your ability to react quickly and correctly to new situations, as well as your overall sharpness of mind and cleverness. In the simplest of terms, Wits measures how quickly (as opposed to correctly) you think. Wits represents shrewdness, sagacity and the capacity to understand problems in the simplest terms.

Those with low Wits are occasionally unable to take appropriate actions because of surprise. A low Wits rating can indicate that you are more easily tricked and fooled than most people, for you are a gullible and unsophisticated student of human (and vampire) nature. If you have high Wits, you are able to react quickly to new situations and are seldom caught off guard by sudden changes in events. Whatever else happens, you are able to keep your Wits about you.

Specialties: Clever, Shrewd, Practical, Combat Nerves

- • Poor: You never doubt your betters.
- •• Average: You know when to pull out of a bad dice game.
- ••• Good: You can respond quickly to accidents or ambushes.
- •••• Exceptional: You'd make an excellent general…or outlaw.
- ••••• Outstanding: Reynard the Fox
- •••••• Inhuman: Your reaction speed borders on precognition.

ABILITIES
TALENTS

Talents describe all the untrained and intuitive Abilities. Talents can never be trained or studied, but can only be learned through direct experience — usually during a story. If your character takes an action using a Talent he does not possess, there is no effect on your roll. A number of dice equal to the base Attribute are rolled. Talents are such natural and intuitive Abilities that it is assumed that everyone has some small capacity in each one.

ACTING

You are practiced at feigning emotions, beliefs or a certain frame of mind. If the situation calls for it, you can easily play the role of someone rather different from yourself. However, simply because you have this Ability does not mean you use it unethically. Honorable leaders have used Acting to lend power and depth to their speeches. You are able to feign tears, anger, friendliness and virtue.

- •   Novice: A rank amateur, you can feign sickness.
- ••   Practiced: You may have been in a passion play or two.
- •••   Competent: You could earn a job with a traveling troupe.
- ••••   Expert: You could play a part well for days on end.
- •••••   Master: You can become someone else whenever the mood strikes you.
- ••••••   Legend: They'd be fooled even if they could read your mind.

Possessed by: Traveling Players, Courtiers, Gamblers, Charlatans, Spies

Specialties: Pretend, Inspirational, Feign Emotions, Religious Awe, Mimicry

ALERTNESS

Over the years, you have become practiced in noticing all that happens around you, even if you are not actively concentrating upon the surroundings. This Talent dictates not the ability to search a specific area, but rather the ability to stay alert for a long period of time. Alertness simply indicates how aware you are of the world around you. It describes how much attention you pay to things other than the rumbling of your belly or the doubts in your mind.

- •   Novice: You tend to be alert to changes, moreso than most.
- ••   Practiced: You are watchful and very attentive to your surroundings.
- •••   Competent: You are highly vigilant.
- ••••   Expert: You are a truly cautious individual and rarely let down your guard.
- •••••   Master: You notice everything that goes on around you.
- ••••••   Legend: You notice when a flea enters or leaves the room.

Possessed by: Sentries, Hunters, Burglars, Messengers, Vagabonds

Specialties: Traps, Ambushes, Forests, Crowds, Noises, Paranoia

ATHLETICS

This Ability describes your general athletic prowess and skill at physical games. It determines your ability to jump across a chasm, swim through a storm, throw a rock, vault a fence or climb a tree. Athletics concerns complex motor actions; physical actions requiring only one type of motor action, such as lifting, do not use the Athletics score, nor do athletic actions classified under another Ability. (Wrestling, for instance, would fall under Brawl.)

- •   Novice: Serf
- ••   Practiced: Squire
- •••   Competent: Trained knight
- ••••   Expert: Skilled juggler or tumbler
- •••••   Master: Paragon among mortals
- ••••••   Legend: You could have beaten any ancient Olympian at any event.

Possessed by: Entertainers, Squires, Barbarians, Youths, Elite Warriors

Specialties: Swimming, Juggling, Tumbling, Dancing, Thrown Objects

BRAWL

You know how to fight unarmed, as well as with casual weapons such as pokers and table legs. This Ability includes such maneuvers as punching, kicking, grappling, throttling, throwing, gouging and biting. Brawling can get quite ruthless, but generally it is a nonlethal form of combat.

- •   Novice: You know what to do, but you haven't had much experience.
- ••   Practiced: You know where to hit people and make it hurt.
- •••   Competent: Nobody in your village bothers you anymore.
- ••••   Expert: You can take a sword away from a robber with little trouble.
- •••••   Master: You can wrestle bears to the ground.
- ••••••   Legend: You have mastered techniques unknown to the greatest fighters of your time.

Possessed by: Soldiers, Bullies, Brigands, Rustics

Specialties: Armlocks, Boxing, Wrestling, Grappling, Throws, Showing Off

DODGE

The most effective way to win a fight is not to be struck. Becoming proficient in the Dodge Talent is a very wise choice. Your score in this area describes your ability to avoid both melee and missile attacks, which includes diving for cover and ducking punches.

- •   Novice: You hit the ground if someone screams, "Look out!"
- ••   Practiced: You can come out of a fistfight without many bruises.

- ••• Competent: You can anticipate where the next sword blow is coming from.
- •••• Expert: They'd have to be lucky to lay a hand on you.
- ••••• Master: You can avoid arrows.
- •••••• Legend: You dance untouched through great battles.

Possessed By: Criminals, Scouts, Light Troops, Canny Brawlers, Animal Trainers

Specialties: Leap, Sidestep, Duck, Find Cover, Dive

EMPATHY

You understand and can sympathize with the emotions of others, and are thus able to respond to them appropriately. You can often discern the motives behind someone's actions by simply listening to him. You can also detect when you are being told lies. Empathy has a down side, however — because you are so open to the feelings of others you often feel the same emotions as those around you.

- • Novice: Gossipy widows feel they can trust you.
- •• Practiced: Occasionally you get sympathetic pains from others.
- ••• Competent: You have an amazing insight into others' motivations.
- •••• Expert: No lies ever get past your scrutiny.
- ••••• Master: You often finish other people's sentences.
- •••••• Legend: You read complicated emotional textures at a glance.

Possessed by: Gossips, Skilled Merchants, Priests, Parents, Fortunetellers

Specialties: Emotions, Truths, Family Problems, Personalities, Background Emotion

INTIMIDATION

The art of intimidation comes in many forms, ranging from a subtle suggestion to outright physical damage. Each method of intimidation has its time and place. You understand the science of being overbearing and know how to use it to get what you want. People with high Intimidation scores seem to radiate an aura of authority.

- • Novice: Stray dogs cross the street to avoid you.
- •• Practiced: You win an occasional staredown.
- ••• Competent: Your gaze is very unsettling.
- •••• Expert: You can dominate foreigners on their home ground.
- ••••• Master: You can make vicious animals turn tail and run.
- •••••• Legend: Demons themselves would quake in your presence.

Possessed by: Brigands, Witch-Hunters, Sovereigns, Torturers, Knights

Specialties: Staredowns, Subtle Hints, Overt Violence, Threats, Political

LARCENY

This Talent actually covers a wide range of criminal activities, including both knowledge of the physical aspect of skills and the ability to find and deal with criminal groups. That said, there isn't much of an organized underworld in medieval Europe. Most criminals act alone or with small bands of friends. Cities are simply too small and communications too poor to support large criminal syndicates. Only in the largest cities — Venice, Genoa, Paris, London — might large groups be found.

However, this Talent is still very useful, both for dealing with these scattered groups and for committing petty crimes. First and foremost, Larceny allows you to blend in with the local scene without drawing attention to yourself. Gossip, felony theft and street slang are also imparted by using this Talent. Finally, those skilled at Larceny can perform minor criminal acts involving sleight of hand (drugging drinks or cutting purses, for instance).

For example, the locks of the Middle Ages may be picked with Dexterity + Larceny (usually difficulty 8); moving a wax seal from one document to another requires an Intelligence + Larceny roll (difficulty 8).

- • Novice: You can get through a simple latched door.
- •• Practiced: You can spot a careless cutpurse.
- ••• Competent: You could make a living at theft.
- •••• Expert: You make an excellent burglar, forger and spy.
- ••••• Master: You could steal a kingdom's crown jewels.
- •••••• Legend: You could borrow the king's eye-teeth.

Possessed by: Robbers, Beggars, Vagabonds, Traveling Players

Specialties: Picking Pockets, Rumor Mill, Fencing, Slang Terms, Lockpicking

LEADERSHIP

You can get people to follow your lead and obey your orders through exerting authority and by example. Leadership isn't so much knowing the techniques of getting people to follow you as it is being the type of person people will follow. Leadership is often used in conjunction with Charisma.

- • Novice: You could organize a work party.
- •• Practiced: Your voice is a dominant one, and you can demand silence.
- ••• Competent: You can rally your neighbors when the need arises.
- •••• Expert: You attract followers without really trying.
- ••••• Master: You could be the next Charlemagne.
- •••••• Legend: They tend to worship rather than follow you.

Possessed by: Nobles, Military Officers, Constabulary, Churchmen

Specialties: Commands, Orate, Compelling, Friendly, Noble, Military

SUBTERFUGE

You know how to conceal your own motives; moreover, you know how to decipher the motives of others and how to use those against them. The secrets and intrigues of others interest you, and you work at understanding their weaknesses. A command of this skill makes you the ultimate conversationalist, or the ultimate spy.

- •   Novice: You understand tact.
- ••   Practiced: You could hold out on the tax collector.
- •••   Competent: You could woo two women at once.
- ••••   Expert: You could sell pig sweat as alkahest.
- •••••   Master: You could, with time, convince your archenemy to trust you.
- ••••••   Legend: They'll never know why the kingdom really fell.

Possessed by: Courtiers, Charlatans, Wooers, Minstrels, Traveling Players, Spies

Specialties: Finding Weaknesses, Seduction, Selective Omission, Fast-Talk, Flattery, Changing the Subject

OTHER TALENTS

Search, Guile, Intrigue, Expression, Painting, Sculpture

SKILLS

Skills are all the Abilities that are learned through apprenticeships or rigorous training. If you try to use a Skill but have no rating in it, the difficulty goes up by one. You are simply untrained in the techniques of that Skill and thus have a harder time accomplishing the task than someone who has at least some idea of what he is doing.

ANIMAL KEN

Animals do not behave in the same way that humans do under the same circumstances. The ability to understand the actions of animals can come in quite handy. Those characters skilled in Animal Ken can not only predict the actions of animals, but can use this knowledge to calm or enrage them. Animal Ken also is the Skill used to train animals. It is worth noting that many animals are uneasy around vampires, and Animal Ken is invaluable for any Cainite planning to ride horses.

- •   Novice: You can befriend a domesticated animal.
- ••   Practiced: You can teach a dog to come when you call.
- •••   Competent: You could train a hunting hound.
- ••••   Expert: You could be the king's own falconer.
- •••••   Master: You could domesticate a wild animal.
- ••••••   Legend: You are one with God's creatures.

Possessed by: Kennel Masters, Falconers, Stablehands, Manor Lords, Squires, Hermits

Specialties: Dogs, Raptors, Horses, Bears, Farm Animals

ARCHERY

You can fire bows and crossbows. You can also string a bow, and care for and make minor repairs to bows, crossbows, arrows and quarrels.

- • Novice: Your father showed you how.
- •• Practiced: You practiced regularly on the village green.
- ••• Competent: You could find work as a forester.
- •••• Expert: You could make extra money at the archery competitions at local fairs and tournaments.
- ••••• Master: Robin Hood or William Tell.
- •••••• Legend: You can put an arrow through your enemy's eye on a moonless night.

Possessed By: Foresters, Poachers, Competitors, Militias, Bandits

Specialties: Target, Forests, Hunting, Moving Target, Quick Shot

CRAFTS

Craft Skills are simply the professional skills most medieval people have, which they use to survive. Remember that almost everyone at this time works with their hands. Some may have two Crafts (e.g., a farmer who also works as a carpenter), but most specialize in one.

Such Skills often include various petty abilities. So, Farming does not just cover sowing and reaping; it includes handling sheep and domestic animals, repairing buildings and driving carts. Goldsmithing allows a character to evaluate gems and metals, to speculate upon the age of jewelry, etc.

Examples of Craft Skills include Farming (the most common), Carpentry, Blacksmithing, Glazing, Stonemasonry, Wheelwright, Tanner, Brewing, Goldsmithing, Dyeing, etc.

- • Novice: An apprentice or part-time worker.
- •• Practiced: A newly qualified craftsman or inexpert farmer.
- ••• Competent: An experienced, competent professional, earning a fair living.
- •••• Expert: A respected master craftsman.
- ••••• Master: An artisan who has elevated his trade to the level of an art, or a farmer who could make crops grow through a drought.
- •••••• Legend: Your finest work is obviously beyond any human craftsman's powers.

Possessed By: Artisans, Farmers, Townsfolk

Specialties: Detail, Working Quickly, Inventive, Organization, Evaluate.

ETIQUETTE

You understand the small nuances of social life and are able to conduct yourself in a manner that is both unobtrusive and gracious. You understand how to get along well with mortal society, whether courtly or rustic. Your specialty is the culture with which you are most familiar. You use Etiquette during actions such as dancing, seduction and haggling. Etiquette is also used when engaging in diplomacy.

- • Novice: You know when to shut up.
- •• Practiced: You know how to address a local lord or alderman.
- ••• Competent: You understand the nuances of courtly manners.
- •••• Expert: You could get along with just about anybody.
- ••••• Master: You can seat blood enemies at the same table and keep them happy.
- •••••• Legend: You could get five Mongols through a royal Spanish ball without offending anyone.

Possessed by: Envoys, Nobles, Heralds, Courtiers, Handmaidens

Specialties: Courtly Manners, Street Culture, Peasants, Foreign Customs

HERBALISM

Important in the Dark Medieval world, this covers the identification and preparation of herbs for cooking, healing and harming. You can find, prepare, blend and preserve herbs for any of these purposes.

- • Novice: You watched your mother prepare herbs.
- •• Practiced: You learned all your mother knew.
- ••• Competent: Village expert
- •••• Expert: People come from surrounding villages to buy your herbs and remedies.
- ••••• Master: You could make an excellent living as an apothecary.
- •••••• Legend: Some whisper you can raise the dead.

Possessed By: Village Wise Women, Cooks, Healers, Bandits

Specialties: Culinary, Medicinal, Poisonous, Narcotic, Herbs as Charms

MELEE

In the Dark Medieval world, skill in armed combat can be vital to a vampire's survival. Proficiency in this Skill allows you to use hand-held weapons. Melee covers everything from simple knives, axes and swords to wooden stakes and 20-foot pikes. Although not every Cainite will have possessed this Ability in life (lords are often loath to teach their vassals to fight), many learn it from their sires or other sources afterward.

- • Novice: You've seen a knife being used.
- •• Practiced: Peasant militia
- ••• Competent: Typical knight
- •••• Expert: Any weapon is deadly in your grasp.
- ••••• Master: Lancelot
- •••••• Legend: No warrior can stand before your whirling blade.

Possessed by: Soldiers, Militia, Robbers, Lords, Barbarians

Specialties: Swords, Axes, Knives, Clubs, Disarms

Music

You can create and play music; you know how to play one instrument for each rating point you have. Of course, the higher your rating, the better you are at playing your instruments, especially the first instruments you learned. This is the ability to create music — the higher your rating, the greater your musical ability. You should decide what instruments you play.

Typical medieval instruments include the recorder, hammered dulcimer, harp, lute and psaltery.

- Novice: You can carry a tune and plink out a chord or two.
- •• Practiced: Your voice stands out during hymns.
- ••• Competent: You could make a decent living as a troubadour.
- •••• Expert: Your skill is haunting and memorable.
- ••••• Master: You could compose before you were three.
- •••••• Legend: They say you can sing tears from the stones.

Possessed by: Minstrels, Singers, Noble Ladies, Monks, Bards

Specialties: Harp, Composition, Lyrics, Chanting, Bawdy Songs

Ride

You are able to ride comfortably on a horse, and with practice might be able to fight from horseback. You can also tell the rough value of a horse, are familiar with their tack (bridles, saddles, etc.) and can spot obvious ailments and defects.

- Novice: Hang on, shut up, and don't try to gallop.
- •• Practiced: You can gallop, clear small jumps, etc.
- ••• Competent: You can ride in a hunt or in battle, jump hedges safely and ride all day without getting saddle-sore.
- •••• Expert: Perfectly at home in the saddle, you could ride for weeks without discomfort.
- ••••• Master: If you wanted, you could stand on the saddle, pluck handkerchiefs from the ground or perform other flashy tricks.
- •••••• Legend: You know your horse's capabilities better than it does, and can make use of them all at will.

Possessed By: Knights, Squires, Nobility, Messengers, Huntsmen, Officers, Wealthy Merchants, Priests

Specialties: Jumping, Speed, Mounted Combat, Tricks, Forest

STEALTH

Stealth is the ability to sneak about or hide without being seen or heard, and is often rolled against another character's Perception. Stealth is of extreme importance when vampires engage in the Hunt.

- • Novice: You can hide in the dark.
- •• Practiced: You can hide in the shadows.
- ••• Competent: You are an accomplished hunter.
- •••• Expert: You could walk silently over two inches of dry leaves.
- ••••• Master: You could sneak up on a pack of wolves.
- •••••• Legend: Assamite elder

Possessed by: Burglars, Spies, Scouts, Hunters, Vampires

Specialties: Prowl, Hide, Lurk, Shadows, Crowds, Crawling, Wilderness

SURVIVAL

The wilderness is a dangerous place, at least for those who do not understand it. The skill of Survival includes seeking shelter, finding a direct route through and relative safety in the wilderness, and tracking. When you use Stealth in the wilderness, you cannot roll more dice for your Stealth rating than you have in Survival.

- • Novice: You can survive a five-mile trek.
- •• Practiced: You are familiar with the wilderness.
- ••• Competent: You can feed yourself adequately for long periods of time.
- •••• Expert: You are at home in the wild.
- ••••• Master: You could live off the land for years on end.
- •••••• Legend: You fear neither desert nor tundra.

Possessed by: Barbarians, Hunters, Bandits, Refugees, Hermits

Specialties: Tracking, Highlands, Edible Plants, Marsh, Hunting

OTHER SKILLS

Cooking, Boating, Painting, Smithwork, Weaving

KNOWLEDGES

Knowledges include all Abilities that require the rigorous application of the mind, not the body, so nothing but Mental Traits can be used to modify Knowledge rolls. Though the ratings discuss Knowledges in terms of college degrees, school is not the only way to gain Knowledges — it is simply the most common. These are scholastic Abilities for the most part, but self-study or tutoring is also possible.

If you do not have a Knowledge, you cannot even attempt a roll that involves it. There are exceptions, however, such as when the Storyteller rules that the roll deals with trivial information that anyone has a chance of knowing.

ACADEMICS

You understand Latin, can read and write, and have been taught something of theology and philosophy. This is the standard medieval education, and requires that you have attended at least a cathedral school or monastery. A high rating indicates that you attended one of the universities, in Paris, Salerno, Oxford or Bologna. This education did not come cheap. You, your parents or your guardians obviously had some wealth.

Remember, most medieval people are entirely illiterate. Without some understanding of Academics you can neither read nor write.

- • Dabbler: You can speak Latin, read and (kind of) write. You've heard of Aristotle.
- •• Student: Your Latin grammar is excellent, and you have a good grounding in math, philosophy and theology.
- ••• Learned: You are well versed in the writings of learned theologians and pagan philosophers like Aristotle.
- •••• Scholar: You are qualified to teach in any university and can debate with the finest minds in Europe.
- ••••• Savant: You are a learned theologian and could teach a thing or two to Aristotle.
- •••••• Visionary: The obscure and forgotten rests lightly on the tip of your tongue.

Possessed by: Ranking Priests, Monks, Teachers, Scribes, Royal Administrators

Specialties: Theology, Mathematics, Calligraphy, Metaphysics, Heresy, Grammar

HEARTH WISDOM

Yours is the common wisdom of the peasant, what some might call "superstition" or "folklore." You may not understand the complexities of Lupine ways or fae Glamour, but you know that the simple items (silver, holy water, cold iron, etc.) have some power over supernatural beings, perhaps more than those beings would care to admit. You may also be able to use such bits of knowledge against your vampiric opponents. Hearth Wisdom can also be used for simple herbal remedies, although it is not as potent as the Herbalism skill; such remedies will be for minor aches, fertility, colds and other small things.

Hearth Wisdom carries certain corollaries with it, however. Folklore can vary from place to place, and what a Russian character knows may mean nothing to his Irish friend. Likewise, while a great deal of folklore may have that kernel of truth in it, the rest is chaff, and only experimentation may prove which is which. Most truth-fiction ratios should run about 20/80 or so, more or less depending the Storyteller and the character. For example, a Romanian may have lots of stories and superstitions about vampires, but may know almost nothing of faeries. The Occult Ability accounts for harder facts and the resources to acquire such facts.

- • Dabbler: You listened to Granny's fireside stories.
- •• Student: You can recognize a creature when you hear of it, and learned from your village wise woman.
- ••• Learned: People come to you for advice and simple cures. You are familiar with lore from neighboring countries, but not well versed in it.

- •••• Scholar: You are a fountain of lore from your native culture and one or two others. Some of that lore comes from personal experience.
- ••••• Savant: Your word is respected, and you speak with authority about certain denizens of the shadow world.
- •••••• Visionary: Your knowledge, although cloaked in riddles and stories, is legendary, and you may be considered a threat by some supernaturals, including your own kind.

Possessed by: Village Elders, Old Wives, Witches, Wise Women, Cunning Men, Hermits, Herbalists, Peasants, Mages, Farmers.

Specialties: Irish, German, Scottish, English, French, Scandinavian, Russian, Italian, Eastern European, Jewish, Middle Eastern, Omens, Cures, Wards, Charms

INVESTIGATION

You are trained to notice all sorts of details others might miss, and at high levels may function as a detective. This Knowledge also reflects a character's ability to do research, both in libraries (rare) and through questioning.

- • Dabbler: You'd notice the footprints on the stable floor.
- •• Student: You can get information by buying a few drinks.
- ••• Learned: You can tell an accidental fire from a deliberate one.
- •••• Scholar: You catch minutiae with a brief scan of the room.
- ••••• Savant: Brother Cadfael
- •••••• Visionary: You could make a living at tracking down Assamites and Nosferatu.

Possessed by: Spies, Constables, Tax Collectors, Abbots, Bounty Hunters

Specialties: Search, Prowl, Locate Informant, Monastery Records, Shadowing

LAW

Prisons do not exist as a formal institution, and a criminal's rights are often whatever the local authorities feel like granting. This Knowledge allows characters to know what is locally illegal and how severely infractions are punished. More often, this Knowledge allows local judges, officials and rulers to settle disputes over property and the like. In a feudal society, the laws of ownership are of paramount importance.

- • Dabbler: Practical knowledge; city guard
- •• Student: Captain of the guard
- ••• Learned: Town official
- •••• Scholar: Experienced judge
- ••••• Savant: King Solomon
- •••••• Visionary: Hammurabi was a pretender next to you.

Possessed by: Constabulary, Judges, Criminals, Sovereigns

Specialties: Courts, Local Law, Punishments, Criminal, Laws of Ownership, Nobles' Rights

LINGUISTICS

It is assumed that you can speak your natural language, but you must purchase any other languages you wish your character to speak. For each level of Linguistics, your character may fluently speak another language. However, Linguistics also gives a character an understanding of the structure of language, which is in turn the basis of thought. With this Ability, you can identify accents. You also have a chance of figuring out phrases from languages related to the languages you know. For instance, you might be able to decipher some vulgar French (a Romance language) if you know Latin. **NOTE: You do not need to purchase this to speak Latin if you have Academics.**

- • Dabbler: One additional language.
- •• Student: Two additional languages.
- ••• Learned: Three additional languages.
- •••• Scholar: Four additional languages.
- ••••• Savant: Five additional languages.
- •••••• Visionary: Eight additional languages.

Possessed by: Travelers, Scholars, Diplomats, Interpreters

Specialties: Curse Words, Technical, Diplomatic, Political

MEDICINE

Medieval medicine is very primitive by modern standards. Even the simplest internal surgery has a difficulty factor of 9. In practical terms, this Knowledge is only useful for basic "first aid" — stopping bleeding, treating burns — and for simple procedures like treating fractures, fevers or stopping wounds from festering.

- • Dabbler: You know a little about binding wounds.
- •• Student: You can bleed someone with little risk.
- ••• Learned: You can diagnose and treat simple illnesses.
- •••• Scholar: You can deliver a child and rarely lose the mother.
- ••••• Savant: You could advance medicine to the next level in your area of expertise.
- •••••• Visionary: Your healing arts are so great some whisper you have a pact with the Devil.

Possessed by: Apothecaries, Midwives, Barbers, Field Surgeons

Specialties: Herbs, Poison Treatment, Battle Wounds, Disease, Leeching, Childbirth, Petty Surgery, First Aid, Diagnosis

OCCULT

This Knowledge is a catch-all dealing with local folklore, arcane texts, ancient legends and most other forms of supernatural facts and hearsay. This understanding of the more sinister side of the world includes knowledge of curses, rituals, magic and mysticism, and contains much that is only speculation and fantasy. This Knowledge is of the utmost interest to many vampires, and pursuit of this Knowledge may indeed become a major facet of your chronicle. A 4 or 5 rating indicates a deep understanding of vampires and other aspects of the occult (mostly what is patently false).

- • Dabbler: You've heard some tales.
- •• Student: You listen to the local wise woman's rambling.
- ••• Learned: You've found proof to back up some of your beliefs.

- •••• Scholar: You have found great secrets hidden among the dross.
- ••••• Savant: Fully initiated in many of the great mysteries. You don't need your sire to tell you what's going on!
- •••••• Visionary: You can recite *verbatim* what even magicians believe to be lost.

Possessed by: Heretical Scholars, Vampires, Pagans, Hedge Wizards, Kabbalists

Specialties: Vampires, Witches, Mystical Powers, Cults, Ancient Wisdom, The Kabbala

POLITICS

This Knowledge provides a familiarity with the politics of the day, including the people in charge and how they got there. It can be applied to almost any organization, from the Church to a local gaol. This can be an essential Ability when attempting to deal with mortal authorities in any way. This Ability even has some influence on being a capable politician yourself. Long familiarity with a subject can sometimes give one ideas....

- • Dabbler: Casual observer
- •• Student: Local herald
- ••• Learned: Aspiring heir
- •••• Scholar: Courtier
- ••••• Savant: Eminence grise
- •••••• Visionary: You know when the rebellions will come.

Possessed by: Lords, Courtiers, Heralds, Jesters

Specialties: Feudalism, City, Religious, Heraldry, Vampiric Hierarchies

SCIENCE

You have at least a basic understanding of metallurgy, botany, biology, engineering and astronomy. Your knowledge is tempered by local beliefs and superstitions; still, you have enough practical learning to be in demand.

- • Dabbler: You've been apprenticed to a smith or monk.
- •• Student: You studied the illustrations in the abbey's library.
- ••• Learned: You know about basic fortification and are a local authority on the animals of the forest.
- •••• Scholar: You can design effective siege engines (and ways to stop them).
- ••••• Savant: Alchemists' hopes everywhere ride on your shoulders.
- •••••• Visionary: You are truly ahead of your time, and would do well in the Renaissance.

Possessed by: Alchemists, Engineers, Hermits, Architects, Metalsmiths, Eastern Scholars

Specialties: Biology, Astronomy, Botany, Astrology, Metallurgy, Engineering

CHAPTER FOUR: CHARACTER

SENESCHAL

During your breathing days (or perhaps in your unlife), you were responsible for managing and maintaining a household or organization. Maybe you were Mother Superior or the abbot of a convent or monastery, or you might have been the chief steward of a nobleman. Perhaps you maintained a cathedral, or you were simply the lady of the house. This reflects your knowledge and experience in balancing the books, keeping inventory of the larder and wine cellar, managing the servants, entertaining guests, keeping the house and lands in good repair, and in general making certain that the household, abbey, cathedral, guildhouse or whatever was in good running order. Even a farmer might have some similar ability in making sure there was enough money for rent and keeping his farm in order.

Along with the attendant experience, this Knowledge may allow you to evaluate how another household is running (and to spot and correct problems), appraise quality of trade goods or entertain a guest even if you're not in your usual household.

- • Dabbler: You can keep a smaller place running without too many problems, and know how much money is available.
- •• Student: You can balance your books and budget for expenses, and guests are never a problem.
- ••• Learned: You can handle a larger household with no one assisting you, and your guests always have a good night.
- •••• Scholar: You can manage a large household or series of smaller households with no trouble.
- ••••• Savant: You can keep your house running even during the most difficult times, and your superiors consider you indispensible.
- •••••• Visionary: Your abilities to handle crises and manage your household are the talk of your social stratum, and other seneschals look to you as an example.

Possessed by: Innkeepers, Noblewomen, Wives, Chief Stewards, Seneschals

Specialties: Kitchens, Hostels, Noble Households, Accounting, Innkeeping, Taverns, Religious Orders

OTHER KNOWLEDGES

Astrology, Philosophy, Cartography, Navigation, History, Theology

BACKGROUNDS

Cuius regio eius religio.
(He who controls the area controls the religion.)
— Anonymous Latin proverb

Background Traits describe the special advantages of your character. However, you must determine why and how you came to possess these particular Traits. Where did you get your resources? What kind of contacts do you have? Where does all of this influence come from? Make sense out of your Background Traits and integrate them into your character concept.

You can make rolls using these Traits to obtain information, resources or favors. Frequently, these Background Traits are used in conjunction with an Attribute, such as rolling Charisma + Influence to set the constabulary on a rival, or Wits + Resources to tap into your cousin's treasury.

ALLIES

Your allies are mortals who help and support you — they could be family, friends or even an organization with which you are friendly. Allies have their own lives to live, so they are not at your beck and call, but they often have influence in the community and access to their own contacts or resources. An ally is ultimately a mortal whom you have befriended, and who protects and aids you out of love or common interest. Be sure to rationalize how it is that you keep contact with your allies if you can only be active at night.

For each point of Allies that you have, consider yourself to have one ally. This individual is a person of influence in the city where you live. An ally could be a sheriff, a town councilor or even (if your rating is a 4 or 5) the burgomeister himself.

Allies are generally very trustworthy and loyal. However, it requires time and energy to maintain the alliance, for the friends expect the aid of the character in return in time of need. Though they likely do not know you are a vampire, they may know something of your powers and thus may come to you for favors. This is often an excellent means for a story to begin.

- • One ally, of moderate influence and power.
- •• Two allies, both of them of moderate power.
- ••• Three allies, one of them quite influential.
- •••• Four allies, one of them very influential.
- ••••• Five allies, one of them extremely influential.

CONTACTS

You know people from many different walks of life, and they comprise a system of information and help that could come in very handy some day.

Contacts are not only the people you can manipulate or bribe to get information, but friends whom you can really count on (major contacts) to provide you with accurate information (in their areas of expertise). You should describe your major contacts as complete characters, either as the chronicle progresses or beforehand. You also have a number of minor contacts spread through the city. When you wish to get in touch with a minor contact, make a roll using your Contacts rating against a difficulty of 7. Each success means you have made successful contact with one of your minor contacts; of course, you will need to bribe or charm her into giving you needed information.

- • One major contact
- •• Two major contacts
- ••• Three major contacts
- •••• Four major contacts
- ••••• Five major contacts

GENERATION

Starting vampires in a Dark Medieval chronicle are assumed to be 12th generation. Although this may seem unusually far removed from Caine, it is assumed that the conditions that support the Dark Ages' vampiric population have prompted vampires to sire many childer. Characters of earlier generations will have serious repercussions on the tone of the chronicle, and it is up to the Storyteller to decide whether a character may take this Background at all. A player should not assume that her Storyteller will allow earlier-generation vampires.

If your Storyteller does allow this Background, these are the advantages for each rank:

- •   Eleventh generation
- ••   Tenth generation
- •••   Ninth generation
- ••••   Eighth generation
- •••••   Seventh generation

HERD

You have built a group of mortals from whom you can feed without fear. This herd also helps protect you and can be used to perform a number of different services. However, the herd is not as tightly controlled or as loyal as are retainers, and is not as closely connected to you as are allies. Ultimately, the Herd describes only the number of vessels you have readily available. Your Herd rating is added to your Hunt rolls, as described in Chapter Nine.

- •   3 Vessels
- ••   7 Vessels
- •••   15 Vessels
- ••••   30 Vessels
- •••••   60 Vessels

INFLUENCE

Influence denotes a character's ability to sway the mortal world. However, it has its limitations. Few things happen during the night in medieval society. Major nobles may hold nighttime feasts and revels, and peasant celebrations may carry on after dark, but generally the night is a time for private pursuits and for sleep — and there are no phones, faxes, computer nets or mail services with which to manipulate events at a distance. How is a vampire going to influence mundane society?

To make use of this Background, a character may have to combine it with another Background like Retainers or Allies. A character would usually require ghouls or other mortal pawns as intermediaries when exploiting this Background.

Also remember that Influence in the medieval world is often highly compartmentalized. A respected monk may have influence within the Church, for example, but not among merchants. A town mayor might be despised by the local nobility. A baron need not have any influence with the Church. Work out exactly where the character's Influence derives from (a reputation for wisdom? powerful relatives? etc.), and keep that in mind when using this Background in your stories.

- •   Moderately influential; you have some sway in a town.
- ••   Well-entrenched; a factor in a city's politics.
- •••   Position of influence; you have some power in a barony or several strong parishes.
- ••••   Broad personal power; you can partially sway a county or diocese.
- •••••   Vastly influential; your suggestions might even reach the king's ears.

MENTOR

This Trait describes one or more elders (your sire?) who look after you. Each rating point of Mentor you possess describes how powerful your mentor is in the community of the Cainites. Your mentor could simply be a vampire who has learned her way around the land, or an ancient who has garnered huge amounts of power in both the mortal and immortal worlds. Your mentor can give you advice, protect you from other elders, caution you when you intrude on the affairs of other elders and inform you of opportunities for power and advancement.

Often a mentor is your sire, though it can be any vampire who has taken interest in you. If your mentor is powerful, it might not be a single person, but a group. Thus, a coterie could be a mentor, as could the ruling council of a clan. Tremere often have the Mentor Background Trait because of the aid they receive from their elders.

A mentor may expect to receive something in return for the aid she provides. Though she may simply enjoy your company, in time of need she may call upon her "apprentice." This may begin a number of excellent stories. In general, however, you do receive more than you need to give out.

- •   Mentor is an ancilla and of little influence.
- ••   Mentor is an elder and is well respected.
- •••   Mentor holds strong influence in the city.
- ••••   Mentor is a prince, and has much power over the city.
- •••••   Mentor has great power beyond her domain.

RESOURCES

A medieval person's assets are unlikely to be static. Most peoples' Resources will be land and animals, which must be farmed to generate revenue. Merchants must trade. Nobles must collect taxes and dues. And of course, all these activities take place in daylight in the medieval world. Realizing assets (selling animals, for example) also requires that the person be able to move about during the day. Tricky.

There are no medieval investment funds or stockbrokers. If a character has Resources, she must either manage her assets in person (hard to do at night) or employ a bailiff (manager); in this case, think about and develop the character's relationship with her proxy. It is also worth specifying roughly what these resources are. Farm animals? Land? Trade goods?

On the other hand, medieval vampires are unlikely to have much use for money. They might want weapons, or cash to pay bribes, but what do they need? They don't need food (on which medieval craftsmen spend 90% of their income), don't need to spend money running a car and are unlikely to pay rent. Markets and traders are only open during daylight hours, so vampires without mortal servants won't even be able to buy anything.

- • Scant resources: You have just enough to afford the bare necessities — shoes and clothes when yours wear thin — but nothing more.

- •• Sufficient resources: You can meet your basic requirements and still have one or two shillings spare per month.

- ••• Comfortable: You might own a small house and have some means of making a comfortable living. You earn five Librum per year (about average), all spending money. Consequently, you have five shillings per month. If you sold up and moved out you would get no more than five Librum.

- •••• Wealthy: You have a large house or small manor. You might own a village or you might be a wealthy merchant. You could afford to keep a horse, and you certainly have a few servants. (How will you keep your secret from them? Those that will stay loyal to you regardless should be counted as retainers.) In addition, you have five shillings per month. In total, your estate is worth around 400 Librum.

- ••••• Vast Wealth: You might own a castle and vast tracts of land (10-20 entire villages), or run a huge trading empire. If you can work out a way to exploit these resources, you could maintain a huge household, including stables, servants, etc., and still have one Librum per month to spend. The estate would be worth thousands of Librum, if you could find anyone wealthy enough to buy it.

RETAINERS

You have one or more servants and assistants who are your loyal and steadfast companions. Retainers may be ghouls who are bound by the Blood Oath to you, individuals whom you have so Dominated over the years that they are incapable of independent action, or individuals whom you have so overwhelmed with your Presence that they would do anything for you. Ghouls are treated as mortals or animals with Potence 1, who may use the Cainite blood they drink much as vampires do.

Retainers must always be controlled in some way, either through a salary, through the donation of your blood or through the direct control of their minds. They may not always be loyal, though typically they are. If given the chance, they may betray you, depending on how well they have been treated.

Retainers should not be supermen, even if they are ghouls. Each should have a weakness. For instance, one retainer might be very loyal, but not very skilled. Another retainer might be very powerful, but have a very independent mind. No retainer should ever be the perfect bodyguard; nothing is that easy in **Vampire: The Dark Ages**. Retainers are meant to be characters in and of themselves, something to add flavor to the chronicle. Do not let them be abused.

- • One retainer
- •• Two retainers
- ••• Three retainers
- •••• Four retainers
- ••••• Five retainers

STATUS

You have something of a reputation and a standing within the Cainite community. It is usually determined by your sire's Status and the respect your particular clan is due.

The more Status you have, the less ill-treated you are by the elders, and the more respected you are. Status is sometimes used in rolls with Social Traits and reflects your prestige in such instances.

- • Known: a neonate
- •• Respected: an ancilla
- ••• High status: an elder
- •••• Powerful: an advisor to the prince.
- ••••• Luminary: a prince

VIRTUES

O conscience, upright and stainless, how bitter a sting to thee is a little fault!

— Dante Alighieri, *Purgatorio*

A character's Virtues describe his orientation on life and his essential integrity and moral strength. These Traits are intended to help you understand and direct your characters, not force a certain action upon them. However, a vampire is a creature of great passion, and sometimes Virtue rolls are required, with failure indicating that the character cannot avoid going into a frenzy, has lost ground to the Beast or is not brave enough to conquer terrifying circumstances.

Your character's Road will determine his Virtues: whether he believes in Conscience or Conviction, or whether he relies on Self-Control or Instinct. Courage is universal; no Road can value cowardice and survive long. (Note: For those players used to the morality codes for the Sabbat for **Vampire: The Masquerade**, Conviction and Instinct are not the same as Callousness and Instincts. Like everything about the Paths of Enlightenment, the Sabbat Virtues were codified long after the Dark Ages, based partly on the Virtues and Roads of previous ages.)

CONSCIENCE/CONVICTION

Conscience and Conviction are Traits of self-awareness which enable you to evaluate your own conduct. The judgments made by Conscience stem from your attitudes, ideals and morals. Similarly, Conviction details your ability to remain reasonable in the face of suffering or need. They are internalized prescriptions of self-worth and the voice of the real self — not the façade you might present to the world. These rolls are made to determine whether you lose ground along your Road by committing immoral (for your Road, that is) acts. A character with high Compassion will feel remorse; a Cainite with high Conviction will recognize her trespass and attempt to overcome it.

- •   Chaste/Steady
- ••   Moral/Sure
- •••   Just/Determined
- ••••   Charitable/Committed
- •••••   Remorseful/Dedicated

SELF-CONTROL/INSTINCT

These Traits represent the amount of control or influence you have over your emotions. Self-Control represents your discipline, your self-mastery. Those with high Self-Control rarely surrender their reason. Instinct is your ability to "ride the Beast," so to speak. It allows a vampire to put frenzy aside in the name of self-preservation.

Self-Control and Instinct are used to resist going into a frenzy. When you use either Virtue, you can never roll more dice than the points you currently have in your Blood Pool. Quite simply, the hungrier you are, the harder it is to resist. (See the Frenzy section of Chapter Seven for more information.)

- •   Calm/Rudimentary instinct
- ••   Temperate/Intuitive
- •••   Disciplined/Animalistic
- ••••   Hardened/Visceral
- •••••   Total self-mastery/Primal

COURAGE

Courage is a quality of the mind that enables you to stand fast in the face of opposition, hardship or danger. Courage is used to resist running away in terror from things a vampire instinctively fears, such as the sun, fire or a cross held by a person with holy powers. (See the Rötschreck section of Chapter Seven for more information.)

- •   Bold
- ••   Dauntless
- •••   Steadfast
- ••••   Gallant
- •••••   Valorous

VIA SCORE

The basic reason to preserve your character's Via rating is simple: if his Via ever falls to zero, he becomes a monster under the Storyteller's control. Permanently. Of course, there are other reasons. For instance, you cannot roll more dice in any Empathy roll than you have in your Via score. The fewer Via points you have, the deeper you sleep, and the more difficult it is for you to wake up in an emergency. You also tend to go into a frenzy more

often in stressful situations, as you find it difficult to control your primal instincts when you are in danger. The actions you take when in frenzy could lead you to lose even more Via points.

This Trait can be seen as what separates a vampire from a human. Vampires with high Via ratings are closest to human (as distinct from humane). Those far behind on their Road are bestial and monstrous, and not by choice.

EFFECTS OF THE ROADS

• To a large extent, a Via rating determines how human a vampire appears and how easily she can pass for human in the general populace. The farther back along a Road a character is, the more bestial she appears.

• Vampires tend to sleep very deeply and, even if there is danger, can be difficult to wake up. During the day, especially after being awakened, you cannot roll more dice on any roll for any action than your character's Via rating. See the Awakenings section for more information on how the Roads affect activities during the day.

• Roads directly affect Virtue rolls when you attempt to resist going into frenzy. You cannot roll more dice than your character's Via rating. Therefore, as you sink into the abyss of bestiality, you cannot long resist the call of the wild. As the Road is lost, the character comes slowly closer to the day when he loses all self-control.

• The length of time spent in torpor is also directly affected by the Via rating. The fewer the character's Via points, the longer he remains in torpor.

THE FORKING PATH

Sometimes, a character's philosophy evolves enough during play to warrant a change of Road. If the Storyteller and player agree that such a change is appropriate, the Cainite may move to a different Road. (For obvious reasons, a vampire cannot spend any real time "between" Roads. Such indecisiveness is fodder for the Beast.) If the new Road uses the same Virtues as the previous one, the character's new Via score is worked out as if the character was newly created (i.e., all dots gained from experience or freebie points are lost). If a Virtue changes, then the new Virtue starts with one dot and cannot be raised higher for at least three sessions. Such a dramatic change in philosophy takes some getting used to.

For example, the Ravnos Taltin began play on the Road of Paradox. However, constant exposure to mortals has begun to soften him, and his personal ethics are beginning to lean toward the Via Humanitatis. His player and Storyteller agree that this change would be appropriate, and Taltin moves to the Human Road. Since his new Road prizes Conscience and Self-Control, and the Via Paradocis valued Conviction and Self-Control, his Conviction must change. His new Virtue of Conscience starts at one dot. His Self-Control, however, can remain at the four dots it previously possessed. Taltin now has a score of 5 on the Road of Humanity.

DEGENERATION

Sometimes a character will take an immoral action, either willfully or despite her best intentions (while in a state of frenzy). In such cases, the Beast might take a little more control of her soul.

ROAD OF THE BEAST

Road Rating	Minimum Wrongdoing for Conviction roll
10	Attacking a clearly superior foe.
9	Not challenging a clearly weak leader for leadership.
8	Killing for any reason other than survival.
7	Avoiding contact with nature or wild animals.
6	Needless torture.
5	Making a sacrifice for someone unrelated to you.
4	Refusing to kill when important to your survival.
3	Failing to defend your territory.
2	Showing mercy to a dire enemy.
1	Abstaining from feeding when hungry.

ROAD OF CHIVALRY

Road Rating	Minimum Wrongdoing for Conscience roll
10	Failing to assist mortals in need.
9	Treating a peer with disrespect.
8	Placing personal desire above duty.
7	Breaking your word to a clanmate or peer.
6	Failing to assist clanmates or peers in need.
5	Striking an unarmed opponent.
4	Failing to provide hospitality to another Cainite.
3	Treating a superior with disrespect.
2	Breaking your word to your lord or prince.
1	Breaking a sacred oath.

ROAD OF BLOOD

Road Score	Minimum Wrongdoing for Conviction Roll
10	Breaking your word of honor to a clanmate.
9	Failing to assist or avenge a clanmate; revealing clan secrets to outsiders.
8	Placing personal desires or ambition above duty.
7	Not killing a non-Assamite vampire when there is need.
6	Failing to pursue blood or knowledge in the face of minor danger.
5	Breaking your word of honor to a mortal.
4	Being disrespectful to clan leaders; not pursuing greater knowledge of Haqim's teachings.
3	Failing to pursue vampire blood or knowledge of Caine when there is moderate danger.
2	Succumbing to frenzy.
1	Ignoring an opportunity to obtain vampire blood of a lower generation than your own, no matter the cost.

ROAD OF THE DEVIL

Road rating	Minimum wrongdoing for Conviction roll
10	Refusing to sire new vampires.
9	Failing to pursue a new form of pleasure.
8	Failing to ride the wave of a frenzy.
7	Avoiding injury to others at the cost of your own pleasure.
6	Refusing to murder humans when it would be in your best interest.
5	Refusing to commit cruel acts that are in your best interest.
4	Refusing to tempt the virtuous when opportunity awaits.
3	Turning down a chance for material gain.
2	Acting altruistically.
1	Aiding servants of virtue, God, or similarly opposed powers.

Road of Heaven

Road Rating	Minimum Wrongdoing for Conscience Roll
10	Failing to show respect to the Church (or similar institution).
9	Failing to speak out against corruption, sin, greed, pride, etc.
8	Being motivated by pride, avarice, gluttony (e.g., for blood) or some other sinful impulse.
7	Theft, robbery, willful vandalism.
6	Causing harm to a pious and virtuous person.
5	Feeding from an innocent without permission.
4	Blasphemous or heretical acts.
3	Allowing a crime or major sin to go unpunished.
2	The murder of an innocent (i.e., not a sinner or criminal) without any cause.
1	Aiding a demon, Infernalist, Setite or other supernatural servant of evil.

Road of Paradox

Road score	Minimum wrongdoing for Conviction roll
10	Refusing to commit diablerie upon an elder of another clan.
9	Refusing to lead a "locked" being into the light — or into destruction.
8	Showing any concern for mortals.
7	Failing to acquire items or knowledge that would affect reality.
6	Failing to trick others when the opportunity arises.
5	Being caught altering another's reality via the select redistribution of possessions (known among the vulgar as stealing).
4	Refusing to destroy an empowered device.
3	Actively joining or maintaining an existing Cainite power structure.
2	Actively hindering change.
1	Actively inducing boredom.

Road of Humanity

Road Score	Minimum Wrongdoing for Conscience roll
10	Accidental wrongdoing.
9	Purposeful wrongdoing.
8	Purposeful infliction of injury.
7	Theft and robbery.
6	Unmeditated murder.
5	Wanton destruction.
4	Deliberate cause of injury.
3	Sadism and perversion.
2	Meditated murder.
1	Only the most heinous and demented acts.

Road of Typhon

Road score	Minimum wrongdoing for Conviction roll
10	Attempting to maintain any sense of self-control, purity or worth.
9	Refusing to succumb to one's own weaknesses (this includes attempting to avoid frenzy or Rötschreck).
8	Failing to destroy a vampire in Golconda.
7	Destroying a foe expediently and mercifully rather than "poetically".
6	Failing to undermine the current social order in favor of the Setites.
5	Failing to replace faith with cynicism and despair.
4	Failing to exploit another's weaknesses.
3	Allowing one's feelings for a mortal to override the need to corrupt said mortal.
2	Refusing to corrupt a vampire for the Setites.
1	Not attempting to awaken Set at the earliest opportunity.

Controlling the loss of Via points is one of the most important elements of the Storyteller's role. If she lets the players get away with anything, then the whole fabric of the game is destroyed. Conversely, if she's too strict, the chronicle will last about three game sessions. These rules are open to interpretation and adjusting, but should never fall by the wayside.

Whenever a character takes an action which the Storyteller believes to be morally questionable (according to his Road), she may decide it is serious enough to warrant a loss of Via score. A degeneration roll is made by rolling Conscience or Conviction, whichever the character has. The difficulty is commonly 6, though it can vary at the Storyteller's discretion.

If the player succeeds in the roll by getting even one success, then the character does not lose the Via point. If he fails the roll, or botches, then the character loses both a point of Conscience/Conviction and a point on his Road. A botch also indicates the character gains a Derangement from the mental trauma involved in such a loss.

REMORSE

The Storyteller should always try to warn a player before she takes an action that will result in her character losing ground on her Road. Players should understand the consequences of what they are doing and be able to savor the anticipation if there is a chance they might not be able to do anything about it (say, they're in a frenzy). When the players get complacent and think they can get away with anything, that's when the Storyteller should start to warn them. However, the Storyteller should never cry wolf by warning them and then not calling for a roll.

THE HIERARCHIES OF SIN

It stands to reason that a character with a score of 3 on the Road of Humanity is less humane than one with a score of 10. The vampire with a high Via score is always very advanced his their chosen morality. However, the farther one goes, the harder it is to keep to the path. The Cainite with a 10 will need to make Virtue checks for even trivial infractions of his Road's ethics; he must be a paragon of his code to keep as far from the Beast as he does. But the vampire with a 3 on the Human Road will only lose ground by committing decidedly cruel acts.

The Hierarchies of Sin are rough guides to help the Storyteller and players know what sort of actions will require a Conscience or Conviction roll. The charts list the minimum wrongdoing that merits a roll. The Storyteller, as always, is the final arbiter of such things. He may ask a player to roll for degeneration even when the rules do not require it. The players should trust their Storytellers in this.

WILLPOWER

Willpower measures how capable a character is at overcoming the urges and desires that may tempt her. However, unlike other Traits, it is not something you roll (at least not often); Willpower is something that you use up. When you use a point of Willpower, you remove it from the character's Willpower Pool (the squares), not from the Willpower rating (the circles). The rating stays constant, while the Pool gets used up during the story.

Willpower from the Willpower Pool goes up and down a great deal during a story. It decreases by one every time the player uses a Willpower point to do something extraordinary, such as to retain self-control or gain an automatic success. Eventually, the character will have no Willpower left, and will no longer be able to exert himself the way he once did. The character is mentally exhausted and can't rouse himself enough to give a damn — he's expended all his Willpower.

•	Weak
••	Timid
•••	Unassertive
••••	Diffident
•••••	Certain
••••••	Confident
•••••••	Strong
••••••••	Controlled
•••••••••	Iron-willed
••••••••••	Unshakable

USING WILLPOWER

Willpower is one of the most active Traits in **Vampire: The Dark Ages**, simply because there are so many different ways to employ, regain and change it. Willpower is such a focus of the game that you will be paying a lot of attention to it, so you had better understand the following rules:

• A Willpower point can be used to give you one automatic success in an action. Only one point of Willpower can be used in this way on a single turn, but it gives you a single guaranteed success. In this fashion it is possible to succeed automatically in any simple action, merely by concentrating. For extended rolls, the extra success can make the critical difference between success and failure. There are some situations in which the Storyteller may not allow such a use of Willpower. Only vampires may use Willpower in this way.

• On some occasions, the Storyteller may tell you that your character does something because of instinct, primal urge or gut reaction. ("You run away from the window in mortal terror as the sunlight streams through.") You can use a point of Willpower to avoid this so you can do as you please. However, the feeling might return, and another Willpower point might be required. Sometimes it will return more times than you have Willpower, while other times you may completely overcome the urge.

• When one of your Derangements is about to cause you to take a course of action you would rather not do, a Willpower point can be used to control yourself. However, each time you attempt to overcome the Derangement, another Willpower point must be spent. Eventually, if enough Willpower points are spent, the Derangement is overcome permanently. This is the only way Derangements can be overcome, though this is not effective on a Malkavian's initial Derangement.

Willpower can only be increased permanently by the expenditure of experience points, but the Willpower Pool can go through enormous changes during a story. Discussed below are the various ways Willpower can change.

RECOVERING WILLPOWER

Characters recover their Willpower Pool whenever they are able to rest or get a chance to restore their self-confidence. It is up to the Storyteller to decide when and how a character recovers Willpower.

Listed below are the three different ways in which a character can regain Willpower. This does not have anything to do with the Willpower rating (which can be changed only with experience).

• At the end of the story (not a game session), characters regain their Willpower — all of it returns, up to the amount of the Willpower rating. The Storyteller may wish to restrict them somewhat by insisting the characters attain some modicum of self-pride or achieve moderate success in the story.

E.g.: The story ends with a partial stalemate. You didn't get everything you were after, but didn't embarrass yourself either. Recover all your Willpower.

• (Optional) You achieve some special success during the story that the Storyteller judges would cause the character to recover her self-confidence (and thus all or some of her Willpower).

E.g.: You rescue your husband from the fire consuming your mortal house. Regain three Willpower points.

• (Optional) Fulfill some criterion of the character's chosen Archetype, thus regaining from 1 to 3 Willpower points, subject to Storyteller judgment. This must be achieved through roleplaying, and approved by the Storyteller.

E.g.: As a Penitent, you give the riches you took from the bandits to a recent (and surviving) victim of yours. Regain two Willpower for your contrition.

If none of the options above suits your style of play, consider allowing the characters to regain one point of Willpower after they wake up each evening. It's a simple way to organize it because they are already subtracting a point from the Blood Pool, and it guarantees a steady recovery of Willpower.

BLOOD POOL

This is simply a measure of how much blood a vampire has in his system. The Blood Pool can be empty, which means that the character has used up all available blood in his body system. He will then lose a Health Level the next time the rules require him to lose a Blood Point (such as when a night passes). In other words, when the Blood Pool is empty, the character may not use Blood Points.

Blood Pool is an important factor in all Self-Control/Instinct rolls. You may never roll more dice on any roll involving the Self-Control/Instinct Trait than you currently have as a rating in your Blood Pool. Thus if you only have three Blood Points left, you can only roll three dice to avoid going into frenzy, even if your Self-Control is 4. This reflects the negative influence hunger has on Self-Control/Instinct.

The size of your character's Blood Pool depends entirely on her generation.

USING BLOOD POOL

Every night of existence uses up one Blood Point (scratch it off after a day of sleep). However, characters can decide to use Blood Points for other purposes. The number of Blood Points a character can use per turn is determined by her generation, though the effect is cumulative over a number of turns.

• One Blood Point can be spent to restore one Health Level, but only if the character is at rest and inactive. It takes one turn to heal one Health Level.

• One Blood Point can add one point to a specific Physical Attribute (Strength, Dexterity or Stamina). The player must announce the expenditure of a Blood Pool point, and for the remainder of the scene she gains one extra die. Only one Blood Point can be used per turn, but the effects accumulate over a number of turns as more Blood Points are used. After three turns and three Blood Points, a character could have +2 Strength and +1 Dexterity. Of course, Cainites of lower generations can often spend more blood in a turn.

• A vampire can give a portion of her Blood Pool to another, thus enabling him to restore Health Levels or take special actions. This necessitates slashing open an artery and letting the other character drink from it. Some characters may frenzy and attempt to drink more than they should, so this action can be somewhat dangerous. Additionally, if this is the third time someone has drunk a certain Cainite's blood, he will become the donor's Thrall unless he is already currently under the Blood Oath to another vampire.

When a character drinks the blood of an animal or human, she gains nourishment — essential for a vampire to live. This is described in the game as Blood Pool. If a character's Blood Pool is full, she is sated and cannot benefit from drinking more. If a vampire drinks all of a person's blood, that person will die. If more than half is drunk, the person will need to be hospitalized and will perhaps die (mortals drop one Health Level for each point of blood lost).

GAINING BLOOD POOL

When a vampire drinks the blood of a human or an animal, she is able to add blood to her Blood Pool. Up to three points of blood can be drained in one turn. The shorter the turn, the less leisurely the character is taking the sustenance. Many Cainites drink very slowly so as to eke more pleasure out of the experience. It is impossible to take more than three points of blood in three seconds (the shortest an action turn gets).

Source	Blood Pool size
Vampire	10 - 50
Lupine	25
Average Human	10
Cow	6
Child	5
Hound	4
Sheep	4
Pig	4
Cat	3
Rat	1/2
Bird	1/4

Once a human is bitten, he no longer resists the attack of the vampire, and indeed becomes a full partner in the ecstasy. Thus, the vampire need not fear the victim once the teeth have sunk in. In the cases of exceptionally strong-willed individuals (9+ Willpower), resistance may continue, but eventually even they are drawn into the seduction of the Kiss. Some mortals, given the opportunity, learn to enjoy the Kiss and may develop a lust for it.

If a vampire drinks more than half of a victim's Blood Pool, that person's life is in serious danger, and some sort of treatment is usually necessary to ensure the victim's survival. If more than three-fourths of a victim's blood is taken, then immediate medical care is required or the vessel will surely die.

A wounded character usually has less blood than normal. Assume that a normal-sized human has one fewer Blood Point for each level of wound. Vampires do not lose blood to wounds in this way. Assume humans regain one Blood Point a day if they do not have a full supply of blood. While some animals may have much more blood than a human by volume, it is far less nourishing and therefore is worth less in Blood Points.

Old blood is never as nourishing as fresh blood, unless it is extraordinarily potent, like the blood of an elder. Such blood will maintain its vitality for some time. If a vampire drinks the blood of an ancient, each point taken may be worth two Blood Points or more. Therefore, it is possible by feeding from such creatures to gain a tremendous amount of Blood Points. Elders are able to concentrate the blood they drink, thereby increasing their effective Blood Pools. Each "point" of their Blood Pool is therefore worth 1/10th of their total Blood Pool.

Essentially, elders have much larger Blood Pools than other vampires, although they are not physically larger. They are able to contain the blood only because they are able to concentrate it. Thus, if another vampire drank that blood, she would receive a highly concentrated dose (which often has special properties as well). The blood of Lupines is just as potent.

HEALTH

This is a measure of how hale and hearty a character is. There are various levels of injury, and each applies a different penalty to the person so injured. A character who is Hurt, -1, would have one fewer die to roll on all her rolls, while a character who is Crippled, -5, would have five fewer dice to roll. If that leaves the player with no dice to roll, then the character cannot take that action.

A vampire who is Incapacitated can take no action whatsoever. She is immobilized, and the only action she can perform is to heal herself using Blood Points or swallow blood that is offered to her. A mortal who reaches this state is very close to death; if she loses one more Health Level, she dies. If a vampire sustains an aggravated wound at the Incapacitated level, then he dies the Final Death as well.

HEALTH LEVELS

Level	Penalty	Description
Bruised:		Character is only bruised and has no action penalties.
Hurt:	-1	Character is only mildly hurt; movement isn't hindered.
Injured:	-1	Minor injuries; little hindrance to movement.
Wounded:	-2	Character cannot run, but can still walk.
Mauled:	-2	Character is badly injured and can only hobble about.
Crippled:	-5	Character is severely injured and can only crawl.
Incapacitated:		Character is completely incapable of movement.

GENERATIONS CHART

	Trait Max Rating	Blood Pool Size	Blood Points/Turn
Third	10	?	?
Fourth	9	50	10
Fifth	8	40	8
Sixth	7	30	6
Seventh	6	20	5
Eighth	5	15	3
Ninth	5	14	2
Tenth	5	13	1
Eleventh	5	12	1
Twelfth	5	11	1
Thirteenth+	5	10	1

Trait Max Rating: This indicates the highest Trait rating a vampire can have. This is especially important when it comes to Disciplines. Note that player characters can only buy a six rating in any Trait with experience points.

Blood Pool Size: Ancient vampires are capable of storing more blood (or its energy) in their system than younger ones.

Blood Points/Turn: This describes how many Blood Points a vampire can use in a single turn for either extra dice or levels of healing.

Chapter Five: Disciplines

As for myself, I walk abroad o' nights
And kill sick people groaning under wall:
Sometimes I go about and poison wells.
— Christopher Marlowe, The Tragical
History of Doctor Faustus

In a latter day, Disciplines might be called supernatural abilities. In the Dark Ages, they are known for what they truly are: the dividing line between humanity and the Beast. Whether they be gifts from God (as some suggest), the marks of Satan (as most believe), Lilith's kiss (as Cainite legends claim), or a simple primal heritage, Disciplines grant vampires powers unknown to mortals.

Each Discipline bestows some special ability. Some forge bonds with animals or grant the powers of illusion. Others convey great strength, inhuman speed or the solidity of stone; allow her to change into beasts at will; or enable her to turn an entire room of strong-willed warriors into slaves. Whatever spawned these mystical powers, their existence defines the might of the undead.

In game terms, Disciplines range from one to five dots (see Traits). Six-dot Disciplines are also included for players and Storytellers running characters of seventh generation and lower. Some Disciplines involve a single ability, like great strength (Potence), while others span several related talents, like sorcerous Thaumaturgy. Depending on the Discipline, each dot either grants a character some new power or enhances a single one to greater levels. Each of the Disciplines listed in this chapter offers a variety of powers and the levels necessary to achieve them.

Each new character begins the chronicle with four dots in her clan's special Disciplines — those abilities her clan has mastered. From there, freebie points may be spent to raise those Disciplines or purchase others. As a character progresses, she may spend experience points to increase her powers still further, potentially rivaling those of a Cainite elder.

Naturally, a character should have some "in-game" reasons behind the increases in her powers. These rationales will depend more upon the vampire or her clan than upon flat rules. A Gangrel might raise her Animalism rating through constant contact with beasts, while a Tremere learns the spells that unlock the animal bond, and a Malkavian devolves to such a bestial state of sanity that he becomes one with the animals when he so chooses. Whatever the story may be, the player should invent the methods her vampire uses to increase her Discipline ratings before she adds on new dots.

It bears repeating that Disciplines clearly mark the character's supernatural origin. While the lowest levels of Celerity or Potence may be passed off with "Oh, she's just quick on her feet (or strong for her size)," most such powers set the character apart from the living. Mortals who see Disciplines in action may fear the Cainite who wields them, or grow jealous and try to have her destroyed. Vampires themselves often express reservations about these powers; even gifts from God take time to grow accustomed to. A freshly Embraced neonate might well wonder how much farther into damnation these uncanny talents would drag him….

Advanced Disciplines

To those with the strength of blood and will, the first five levels of each Discipline are just the beginning of a vampire's potential. Unusually talented vampires may advance beyond the basic five levels and develop their own variations on the power.

At the sixth level (or higher), a vampire achieves such mastery that her Disciplines mirror her inner nature. A vicious Brujah with six dots in Dominate may terrify a roomful of people through some unique power, while a more subtle member of the same clan could shame an incubus with his seductive influence. Each Discipline lists several options for sixth-level powers; at the Storyteller's discretion, a player may create a new, individual power. Whichever option a player chooses, the manifestation of the power should reflect the vampire's personality.

With enough experience (and good reasons behind new powers), a player may buy more than one sixth-level Discipline power. Naturally, this requires plenty of experience points; obtaining even one Level Six power costs 30 points, and each additional one costs another 30. Vampires' lives are measured in millennia, of course, so slow advancement is not much of an inconvenience. Any clever Cainite may think of dozens of uses for even the lowest Discipline levels; the additional powers are simply spice to an already savory gruel.

Truly ancient vampires may command talents beyond even the sixth level; Storytellers are encouraged to invent awesome powers in addition to those offered here, or give godlike elders a variety of Level Six Disciplines. Thus, an ancient Cainite who has achieved a Dominate rating of 8 may have more than eight Dominate powers. Fear your elders, childe....

ANIMALISM

In the Dark Ages, humanity's conquest of nature is far from complete. The forests are filled with beasts capable of giving even an experienced huntsmen a fearsome match. Killing a pack of ravenous wolves means an up-close and bloody confrontation with rabid beasts.

Humanity's ignorance of the behavior of wild animals has spawned fear and hatred of many species like the wolf and the bat. Conversely, humanity's dependence on domesticated animals, as beasts of burden, food sources and protection, links people closely to the animal world.

The Discipline of Animalism gives a Cainite intense empathy with and rulership over all animals, domestic or wild. Animalism also provides some measure of control over the Beast which lurks within the soul of every vampire.

Animalism is found primarily among the Gangrel, Nosferatu, Ravnos and Tzimisce clans. The Gangrel are especially renowned for running with beasts through the dark forests of Europe. Other clans have difficulty developing this Discipline, as few members of the above clans are especially predisposed to tutoring others in the art.

Lacking this Discipline or the Skill of Animal Ken leaves a Cainite with the curse of being offensive to animals. Beasts are distinctly uncomfortable around the undead and do all they can to move away or perhaps attack.

Animalism is one Discipline which pious vampires tend to view positively, citing the apparent use of such powers by Noah, Daniel and even Jonah to support a claim that the power may stem from above rather than below. While these Cainites are a minority among those who possess Animalism (most Gangrel being pagan barbarians and Tzimisce believing themselves gods), they zealously cling to their interpretations.

Whenever characters interact with animals, the Storyteller should give the creatures unique personalities and manners of speech. Animals may eventually befriend characters, so the better a creature is portrayed, the longer it remains interesting to the player. Remember that animals are generally simple-minded and take things quite literally.

Depending on what level of fantasy you choose to inject into your **Dark Ages** chronicle, Animalism may aid Cainites' interaction with supernatural beasts (griffins, manticora, etc.). The difficulty of powers is increased by one or two when using Animalism on such creatures. Also, fantastic beasts are usually much more intelligent than common ones.

• FERAL SPEECH

God's gift of speech was not reserved for humans alone. Feral Speech allows a Cainite limited communication with animals, allowing for specific requests of creatures. To invoke this power, the Cainite must look into the animal's eyes. Once contact has been made, the vampire may issue the creature commands by speaking in its tongue, whether in chirps, hisses or barks. Some Nosferatu are said to be able to give orders silently, but they must maintain eye contact with the animal throughout the conversation and must reestablish contact to give the animal any new instructions.

Feral Speech provides no guarantees that an animal will want to deal with the vampire, but the animal usually becomes better disposed toward her. Smaller animals may be cowed into accepting commands, while orders for large predators are better couched in terms of requests. It is highly recommended that all communication be roleplayed.

If communication is effective, the animal tries to perform the command to the best of its ability and intellect. Highly complex commands (like anything with conditional logic) are lost on all but the very brightest animals. Commands are deeply implanted, though, and may affect the animal for some time.

System: No roll is necessary to talk with an animal, but the player must make a Manipulation + Animal Ken roll (difficulty 6) to get it to do favors. This difficulty can be adjusted by circumstances and roleplaying skill. The character's approach to the conversation depends heavily on his Nature. The character might try intimidation, teasing, cajoling, rationality or emotional pleading. The player should understand that he does not simply play his character, but the Beast within as well.

•• NOAH'S CALL

This power allows the Cainite to cry out in the voice of a specific type of animal. All such animals within earshot are summoned, but may choose whether or not to respond. Those that do will not necessarily provide immediate assistance to the vampire. However, they are favorably disposed toward the Cainite, and most offer assistance.

The few Cainites who cling zealously to their Christian beliefs and who achieve mastery of Animalism liken this power to that of Noah, who called to him two of all creatures and shepherded them into the ark.

System: The player must roll Charisma + Survival (difficulty 6) to determine the response to the call. Consult the table below. The only animals that might respond are those that hear the call.

At the player's discretion, the call can be targeted to even more specific groups of animals. For example, a vampire could call for all gray-furred wolves in the area, for only a certain wolf pack or for only the alpha male of the wolf pack.

1 success	One animal responds.
2 successes	A quarter of the animals within earshot respond.
3 successes	Half of the animals respond.
4 successes	Most of the animals respond.
5 successes	All of the animals respond.

●●● COWING THE BEAST

Cainites are the supreme predators of the natural world. Many Cainites believe that within each of them lies the spirit of a ravenous Beast, similar to but also superior to the Beast that lies in every mortal heart. With this power, a Cainite may touch any mortal human or beast and for a brief moment connect their bestial spirits. That brief contact is enough to make the subject's Beast cower before the Cainite's.

The subject loses all courage, hope and inspiration. The most courageous mortals simply become apathetic and depressive, while sensitive ones may suffer from phobic Derangements while under the power's influence.

Christians among the Nosferatu purport that this power was manifested by Daniel when he was cast into a den of ferocious lions in ancient Babylon and emerged unscathed the next day. Most religiously orthodox Cainites, like these Nosferatu, believe this power will not take effect if they have recently been unfaithful to their beliefs. Conversely, Tzimisce simply see the power as further evidence of their superiority over lesser beasts. Ravnos don't particularly care where the power comes from, but find it useful to calm the mortals they have just thieved. Gangrel and some Nosferatu are said to use a similar power that soothes the subject's Beast into a state of utter complacency rather than oppressing it through fear. This power functions identically to Cowing the Beast, but is known as Song of Serenity.

System: The player must roll Manipulation + Intimidation (or Empathy if using the soothing Song of Serenity) at difficulty 7. It is an extended action and the player must collect as many successes as the target has Willpower (5 for most animals). Any failure indicates that the vampire must start over from the beginning, while any botch indicates that he is never again able to affect that subject's Beast.

When a mortal's Beast is cowed or soothed, he can no longer use or regain Willpower. He ceases all struggles, whether mental or physical. He cannot even defend himself if assaulted, though the Storyteller may allow a Willpower roll if the mortal's life is threatened. To recover from this power, the mortal may roll Willpower (difficulty 6) once per day until he accumulates enough successes to equal the Cainite's Willpower. Cainites themselves cannot be affected by this power.

●●●● RIDE THE WILD MIND

In the Dark Ages, religious doctrine asserts that animals have no souls, only spirits. Using this power, Cainites believe they are able to fill that vacancy by moving their own souls into the bodies of animals. By staring into the eyes of an animal, the vampire can move her *anima* — her conscious mind — into the animal and possess it. The vampire's body falls into a motionless state like torpor, but her mind takes control of the animal's actions.

Tzimisce seldom use this power, considering it debasing to enter the body of a lesser creature. When they do, they only possess predators. Ravnos make a habit of killing and sucking the vitae from animals after the possession, for fear that their souls will be retained in the animals.

System: The player must roll Charisma + Animal Ken (difficulty 8) as the character looks into the animal's eyes (only animals with eyes can be possessed). The number of successes

obtained determines how thoroughly the character's soul overrides the spirit of the animal. Multiple successes allow the character to utilize some mental Disciplines while possessing the animal. Fewer than three successes means the player must use Willpower points to take any action that directly violates the instincts of the animal in question.

1 success	Cannot use Disciplines.
2 successes	Can use Auspex.
3 successes	Can also use Presence.
4 successes	Can also use Dominate, Dementation.
5 successes	Can also use Thaumaturgy, Chimerstry.

The possessing character behaves much like the animal if fewer than five successes are obtained — her soul is clouded with needs and impulses from the animal's spirit and body. Because the character's soul and the spirit of the animal become so entwined, the character may continue to think and feel like that animal, even after the connection has been broken. This should be roleplayed. The effect continues until a total of seven Willpower points are spent to resist and overcome the animal's nature.

At the end of any particularly exciting incident during possession, the player should roll Wits + Empathy (difficulty 8) for the character to retain her own mind. Failure indicates that the character's mind returns to her own body, but still thinks in purely animalistic terms. A botch sends the character into frenzy upon returning to her own body.

When employing this power, it is possible for a vampire to travel about during the day, albeit in the body of an animal. However, her body must be awake to do so, and therefore the player must successfully make a roll to stay awake (see Chapter Seven).

●●●●● DRAWING OUT THE BEAST

At this level of Animalism, the Cainite has a keen understanding of the Beast within. Whenever the predator spirit threatens to overwhelm the vampire's soul and send her into frenzy, she may instead fling the spirit of the Beast out of her body and into another's. The recipient of the Beast's raging spirit is instantly overcome by frenzy. Since the victim receives the Cainite's own spirit, the behavior and expressions of the Cainite are evident in the victim's frenzied actions. Facial expressions, body language and even changes in vocal inflection mirror the Cainite's own.

Gangrel are especially fond of passing their Beasts onto their ghouls during combat. Autarkis Gangrel have been known to send bands of their ghouls sweeping through hamlets in frenzied fervor while their masters follow to feast upon the destruction. By the time the hamlets' protectors can arrive, both madmen and monsters have escaped into the night.

System: To use this power, the vampire must be in frenzy or close to it, and the player must roll Manipulation + Animal Ken (difficulty 8). The player needs to announce his preferred target prior to rolling; it must be someone within sight. Refer to the table for the results:

1 success	The character transfers the Beast, but releases it upon a friend.
2 successes	The character is stunned by the effort and may not act next turn, but transfers the Beast.
3 successes	The character is completely successful.

If the attempt fails, the intensity of the frenzy actually increases; as the character relaxes in expectation of relieving himself of savage desires, the Beast takes that opportunity to dig deeper. The frenzy lasts twice as long and is twice as difficult to shrug off; it is also many times more severe than normal. A botch on this roll is even more catastrophic. The heightened frenzy is so extreme that not even expending Willpower effectively curbs its duration or effects.

If the character leaves the target's presence before the frenzy concludes, he loses his Beast, perhaps permanently. While no longer vulnerable to frenzy, the character is not able to use or regain Willpower and becomes increasingly lethargic. To recover the Beast, he must find the person who now possesses it (who probably isn't enjoying herself very much) and retrap the Beast. He must behave in ways that make the Beast want to return; the Beast does not always wish to do so.

• • • • • • Quickened Unity

With this power, a vampire may touch an animal and link the spirit of his own Beast to the spirit of the animal. Once the two are linked, the Cainite can pull the thoughts, memories and experiences from the animal, mentally reliving the animal's past. The longer the vampire maintains the link, the more information he can gather. However, if the link is maintained too long, the vampire may become confused as to which memories are his own and which are the animal's.

Cainites use this power for all manner of purposes. For example, wild stags know the lay of the surrounding forest, war horses remember how various battles fared, and rats know all the crawlways into a castle and what lies below that castle.

System: Use of this power requires a Perception + Animal Ken roll (difficulty 6). Each turn after the first spent in this melded state requires the character to spend a Willpower point. It usually takes two turns to locate and extract a precise memory, and about five turns to share spirits completely.

Auspex

A vampire with Auspex sees with the eyes of a god. At low levels, she notices things no mortal could perceive. The more esoteric abilities allow her to expend her consciousness enough to leave her body behind for short periods. Auspex powers usually require Perception rolls; the better the roll, the more the Cainite understands.

Naturally, the vampire who senses more than most has a distinct advantage in these dim times. Whether such talents let her view a distant battle, sense a duke's mood before an audience, or pluck the hidden sins from the minds of saints, Auspex is a powerful tool. A sensitive vampire may, of course, become easily distracted by beautiful things, loud noises or foul smells; sudden or potent events might even disorient the vampire unless she makes a Willpower roll to ignore them. The more potent the source of distraction, the higher the difficulty will be. Failure overwhelms the character's senses, and she may notice nothing else for a turn or two. The notorious weakness of the Toreador illustrates this point.

• Heightened Senses

By sharpening all five of her senses, the character may double the usual range of her hearing and sight. This happens at will and lasts as long as she wants it to. Although her other senses — taste, touch, smell — do not extend any farther than usual, they become far more acute; she might be able to taste the ale in a vessel's blood or smell a distant horse long before a hunter comes into sight.

Occasionally, this talent provides insights that transcend the usual five senses. Odd premonitions or flashes of empathy are common, if unfocused, examples. These perceptions should be left up to the Storyteller's discretion.

This insight has a price. Bright lights or strong smells present a hazard while the vampire uses the power. In addition to the distractions mentioned above, an especially sudden stimulus — like a flaring bonfire or a clap of thunder — might actually blind or deafen the character for an hour or more. So long as she avoids such events, however, the Cainite may detect things her companions miss.

System: Although this power is best defined by Storyteller descriptions and the player's imagination, dice are sometimes necessary. Whenever some threat could be revealed, the Storyteller rolls the character's unmodified Auspex rating. The roll's difficulty varies according to the circumstances (and whim). For instance, a warning that a goblet of fresh vitae has been laced with poisons might require a 6, while the sudden realization that a rival lord in the next county is mobilizing against you might require a 9.

•• SOULSIGHT

By peering past the layers of a target's personality, a vampire may discover clues about his true nature or intent. This power allows the Cainite to read the mystical halos surrounding all things; the colors she sees may tell her much.

Even the simplest peasant has many shifting hues within this halo; strong emotions predominate, while minor undercurrents or deep secrets trickle through. This Auspex level lets the Cainite detect vampires (their halos are pale), magicians (who often crackle with suppressed power) and werebeasts (whose colors seem brighter and more frantic than any mortal's should be). As the target's emotional state changes, the colors in his soul-halo shift, blend or surge into dancing patterns. The stronger the emotion, the brighter the colors become.

System: The player must make a Perception + Empathy roll (difficulty 8). The Storyteller may wish to make this roll so the player doesn't know whether she failed or botched. Each success indicates how much of the target's halo can be seen and understood (see the chart). A botch indicates a misleading interpretation.

1 success	Can only distinguish the shade (pale or bright).
2 successes	Can distinguish color as well.
3 successes	Patterns can be recognized.
4 successes	Subtle shifts can be detected.
5 successes	Can identify mixtures of color and pattern.

The Halo Colors chart offers examples of some common colors and the emotions they represent.

A character may only view another's halo once; if she tries to look at it again, any failure should be considered a botch. It is very easy to imagine seeing what one wants to see when judging someone's intentions.

••• THE SPIRIT'S TOUCH

Each being leaves traces of its essence upon the objects it touches. With this Auspex level, a character can read these impressions and see who has handled an item, when he last held it, and why. If a Cainite turned her attentions to a dagger, for instance, she might get some insights into the last person to hold the blade. For the most part, these visions offer a momentary glimpse of the item and its "owner." a short look might not tell the reader much, but a successful one might reveal a wealth of details: what the dagger's owner looked like, how the weapon came into his possession, and possibly even a vision of the murder it was used in.

Obviously, each clan uses this power differently. The Cappadocians are said to utilize it to discover objects precious to the shades of the dead. Ancient Toreador reexperience the rapture of creativity when handling works of art, while Tremere scholars may sense the hidden power of those standing before them. No matter what use the vampire prefers, she must hold the object and enter a shallow trance while concentrating upon the information she wants to uncover. Although most visions concern the last person to handle the item, a long-time owner will leave stronger impressions than someone who picked up the item once.

System: The character must make a Perception + Empathy roll. The difficulty is determined by the age of the impressions and the mental and spiritual strength of the person or event that left them. The number of successes scored determines the amount of information gained.

Events involving strong emotions (a gift-giving, a murder, a long family history) leave stronger impressions than does short or casual contact. Assume that each success offers one piece of information. While one success would only tell her "a man held this dagger last," three would reveal that he was cruel, middle-aged and afraid. Four successes would reveal her his name, and five or more would reveal his connection to the knife and the things he did with it.

•••• STEAL SECRETS

By forming a bridge between her mind and another's, the character may speak without words or read a victim's deepest fears. Thoughts "stolen" thusly are as audible to the Cainite as normal speech would be. Naturally, such a talent makes its wielder one to be feared among the courts of Europe. While the Tremere and Tzimisce manipulate their mortal servitors through mindplay, some Malkavians disturb their victims by babbling a person's thoughts aloud (often adding their own mad rantings to the torrent).

System: The player must make an Intelligence + Subterfuge roll, with the subject's current Willpower as the difficulty. One success must be rolled for each individual item of information plucked or for each layer of thought the vampire strives to reach. Deep secrets or buried memories are harder to obtain than surface emotions or unspoken retorts.

Such powers do not normally work upon the undead mind; by expending a Willpower point, however, a character may attempt to do so. After the point is spent, the normal roll applies.

Storytellers are encouraged to describe thoughts as flowing streams of impressions and images. Rather than using flat statements like "He's planning to kill the captain of the guard," say "You see a fleeting series of visions: Von Mark, the captain of the guard, deep

HALO COLORS

Condition	Halo Colors
Afraid	Orange
Aggressive	Purple
Angry	Red
Bitter	Brown
Calm	Light Blue
Compassionate	Pink
Conservative	Lavender
Depressed	Gray
Desirous or Lustful	Deep Red
Distrustful	Light Green
Envious	Dark Green
Excited	Violet
Generous	Rose
Happy	Vermilion
Hateful	Black
Idealistic	Yellow
Innocent	White
Love	Blue
Obsessed	Green
Sad	Silver
Spiritual	Gold
Suspicious	Dark Blue
Vampire	Appropriate color is pale
Confused	Mottled, shifting colors
Daydreaming	Sharp flickering colors
Diabolist	Black veins in aura
Frenzied	Rapidly rippling colors
Psychotic	Hypnotic, swirling color
Magic Use	Myriad sparkles

in thought; a dagger, larger than any you've ever seen, in your own hands as you advance through the shadows; your own heart, mortal now and hammering with panic as you raise the knife; and above all, the cold fear of discovery." Such descriptions not only add to the story, they also force the player to decide for herself what she reads. Understanding minds — especially the minds of the deranged — can be a difficult and puzzling task.

••••• ANIMA WALK

By expanding her senses beyond her physical shell, the character can step outside her body and travel quickly to any place she can imagine. She may "fly," cross oceans and descend beneath the ground, so long as she remains below the moon's orbit. Through this power, the ancients are said to watch over their childer. Even Caine himself may still walk the world this way....

While the Cainite's *anima*, or mental self, is separated from her body, that husk lies in a torpid state. Anything can happen while the vampire is gone, and she will never know about it until she returns. During the journey, an ephemeral silver cord connects body to mind; if this cord is severed, the *anima* becomes

hopelessly lost in the world of shades. Returning to one's body after such an experience — if possible — is a long and terrifying ordeal. The obvious risks of travel keep many Cainites from leaving "home" for long. Those who dare, however, may discover much.

System: Leaving the material self behind requires a point of Willpower and a Perception + Occult roll (difficulty varies depending on the distance and complexity of the trip, with 7 being average and 10 reflecting a trip far from familiar territory — to unknown Cathay, for example). The better the roll, the easier and more productive the journey is. Failing or botching this roll can have nasty consequences.

Each time the vampire changes her destination, she must roll again; failure indicates that she has lost her way and must retrace the path of her silver cord. A botch at this stage means the cord has snapped and the *anima* is stranded in the mysterious spirit worlds.

An *anima* may travel at great speeds and carries no clothing or material objects of any kind. Some artifacts are said to exist in the spirit world as well, and these may be taken along if they are found. The *anima* is a witness only; it cannot interact with the material world unless the character spends an additional Willpower point to manifest into a ghostlike shape. This lasts one turn, then fades. Auspex powers may be used normally, however.

If two *anima* encounter each other, they interact as if they were solid. They may talk, touch and even fight as if both were still in the material world. Since their bodies have been left behind, two *anima* travelers may try to cut each other's silver cords. When fighting this way, consider Willpower points to be Health Levels; when all of a combatant's Willpower is lost, the cord is severed. Because Physical Traits mean nothing in this state, the character's Mental ones take their place: Dexterity becomes Wits, Manipulation replaces Strength, and Intelligence becomes Stamina.

Although a vampire in this state remains in the reflection of the mortal world (the Penumbra, for those familiar with other World of Darkness games), she may occasionally go farther into the spirit realms, especially if she becomes lost. Some beings, such as werewolves, ghosts and even rare magi, travel the spirit world as well, and can see and affect an *anima* normally. Storytellers are encouraged to make *anima* trips as wild and mysterious as possible. The world of spirit-borders is a vivid and fantastic place where the true nature of things becomes stronger than their earthly appearances.

•••••• FARSIGHT

At this level of ability, distance becomes immaterial to the Cainite. With a minor effort, she can see and hear distant activities without leaving her body. By concentrating upon a given place, thing or person, she may hear or see everything around it as if she were there herself. Naturally, she must be familiar with that place or person before she can spy on it, but immortals have plenty of time to build up such familiarities.

System: The player must make a Perception + Empathy roll (difficulty 6) to home in on her target. Once she finds it, she may use other Auspex powers normally. She might scry a clearing at the edge of her land, heighten her senses to discover the intruder lurking there, and use Soulsight to discover who he is and what he wants. Each power used in this manner must be rolled and accounted for in the normal ways.

CELERITY

For some Cainites, the mortal world moves in slow motion. In times of stress, vampires with Celerity can move with amazing speed, becoming blurs of motion to anyone, mortal or immortal, who does not possess the Discipline.

Celerity is common to the Assamite, Brujah and Toreador clans. The Assamites utilize the Discipline to strike down their foes before they can mount a counterattack. Toreador are more likely to use the Discipline to lend supernatural grace to live performances such as dance, but can be as terrifying as Assamites if they are angered.

System: Characters with Celerity may take multiple actions in a single turn. While anyone can decide to split his Dice Pool during a single turn, a character with Celerity can perform extra actions (including full movement) without penalty.

Each point of Celerity allows up to one extra action, and the vampire may use his entire Dice Pool for each additional action taken. The vampire must spend one Blood Point per extra action taken per turn and may spend a number of Blood Points on this power per turn equal to his Celerity rating. (The normal limits on the expenditure of Blood Points do not affect the use of this Discipline.) For instance, if a vampire has a Celerity of 4 and wishes to take five actions in a single turn, he needs to spend four Blood Points.

CHIMERSTRY

The Ravnos have a well-earned reputation as the masters of trickery and deceit. Beyond their cunning and wit, they have earned this reputation through their Chimerstry Discipline. Chimerstry allows the Ravnos to create compelling illusions and hallucinations that befuddle the senses of others.

Basic illusions may create distractions in market squares or make a copper penny seem to turn into a gold crown. Advanced Chimerstry illusions affect their victims on a deep psychological level, such that an hallucinatory wooden stake could actually hurt a vampire and make her believe she is paralyzed.

Since most people in the Dark Medieval period believe in magic and would not be entirely surprised to see someone conjure an item out of thin air, Chimerstry powers rarely face resistance rolls. Conversely, the same folk who believe in magic have also heard tales of faerie gold and other illusions; pervasive belief in magic engenders skepticism of objects offered by known magicians. When it comes to scaring a peasant lynch mob, an illusion could send superstitious mortals running or could fuel them with religious fervor against the "diabolist."

An illusion cannot be created if the vampire making it cannot sense it. A blindfolded Cainite cannot use Ignis Fatuus to create an image of a sword. However, she can use Dweomer to create one in her hand because she can touch it, and other people could still see, smell, feel, taste and smell the sword.

The Ravnos believe their Chimerstry power originated from drinking the vitæ from the true masters of illusion, the fae. Every time a Ravnos sets out to learn a new Chimerstry power, she must first seek out a faerie and drink its blood. The custom has led to a painful initiation ritual among Ravnos who seek to learn this Discipline. It has also created mixed relationships among the fae and Ravnos clan. Fae who have been attacked for their vitæ

despise the clan, while other fae have traded blood for favors. These favors are bartered among different fae like currency, and some Ravnos end up owing debts of service for hundreds of years to faeries they have never met.

• IGNIS FATUUS

These minor, static illusions affect one sense. Anyone in the area can detect the illusion with that sense, but not with any others. Note that even if an illusion can be detected by touch, it is not really there. Thus, an invisible Ignis Fatuus wall could be touched, just as an illusory slap could be felt, but the wall could not bar a person's passage, nor could an illusory bridge be used to cross a river.

System: An illusion costs one point of Willpower to create, and lasts until the character can no longer sense it, decides to end it or it is seen through in some way. Ending an illusion takes no time or effort and occurs whenever the creator wishes.

• • DWEOMER

An illusion created with this power can be detected by any or all senses, as decided by the creator of the illusion. Once again, the illusion is not really there, and tactile ones can be passed through.

System: Like the illusions created by Ignis Fatuus, these are static and cannot be moved once created. They cost two Willpower points to create and disappear per Ignis Fatuus illusions.

• • • APPARITION

This power is used in conjunction with either of the above powers. Apparition allows the illusion in question to have a full range of motion. This motion appears perfectly natural as long as the vampire maintaining it is familiar with the proper movement of the subject.

System: The creator spends one Blood Point to make an illusion move in one specific way; she can change or stop this motion, but only if she has done nothing save concentrate on the illusion after creating it.

• • • • PERMANENCY

This power, also used with Ignis Fatuus or Dweomer, allows an illusion to continue even when the vampire is not in its presence. Even illusions that have a range of motion through the use of Apparition can be made permanent, though the vampire must first concentrate on the illusion as it goes through the range of motion desired. The illusion then continues to follow this pattern for as long as it exists. Note that this power only affects illusions created by Chimerstry and has no effect on other Disciplines or objects.

System: The vampire need only expend a Blood Point, and the illusion remains intact until dissolved.

• • • • • HORRID REALITY

This power is only effective against one person at a time. Essentially, the victim of Horrid Reality believes completely and totally that the illusion exists. A fake fire burns him, a fake wall bars him passage, and a fake arrow wounds him.

System: A Horrid Reality costs two Willpower points to create. If the vampire attempts to damage a foe with this power, the player must roll Manipulation + Subterfuge (difficulty of the victim's Perception + Self-Control/Instinct). Each success inflicts one Health Level of damage upon the victim, though the character can do less than the full amount if, before the dice are rolled, she announces a maximum amount of damage she wants to inflict. A person cannot actually be killed in this manner, and all injuries disappear once the victim is truly convinced that he has not been harmed (which can and will take a considerable amount of time; assume that the "dead" victim later awakens from unconsciousness to find himself perfectly healthy).

• • • • • • MASS HORROR

This power causes more than one person to experience a Horrid Reality. Anyone in the same general area of the illusion senses it as if it were actually present. Thus, if an illusion of a dragon is created, the dragon can blast its fiery breath on several people.

System: This power works exactly as Horrid Reality, except that multiple targets can be affected. A vampire can generally affect a number of individuals up to her Willpower.

DAIMOINON

This Discipline is included for Storyteller use only; Baali are not known for their ability to work with others and therefore do not make suitable player characters during this period. Their power is that of the Devil himself, and through the use of Daimoinon they draw upon the forces of Hell to demoralize and cripple their enemies. It is for this reason that all Cainites stand united in their hatred of the Baali, whose lust for power threatens to undermine vampire society.

• SENSE THE SIN

It is said that creatures of evil can turn even the most pious man to evil, for does not everyone fear the capacity for sin? This power allows the Baali to see into the soul of his victim, to ferret out her greatest weakness.

System: By making a Perception + Empathy roll against a difficulty of the target's Self-Control/Instinct + 4, the Baali can sense the subject's greatest character flaw, be it a low Virtue, a weak Willpower, a Derangement or whatever. The Storyteller should use discretion should the "flaw" be something without a stat, such as the subject's guilt at having killed her sire.

• • FEAR OF THE VOID BELOW

Through the use of this Discipline, the Baali can send those who listen to her into fits of terror at the damnation that awaits them in the afterlife. This power is feared by pagan and Christian alike, for such is its power that even blasphemers tremble at the Baali's words.

System: The Baali must first use Sense the Sin (above) to discern the tragic flaw of the target. She must then speak to the target, telling him of his inevitable damnation. If the Baali makes a Wits + Intimidation resisted roll against the target's Courage + 4, the victim falls into Rötschreck; if the Baali scores three or more successes, the target collapses in panic.

• • • FLAMES OF THE NETHERWORLD

By using this power, the Baali may hurl blasts of flame at his enemies — a truly spectacular sight which will instantly convince any onlookers that the Baali is indeed a creature of Satan.

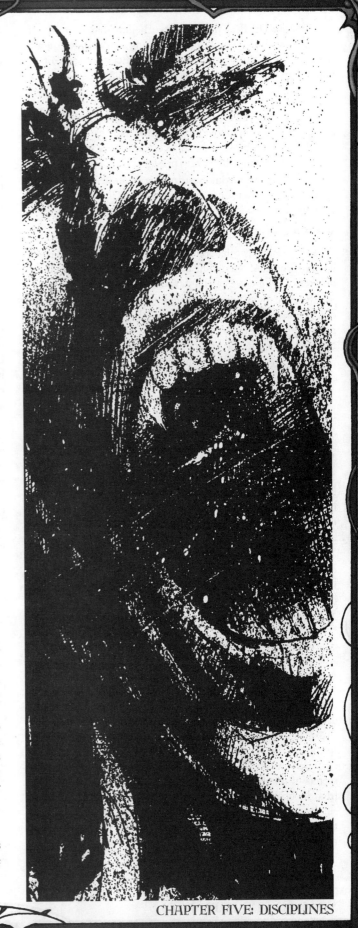

System: The Baali throws blasts of hellfire that do one die of damage per Blood Point spent. Striking an intended target requires a Dexterity + Occult roll with a difficulty dependent on range. This eldritch fire does aggravated damage.

•••• PSYCHOMACHIA

The Baali is able to summon the Beast in an individual. After using Sense the Sin (above) to discern weakness, the Baali can actually coax the Beast to the surface, causing her victim to lose control and become ruled by his passions.

System: The victim must roll his greatest weakness (i.e., lowest Virtue) against a difficulty of 8 or fly into a frenzy; any Derangement possessed by the victim manifests violently.

••••• CURSE

The Baali may call upon his hellish powers to inflict a curse upon his enemies, often disfiguring or crippling them. The Baali may remove this curse at will, should he choose. Few ever do.

System: By making an Intelligence + Occult roll against a difficulty equal to the target's Willpower, the Baali may cast a curse on the target. One of the target's Traits, chosen by the Baali, drops to zero for a duration dependent on the number of successes:

1 success	One night
2 successes	One week
3 successes	One month
4 successes	One year
5 successes	Permanent

•••••• IGNORE THE SEARING FLAMES

At this level of mastery, the Baali is no longer harmed by fire. Her skin may take on a slightly iridescent sheen as it becomes immune to this bane of vampiric existence. Rötschreck check are not required in the presence of flames. Note that the character is still vulnerable to sunlight.

System: The character becomes immune to the damaging effects of fire. A blow with a lit torch or red-hot branding iron still inflicts bludgeoning damage, but the damage is solely from the object itself and not from the fire.

DEMENTATION

To the medieval mind, madness is a curse, or synonymous with demonic possession. The Malkavians know that their madness is a malediction laid on their bloodline by Caine himself. Indeed, some claim that the natural state of vampires is insanity, and that they alone are sufficiently pure of blood to have such divine lunacy. The Discipline of Dementation is an offspring of this madness. Dementation grants a Malkavian the power to spread his lunacy to a victim, drawing the subject into his shattered world. The Malkavians do not zealously guard the secrets of this Discipline; they claim that protecting vampires from lunacy is akin to heresy. In some ways, Dementation is similar to Dominate. The frightening part is that it catalyzes more than it controls, meaning that madness is not so alien to the mortal — or Cainite — mind.

• INCUBUS PASSION

The Cainite using Incubus Passion doubles or triples her victim's emotional intensity. The vampire cannot choose the emotion, merely amplify what is already present. This power works on other Cainites as well as mortals.

System: The player rolls Charisma + Empathy (difficulty of the victim's Via score). The number of successes determines the duration (and, at the Storyteller's discretion, the intensity). Properly timed use of this Discipline increases the target's difficulty to resist frenzy or Rötschreck by one per success, to a maximum difficulty of 10.

1 success	One turn
2 successes	One hour
3 successes	One night
4 successes	One week
5 successes	One month

•• HAUNT THE SOUL

The vampire may stimulate the victim's mind, flooding it with intense visions. The images appear to be fully real, but can only be seen for a second or out of the corner of the eye. The Cainite has no control over what his victim sees, and the visions haunt the unfortunate target for a night, a fortnight or possibly even months. The vivid images visit sporadically, mostly at night and usually when the person is alone. They can be anything from visions of devils and succubi to nightmares from the victim's deepest memory. The Storyteller should let her imagination run wild in describing these visions; St. Anthony's temptation is only one of the possible inspirations for an exciting and disturbing use of Haunt the Soul.

System: The player rolls his Manipulation + Subterfuge (difficulty equal to the victim's Perception + Self-Control/Instinct). The number of successes determines the duration of the period during which visions manifest.

1 success	One night
2 successes	Two nights
3 successes	One week
4 successes	One month
5 successes	Three months

••• EYES OF CHAOS

Through this unusual power, the Malkavian can weigh the taint of sanity on a person. He can perceive another individual's true Nature, although the form such a vision takes varies from Cainite to Cainite. The Eyes of Chaos also reveal the "mark of Caine's purity" on a soul (the Malkavian euphemism for madness). This power reveals the blight of lunacy in its tatterdemalion, oh-so-delicate patterns, even those designs invisible to the most sagacious individuals.

System: The player makes a Perception + Occult roll. The difficulty depends on the intricacy of the soul's pattern and the time the Malkavian has to study it. To discern the Nature of a passing pilgrim requires a 10, but scrying his soul after journeying with him for a week resets the difficulty at 8. Assaying a secretive Cappadocian who is careful to hide all evidence of his doings would be an 8, while discerning the mind behind a code buried in apocryphal scripture would be a 7. The Malkavian can even detect an unseen hand in seemingly random events, such as the circling of bluebottle flies or the patterns of smoke rising from a bonfire (both at difficulty 6). These patterns likely bear no meaning, but might hold the Cainite's attention for hours by their intricate form and possibilities.

•••• CONFUSION

The Cainite may cloud her victim's senses just by making eye contact and conversation. The target loses all sense of time, cannot recall most of his memories, and generally wanders aimlessly until the confusion lifts. The victim often allows himself to be "aided" during this time; this tractableness can lead to a gruesome fate.

System: The vampire must meet her victim's gaze and speak to him, while the player rolls Manipulation + Intimidation (difficulty equal to the target's Perception + Self-Control/Instinct). The duration depends on level of success.

1 success	One turn
2 successes	One hour
3 successes	One night
4 successes	One week
5 successes	One month

••••• HOWLING LUNACY

The vampire with this power may drive his victim, whether serf or saint, mortal or scion of Caine, completely mad. The victim suffers five Derangements (see Page 203) of the Storyteller's choice. To enact this ability, the vampire must gain his victim's undivided attention for at least one turn. Most Malkavians cloak this power amid fervent conversation; more than one hapless wayfarer has stopped to talk with an innocent-seeming hermit, only to flee gibbering into the woods or fall into an unseeing, unhearing stupor.

System: The Player rolls Manipulation + Intimidation (difficulty equal to the victim's Willpower rating). The number of successes determines the duration of the lunacy.

1 success	One turn
2 successes	One night
3 successes	One week
4 successes	One month
5 successes	One year

•••••• KISS OF THE MOON

The Cainite with mastery of this dread power may drive his victims permanently mad. The vampire makes eye contact and speaks quietly to the target, describing the lunacy he wants the victim to manifest. Kiss of the Moon works equally well on vampires and mortals.

System: The player makes a resisted Manipulation + Empathy roll against the victim's current Willpower rating. If the vampire scores at least two successes, the victim takes on a permanent Derangement of the Cainite's choice.

DOMINATE

Dominate is used to control the thoughts and actions of others by superimposing aspects of the controller's will upon her victim. To manipulate the soul of another is thought by many to be tempting fate, and thus many during this era shun those who use Dominate. By removing the victim's free will, the vampire may imperil her own soul. Of course, there are many among the ranks of the undead who do so without compunction or hesitation.

Use of Dominate requires that the vampire capture his victim's eye, and can only be used against one person at a time. Commands must be issued verbally to those under the vampire's sway, which means that a Russian vampire may not give a French princess a command, unless they both speak a single language, whether French or Russian. Certain orders, particularly one-worded, may be given with signs (a pointed finger and stern expression to indicate "Go!"). Latin may be a good common language if both vampire and subject are educated, but will be of little use with the average peasant.

Dominate can only be used against one person at a time. Commands must be issued verbally to those under the vampire's sway. The extent to which control may be extended is determined by the levels of the Discipline.

Cainites who make use of the Dominate Discipline often cast their wills about before ever being Embraced. Their prideful taints were already evident, and were perhaps what drew would-be sires to their next childer. Characters with high Dominate scores may be unable to spend experience points to increase Abilities such as Empathy.

Mortals who can resist Dominate are few. The Church may be the only recourse for most mortals; learned clergymen have written of rituals that make individuals and even whole congregations immune. There is even word of people who bear this divine protection and hunt Cainites.

Restrictions: It is impossible to Dominate another vampire who is of stronger blood — the character must be of a lower generation than the subject for Dominate to be effective. Vampires may resist any attempt at Dominate by spending a Willpower point for each success scored on the Dominate roll. The subject is then immune to attempts at Dominate for the rest of the scene. The target must spend the full Willpower; partial expenditures do no good.

If a Dominate roll botches, the target is rendered immune to future attempts by the same vampire for the rest of the story.

• OBSERVANCE OF THE SPOKEN WORD

By intruding upon a subject's communion with the divine, a Cainite can impose a one-word command which must be instantly obeyed. The command must be clear and unambiguous — run, cough, fall, yawn, laugh, sneeze, burp, follow. If the command is at all confusing, the subject may be slow to respond or clumsy in his performance. The command may be sown into a sentence and stressed like a prominent stitch, concealing the vampire's intent to the ignorant or unwary.

System: The character must make a Manipulation + Intimidation roll (difficulty of the target's Willpower). More successes force the target to act with greater vigor.

•• MURMUR OF THE FALSE WILL

The Cainite can impose false thoughts and revelations upon another mind. The False Will requires intense concentration between vampire and victim, and orders or instructions must be precisely and clearly worded to be carried out. The imposed inspiration may be acted upon immediately, or worldly events may recall it later. Eye contact is required while the command is imposed.

The Cainite's command may be clear and unquestionable, such as "return to the refectory" to "drop your sword." Control can also be protracted and much more subversive. Vampire and victim need look into each other's souls no longer than it takes to make the initial suggestion.

Commands issued cannot force the subject to harm herself or defy her innate Nature. Only one idea may be inspired in a subject at a time.

System: The player must roll Manipulation + Leadership (difficulty equal to the target's Willpower). The number of successes determines how well the suggestion is implanted. At fewer than three successes, the subject cannot be forced to do anything that seems strange to her. The subject might walk outside, but is unlikely to pretend to be a chicken. At fewer than five successes, the suggestion is effective unless heeding it would endanger the subject. A merchant won't pick a fight with someone, but a bravo will in a heartbeat. At five successes, nearly any sort of command can be issued.

••• REVELER'S MEMORY

With this power, a vampire can steal and recreate the memories of another. A subject's mind can be altered only slightly to eliminate memories of meeting or even being fed upon by the vampire, or the vampire can utterly undo the victim's awareness of his self, life and virtues.

Fortunately for the subject, the power is not always completely effective; the victim may remember being bitten, but believe it to have been by an animal in the manor copse. Other times, the victim might recall her altered experiences through a trigger such as an odor or spoken phrase or subconsciously through dreaming.

If another's memories are known to have been altered by use of this power, the Cainite can restore them. Others' falsified memories can also be recognized in this manner. Unfortunately, the vampire cannot use this power on himself.

System: Roll Wits + Subterfuge (difficulty is the target's Willpower score), and then consult the following table to see how much may be done to the subject's memory.

To attempt to uncover removed memories or detect created memories, the character must possess at least the level of Dominate of the vampire who made the alterations, and must roll Wits + Subterfuge (difficulty equal to the Willpower score of the original vampire), gaining more successes than did the character's predecessor.

1 success	Memory loss lasts a day.
2 successes	May remove, but not alter memory.
3 successes	May make slight alterations to memory.
4 successes	May alter or remove entire scene from subject's memory.
5 successes	Whole periods of subject's life may be reconstructed.

•••• LURE OF SUBTLE WHISPERS

Through constant manipulation and subtle temptations, a Cainite may make the subject more pliant to suggestion. Over time, the soul cannot resist the vampire's Dominate and is more resistant to the corrupting efforts of other immortals. Complete control over a victim's mind is no small task, taking weeks or sometimes months to accomplish.

Cainites often fill their servants' heads with subtle whispers and distractions, ensuring these mortals' loyalty. Yet vampires must pay a high price for the souls they purchase: retainers who have been Dominated over time have little passion and certainly no soul. They follow orders in letter rather than spirit; Dominated retainers become like the walking dead.

System: The player must roll Charisma + Leadership (difficulty is the target's Willpower). Conditioning is an extended action. The Storyteller determines in secret how many successes are required, and keeps track of how many are gained. Typically between five to 10 times the subject's Self-Control is required. Only through roleplaying may a player discern whether a target is successfully conditioned.

The subject becomes so completely Dominated that neither the vampire's presence nor eye contact is required to maintain absolute control. He does exactly as he is told as long so he is within earshot of his master. No command roll is necessary, unless the subject is totally isolated from the vampire. Even if a command roll is failed, the subject is still likely to carry out part of the orders given. Additionally, others find the subject more difficult to Dominate, as conditioning raises others' difficulties by two (to a maximum of 10).

••••• VESSEL

This power allows the vampire to perform the atrocity of taking complete control of another's body and mind, making that person the Cainite's vessel. By wholly stealing the mind of another, a Cainite has absolute control over the subject's body, and may use it as freely as he uses his own.

As with the power Lure of Subtle Whispers, such control comes at a price. While the vampire controls his victim, the immortal's body lies motionless, as if in torpor, and defenseless against attacks. Vampires cannot use each other as vessels in this manner. Such control over other vampires is only possible through a Blood Oath.

System: In order to make a vessel of another individual, a character must completely strip away the target's Willpower. The two square off in an opposed roll; the subject rolls Willpower, while the vampire rolls Charisma + Intimidation (difficulty 7 for both). For each success the attacker obtains over the other's total successes, the target loses a point of Willpower. A victory by the subject does nothing but prolong the struggle, for each success provides her with that many extra dice to roll on the next turn. A botch by the attacker, however, makes the subject permanently immune to a character's Dominate attempts.

• • • • • • FEALTY

Fealty allows a vampire to ensure the loyalty of those who voluntarily swear allegiance to her. Whenever a mortal or Cainite freely makes an oath to a vampire who then uses Fealty, the subject is locked into fulfilling the oath to the best of her ability. Whether the subject has false intentions or is sincere but later changes her mind, the oath is binding once it's uttered and Fealty is invoked. The subject is unable to resist upholding the oath, though she may act against the vampire in any matter not covered by the oath.

The Lasombra are said to manipulate their victims into freely making oaths on even the worst deals, and then binding them with Fealty.

System: The player rolls Charisma + Leadership (difficulty is the target's Willpower). The number of successes determines the duration of the Fealty, as follows:.

1 success	One day
2 successes	One week
3 successes	One month
4 successes	One year
5 successes	10 years

FORTITUDE

While all vampires possess a supernatural constitution that allows them to quickly heal injuries to their undead bodies, Cainites who possess the Discipline of Fortitude are able to withstand truly devastating physical punishment without flinching. On the battle-field, these Cainites shrug off sword blows and leap through storms of arrows undeterred. Ventrue have been known to mock opponents during duels by letting themselves be stabbed, just so the Ventrue can trap their opponents' blades and deliver fatal counterattacks.

In addition, whereas most Cainites are very susceptible to sunlight and fire, those with Fortitude are not easily bowed by even these elemental forces.

System: Fortitude provides the ability to resist sunlight and fire. For each level of Fortitude a character possesses, he may roll one die to soak damage from fire and sunlight. A character's rating in Fortitude is also added to his ability to soak other wounds (see Chapter Seven).

MORTIS

This Discipline was developed by the Cappadocians in an attempt to uncover the secrets of death. It seeks to explore many aspects of death, from outright cheating it, to causing it with a single touch. Rumor has it that masters of Mortis are able to defy death itself. Practitioners of Mortis are often consumed with all aspects of death and the afterlife.

• MASQUE OF DEATH

This power allows the vampire or a chosen subject to assume a visage of death. Flesh becomes taut and sallow, and joints grow rigid and stiff. Assuming the appearance of a corpse can be quite useful — if a hunter searches a mortuary for a vampire, he would be likely to ignore one under the effects of this power. The Discipline may also be used as a dreadful curse, causing another to appear as the walking dead.

System: The character assuming this form must simply spend a Blood Point. If attempting to use the power on another, the intended victim must be touched, a Blood Point must be spent, and the player must make a Stamina + Medicine roll (difficulty equal to the victim's Stamina + 3). The effects of this power last until the next dawn or dusk. Characters under the influence of this power subtract two from their Dexterity and Appearance ratings (minimum of 1). A vampire affected by this power may spend two Blood Points to remove its effects.

• • BLIGHT

This power allows the character to cause rapid aging in an opponent. The victim begins to suffer the effects of old age: skin becomes pallid and thin, bones become brittle, and the victim may even begin to experience advanced effects of arthritis or other ailments of the elderly.

System: This power requires the character to touch his opponent. The player must then score a number of successes on a Manipulation + Medicine roll (difficulty of the opponent's Willpower) and expend one point of Willpower. Use of this ability causes the victim to suffer the effects of extreme old age (subtract three from all Physical Attributes, down to minimums of 1). Cainites are affected by this power just as mortals are; it is as if they were Embraced at a later age, though blood can still be spent to increase Attributes.

A mortal who undertakes strenuous activity while under the effects of this power risks heart failure. For each round the mortal maintains such activity, she must make a Stamina roll (difficulty 6), or suffer a heart attack. The effects of this power last until the following dawn or dusk.

• • • AWAKEN

A character who possesses this power can pry himself from death's grip. The character can awaken himself or another vampire who is in torpor.

System: By expending two Willpower Points, the character can attempt to awaken himself or another vampire from torpor. The character must then roll his permanent Willpower (difficulty varies depending upon the target's Via). To obtain the difficulty, subtract the target's Via from 10. Thus, the difficulty to awaken a character with a Via of 6 would be 4. If attempting to awaken another vampire, the character must touch the vampire he intends to awaken. If the subject of this power was driven into torpor due to blood loss, she awakens with one Blood Point.

• • • • DEATH'S WHISPER

For a brief time the character sloughs off Caine's curse. While the character is under the influence of this power he is not affected by any of the traditional banes against vampires. His body is not burned by sunlight, and holy water does not harm him in any way; however, his body becomes nothing more than a corpse. A character who is staked through the heart while under this power is still paralyzed once the power's effects wear off. This state is beyond that of even torpor; the character cannot use Disciplines of any kind, and is unaware of anything that transpires around him. For the duration of the power, he is truly dead.

System: There is no cost to assume this form, although the character must expend two Blood Points to awaken. While the character is in this state he may take no actions whatsoever, and even mental Disciplines may not be used.

●●●●● BLACK DEATH

By touching an individual, the character can cause the victim to experience an early death (or, in the case of vampires, to enter torpor). The victim, if mortal, begins to exhibit signs of plague: sunken and blackened eyes, swollen lymphs and a sickly pallor of the skin. Within one day, all bodily functions cease. Cainite victims of this power enter torpor immediately.

System: The vampire must touch the intended victim, and the player must roll Stamina + Occult (difficulty equal to the target's Willpower) and expend two Willpower points. Success indicates that the vampire has caused his target to expire (or go into torpor).

●●●●●● VIGOR MORTIS

By feeding a corpse some his blood, the Cainite may reanimate the body, creating an undead servant that serves its master until it falls completely into decay. This walking corpse cannot talk (though some have been known to utter a low moan), but is servant to its creator through the Blood Oath.

System: In order to reanimate a corpse, the character must feed it three Blood Points. As soon as the first drop falls onto its lips, the corpse animates and begins to drink of its own accord. This can be a dangerous time for the Cainite, as some corpses have been known to continue feeding after the initial Blood Points have been taken.

A zombie created in the method has the same Physical Attributes as the original person, and the body appears as it did at the time of creation. These creatures do possess some degree of intelligence (lower all mental Attributes by one), but are so overwhelmed by the bond to their masters that they seldom exhibit free thought. They possess three extra Health Levels, do not suffer wound penalties, and are destroyed when they reach Incapacitated.

These automatons crumble to dust on the third sunrise after their creation. The duration of their existence can be extended by feeding the creatures more blood at the time of creation — they remain in existence for one additional day for each additional Blood Point spent.

OBFUSCATE

The Devil, it is said, can hide himself from even the honest man's sight. Certain Cainites may conceal themselves from mortal vision through this uncanny power. By simply wishing to remain unseen, a vampire skilled in Obfuscate can disappear, even if he stands in full view of a crowd. Although his substance stays the same, any observers who might see him are deluded into thinking that he has vanished. Nor do the deceptions stop there. This Discipline's more potent applications include changing faces, concealing other people and objects, or even hiding one's true thoughts behind a mask.

Although several clans use this power, it stands as the hallmark of the hideous Nosferatu. Common lore suggests that Caine, or even God Himself, was so affronted by the original Nosferatu's appearance that He cloaked the childe in secrecy so that He would not have bear the sight of him. A lesser-known legend tells of Lilith's motherly

compassion for her disfigured foster son. Through her arts, she taught him to hide from his own reflection. Whatever the origin of this power, the Nosferatu are most closely associated with its mastery.

Obfuscate and Auspex oppose each other. When a vampire attempts to use her heightened perceptions to discover a hidden opponent, she sees him if her Auspex rating is higher than his Obfuscate. If his Obfuscate outranks her Auspex, he remains undiscovered. If the two are equal, both vampires make a resisted roll of Perception + Subterfuge (Auspex) verses Manipulation + Subterfuge (Obfuscate). The difficulty for the roll is 7, and the character with the most successes wins.

Under most circumstances, few mortals can penetrate Obfuscate's devilish disguise. Many animals, however, may sense (and fear) the vampire's presence, even if they cannot see him. Children, saints and other innocents might also be able to pierce this dark art, at the Storyteller's option.

• CLOAK OF SHADOWS

A Cainite who has not yet mastered the art of deception may warp nearby shadows to cover his presence. In well-lit rooms, the vampire can hide behind more solid obstacles like tapestries, furniture and shrubbery. Since shadows are exceedingly common in this candlelit world, finding suitable cover is rarely a problem. So long as something exists that a person could hide within (or behind), the Obfuscating vampire may remain hidden.

Once concealed, the Cainite must stand silent and still. If he moves, attacks or falls under direct light, the Cloak disappears and the creature stands revealed. The deception also cannot stand close observation without fading.

System: If the character fulfills the criteria above, no roll is necessary. So long as he remains quiet and motionless, no one but a vampire with a high Auspex rating can see him.

•• UNSEEN PRESENCE

With a bit of experience, the vampire can move around without being seen. Shadows seem to cling to him, and others avert their eyes as he passes by. Unless someone deliberately seeks out the Cainite, he stays out of mind as well as sight. People look away without realizing they have done so, and often scurry off in nameless fear. So long as the vampire disturbs nothing, he may come and go as he pleases, staying out of sight indefinitely.

System: Again, no roll is necessary unless the character speaks, attacks or otherwise draws attention to himself. If he wants to cross a squeaky floor, tangled underbrush, water or some other surface that might show where he's been, the player may have to make a Wits + Stealth roll to determine how well the vampire avoids a disturbance. Speaking without giving one's position away demands three successes or more.

••• MASK OF A THOUSAND FACES

The Cainite with this power may masquerade as someone else! This tactic is a favorite Malkavian trick. Although the vampire's body itself does not change, any observer who cannot sense the truth sees whomever the Cainite wishes him to see.

System: The player rolls Manipulation + Acting (difficulty 7) to determine how well the disguise works. If the vampire tries to be someone else, it helps to know some facts about that person. This is a more intimate age than the modern day, after all; when someone shares a room with his friends or family, it is difficult to impersonate him to their satisfaction. For especially difficult deceptions, like fooling a lover, lieutenant or manservant, some bit of personal knowledge or habit may be essential.

1 success	The vampire looks much the same as he always does, with slight differences.
2 successes	He looks somewhat different; people don't easily recognize him or agree about his appearance.
3 successes	He appears the way he wants to appear.
4 successes	Gestures, mannerisms, appearance and voice completely transform.
5 successes	He may masquerade as someone of the opposite sex or of a vastly different age or size.

•••• VANISH FROM THE MIND'S EYE

This power is so advanced that the Cainite who knows it may disappear from plain view. Even if he stands face-to-face with some other person, he may simply fade away whenever he chooses. All but the most jaded mortals would be stunned for a turn or two if the person in front of them suddenly disappeared; one or two among a large group might be able to react. Most people simply panic. Especially weak-willed peasants or serfs wipe the memory of the character from their minds, or cross themselves with fear and hide away. Although vampires are not shaken so easily, even the undead may be disconcerted if a companion vanishes this way.

System: The player rolls his character's Charisma + Stealth to activate this power. The roll's difficulty equals the target's Wits + Alertness (use the highest one in the group if he disappears in front of a crowd). With more than three successes, the vampire disappears completely. With three or fewer, the character fades but does not vanish, becoming an indistinct, ghostlike figure. If the player scores more successes than an observer's Willpower rating, that person forgets that the vampire exists at all. So long as he does nothing to refresh the observer's memory, she will recall him only in vague and tortured dreams.

••••• CLOAK THE GATHERING

By extending his deceptions to cover a large area, the Cainite may conceal others the way he once disguised himself. Any Obfuscate power may be bestowed upon others nearby if the vampire wants to do so.

As with anything, there is a price attached: any protected person who compromises the Cloak exposes himself to view. If the one who invokes the Discipline gives himself away, the Cloak falls and everyone becomes visible. Tales tell of small armies hidden this way during interclan warfare; when the Nosferatu masters withdrew their veils, screaming ghoul warriors charged into battle, often behind enemy walls. It's said that many Ventrue forbid this practice within their domains.

System: The vampire may conceal one extra individual for each dot of Stealth he possesses. Each power must be accounted for in the usual ways (see above), but one roll counts for everyone.

•••••• SOUL MASK

Not all disguises run skin-deep. With this advanced power, the vampire may conceal his soul-halo from another's Soulsight. Although it works in all ways like the Mask of a Thousand Faces ability, the Soul Mask disguises the character's true nature, not his features. If it suits him, he may appear mortal, innocent or more corrupt than a thousand Vandals.

System: The player may choose only one "disguise" color per time he purchases this power. If he wants his halo to appear blue-white, for instance, it will be blue-white every time he uses the Soul Mask. To change his color to red, he must buy this power a second time. Otherwise, it works like the Mask of a Thousand Faces. Low rolls only tint the halo's true color, not conceal it entirely.

OBTENEBRATION

This disturbing Discipline is practiced primarily by the Lasombra, for they desire nothing less than power over all things, even over the primordial abyss itself. Certainly, this power smacks of sinister, pre-Christian forces, and few outside the Lasombra clan would dare to wield powers of such problematic origin.

Obtenebration allows its practitioner to evoke a strange force of "living darkness," the very stuff of shadow made tangible. The exact source of this amorphous blackness is a subject of great debate among the clan. Some Lasombra speculate of a great abyss surrounding the planetary spheres, perhaps Hell, perhaps pagan Stygia, perhaps something else entirely. Others, particularly those on the Via Diabolis, sneeringly rebut that the darkness is nothing more than the manifestation of its wielder's sin-tarnished soul.

This Discipline is exceedingly unnatural and intimidating to most of God's creatures. Protracted use of Obtenebration almost inevitably sends normal animals into a panic, and mortals must often make Courage rolls upon confronting Obtenebration effects. Areas blanketed with Obtenebration often lose their color, becoming bleached or stained.

The competitive Lasombra often view their use of this Discipline as a "struggle for supremacy" with the forces of the outer darkness. Lasombra who employ Obtenebration overmuch sometimes find their steps haunted by mocking shades, and some ambitious Lasombra have been known to disappear forever into the shadows they have summoned.

• SHADOW PLAY

The vampire can manipulate shadows, shroud areas, dim (though not extinguish) ambient illumination, and play other "tricks of the light." Among other things, this allows the vampire to warp or erase her own shadow, cloak herself or make her silhouette more intimidating.

System: The vampire must spend a Blood Point to evoke the power. The difficulties of all Intimidation and Stealth rolls the vampire makes are reduced by one, and the difficulty to be hit by missile weapons increases by one (the shifting shadows throw off depth perception).

Additionally, this power is very disconcerting to mortals and animals. Whenever this power is used in a mortal's vicinity, that mortal must make a Courage roll (difficulty 8) or reduce all Dice Pools by one due to creeping unease. Once a particular mortal has

successfully made a Courage roll against this power, he need never do so again. Animals always lose a die and never overcome their fear; indeed, most animals flee on exposure to this power.

•• Nocturne

The vampire may blanket a swath of ground or sky with an impenetrable inky darkness. This darkness is deeper than a moonless night; only the subterranean caverns of inner earth compare to it. Beings swallowed by this viscous matter find it greatly disorienting and unnerving.

System: The vampire may automatically cloak a 10-foot-diameter area (more or less — the darkness constantly roils, seethes and extends "psuedopods"). The power can be projected to a range in yards equal to 10 times the vampire's Perception + Occult total. Each success with a Manipulation + Occult roll (difficulty 7) enables the vampire to double the diameter of the power. The darkness extinguishes light and even obscures sound; most opponents are completely blinded and disoriented, and even those with Heightened Senses or Witness of Darkness suffer three-dice penalties to most actions. Furthermore, mortals and animals swathed in the pitchy stuff must make Courage rolls as under Shadow Play, above, or panic.

If the vampire uses the power to envelop a flame or flames (torches, a hearth fire, etc.) and spends a Willpower point (more for pyres and conflagrations), he can actually douse the flames.

••• Arms of Ahriman

The vampire can summon one or more "tentacles" of solid darkness from a shadowy area. These tentacles may grasp, restrain or even constrict foes.

System: A Manipulation + Occult roll (difficulty 7) must be made; each success enables one tentacle to be evoked. A tentacle is six feet long and has Strength and Dexterity scores equal to the vampire's Obtenebration rating; Blood Points may be spent ("fed" to the tentacles) to increase these parameters (each Blood Point spent increases Strength by one, Dexterity by one or length by six feet). A tentacle does Strength + 1 crushing damage, has four Health Levels and takes damage from fire and sunlight.

•••• Nightshades

The vampire may evoke shadowy illusions. These illusions are monochromatic and murky, but may be of anything: the vampire himself, monsters, walls, etc. The illusions are human-sized, but successes may be spent to create larger images. Alternatively, the vampire may use this power to infest an area with a chaotic saraband of whirling shadows, disorienting all in the vicinity.

System: Each success on a Wits + Occult roll (difficulty 7) allows the vampire to evoke one Nightshade or double the size of a previously evoked Nightshade.

Alternatively, the vampire may blanket the scene with flitting, writhing shadows. All in the turmoil who do not possess Obtenebration increase initiative difficulties by three and suffer a one-die penalty to all Dice Pools. Additional successes allow the vampire to direct the Nightshades more precisely, perhaps sparing allies or leaving certain areas unshrouded.

••••• Tenebrous Form

The vampire can turn her body into a slithering, undulating shadow. Vampires in this form are virtually invulnerable, may slither through the narrowest cracks, and may see in the deepest darkness.

System: Three Blood Points must be expended to use the power, and the change takes three turns to occur. The vampire is immune to physical attack, but may not physically attack others (though she may wrap around and ooze over victims like a vast, probing slime mold; such contact is extremely disconcerting and may prompt a Courage roll to avoid panic). Fire and sunlight still inflict normal damage, and indeed are more painful to vampires in this form; all difficulties to avoid Rötschreck from these banes increase by one so long as the vampire maintains this form.

•••••• Walk the Abyss

The vampire may step into a human-sized or larger shadow and exit another (of similar size) at another location. He may also reach into a shadow and have his hand and forearm protrude through another shadow at a different location — for example, to grab a victim or object resting near the other shadow. Once grasped, the object may be jerked through the "destination" shadow to the vampire's own.

System: The vampire must decide his exit point and inform the Storyteller. Successfully traveling anywhere requires an Intelligence + Stealth roll (difficulty 6), while successfully pulling someone/something through requires an Intelligence + Brawl roll (difficulty 7; one success needed to grasp, two successes needed to pull the victim through). Failing the roll means the vampire goes/reaches nowhere; a botch means *something* from the abyss comes out.

The vampire may travel/reach a maximum distance equal to five yards times his Intelligence + Stealth total. Additionally, anyone who travels (or is pulled through) the "abyss" must make a Courage roll (difficulty 5 for the power user, 6 for a willing traveler, 8 for a hapless victim) or enter panic/Rötschreck upon reemergence.

Potence

Vampires with the Potence Discipline possess physical strength beyond mortal bounds. Potence allows vampires to leap great distances, lift massive weights and strike opponents with terrifying force. Vampire nobles have been known to break open fortress gates with their bare hands and cut war horses in two with one stroke of a greatsword. In an age when military matters boil down to the clashing of sword against sword, a knight with the strength of 10 men can turn the tide of battle.

Members of Clans Brujah, Lasombra and Nosferatu often possess the Potence Discipline, although almost every clan finds some use for it. Some Nosferatu believe that they will temporarily lose their superhuman strength if they do not periodically dine on the vitæ of oxen, bears or similar physically powerful animals.

System: The character's rating in Potence provides her with automatic successes on nearly all Strength rolls — one automatic success per rating point. Thus she can succeed at most Strength feats automatically without needing to make a roll at all. In melee and brawling combat, the automatic successes count on the damage roll.

Presence

This is the Discipline of supernatural attraction. With it, the Cainites raise mobs, lead armies and sway the opinions of the highest in the land. Presence is a subtle power, and while it has disadvantages, it is one of the most useful Disciplines a vampire can have.

First, quite aside from its deliberate uses, Presence conveys upon the vampire an indescribable mystique. Whatever her class or appearance, the Cainite is always noticed, even by those above her station. In fact, it is quite easy for viewers to believe that she is actually from a social position a step or two above that which she seems — but the façade needs to be bolstered by the right mode of speech and proper courtesies. In the Dark Ages, etiquette is more important to a disguise than looks, and Presence is most useful to those who can shift their manners to fit the audience.

Second, some of these powers can be used on entire crowds of people at once. The vampire's face must be clearly visible to whomever she wishes to affect, but unlike Dominate eye contact is not required.

Third, Presence transcends race, religion, gender, class and (most importantly) generation. The vampire's basic noticeability works on anyone, and the active powers have as much chance (in theory) to work on a Methuselah as on the local blacksmith. In practice, the older and tougher the Cainite, the more likely he is to realize what is being attempted, and resist.

Anyone can resist Presence for a turn by spending a Willpower point, but the affected person must continue spending points until she is no longer watching the vampire. The simplest way to deal with this is to turn around and stop looking. Normal humans in this time will not think of this, though pagans and other wisely superstitious folk have signs that ward off the "evil eye" by covering both of their own.

The major drawback of this Discipline is that it controls only the emotions. The reason and the will are both left intact, and the Cainite cannot give direct verbal orders to those affected. Though the peasantry might follow commands, most free mortals will not, and the resentment the commands engender may mean losing control. However, persuasion of the long-winded or monetary variety is very useful when combined with Presence, and the Ventrue, at least, are adept at using Presence and Dominate in efficient combination.

• Awe

Awe is very simple. Once the vampire employs this power, those who are near her want to be closer to her. It is an immediate and intense attraction, but not so overpowering that those affected lose their sense of self-preservation.

Danger breaks the spell of fascination, as does leaving the area. Victims will remember how they felt, though, and this will affect their reactions should they ever encounter the vampire again.

Awe is extremely useful in mass communication. It does not matter what is said — the hearts of those affected will lean toward the user's opinion. The weak want to agree with the vampire; the strong-willed soon find themselves outnumbered.

System: The player must roll Charisma + Acting (difficulty 7). Those affected can use Willpower points to overcome the effect, but must continue spending Willpower every few minutes for as long as they remain in the same area as the character. However, as soon as a number of Willpower points equal to the number of successes rolled is spent, the Awe is completely shaken off, and the subject can't be affected for the rest of the scene.

The number of successes rolled also determines how many people can be affected:

1 success	One person
2 successes	Two people
3 successes	Six people
4 successes	20 people
5 successes	Everyone in the vampire's immediate vicinity (e.g., an entire church or audience chamber)

•• DREAD GAZE

This power engenders unbearable terror in its victims. Dread Gaze, like the legendary hypnotism of the cobra, stupefies the victim into madness, immobility or reckless flight.

To use this power, the vampire merely shows the mark of Caine upon him — baring claws and teeth, hissing loudly and with malice. Any vampire can do this, but students of this Discipline are more insanely terrifying than mere sight can explain.

System: The player must roll Charisma + Intimidation (difficulty is the victim's Wits + 3). Any success indicates that the target is cowed, while three or more successes indicate that he runs away in fear. Moreover, each success subtracts one from the number of dice the victim is allowed to roll the next turn.

This roll may only be attempted once per turn, though if performed in successive turns, the vampire may collect successes as an extended roll in order to subjugate the target completely. Eventually the target may lose so many dice that he becomes unable to do anything but curl up on the ground and weep. Failure indicates that the attempt has faltered. All collected successes are lost, the victim may act normally again and the player must start over next turn. A botch indicates the victim is not at all impressed, and any further use of Presence by the character is ineffective against him this story.

••• ENTRANCEMENT

This power turns others into the Cainite's willing servants. Out of what seems to them true and enduring devotion, those affected heed the vampire's every desire and command. They retain their creativity and free will.

These spirited, obedient minions are more pleasant than the mind-slaves created by Dominate, but somewhat unpredictable. In addition, the uncertain duration of the effect can be troublesome. The disenchanted are also often displeased. Wise Cainites either dispose of those they Entrance or bind them more securely by a Blood Bond, made much easier by the minion's willingness to serve.

System: The player must roll Appearance + Empathy (difficulty of the target's Willpower) to Entrance a subject . The number of successes determines how long the victim is Entranced. There is no way to extend a period of Entrancement.

1 success	One hour
2 successes	One day
3 successes	One week
4 successes	One month
5 successes	One year

•••• SUMMON

With this power, a Cainite can call to herself any person she has ever met, across any distance. The summoned one comes, perhaps not knowing why, as fast as he is able. He knows exactly how to find the summoner, though not until he is about to take each step. If the vampire moves between calls, the summoned one goes to the new location — he is coming to the vampire, not following orders to meet the Cainite at a specific place.

Though this ability is very powerful, it is more useful locally. While a vampire in England could summon her bondsman back from the Crusades, the journey from the Holy Land might take years. Though a loyal servant could be trained to continue the journey after only one call, in order to bring anyone else, the Cainite would need to Summon every night until the person arrives. Class distinctions are also a factor; if the subject has no great resources at his disposal, the journey will take longer. The only good news is that it is possible (in theory) for the poor bondsman to walk and swim from any corner of the "known" world to any other corner.

System: The player must roll Charisma + Subterfuge. Normally the difficulty for a Summon roll is 5, but if the subject is a stranger, the difficulty increases to 7. If the Cainite has successfully used the Presence Discipline on the subject in the past, then the difficulty is only 4, but if the target previously resisted the vampire's Presence attempt it is an 8. The number of successes indicates the subject's reaction:

1 success	Target approaches, but slowly and hesitantly.
2 successes	Target approaches reluctantly and is easily thwarted by obstacles.
3 successes	Target approaches with reasonable speed.
4 successes	Target comes with haste, overcoming any obstacles in his way.
5 successes	Target rushes to the character, doing anything to get to him.

••••• MAJESTY

This power heightens the general Presence mystique a thousandfold. The beautiful become paralyzingly lovely; the hideous become positively demonic. The Cainite inspires respect, devotion, fear or all in almost everyone who sees her. Serfs obey without thinking, free men treat her with the deference due royalty, and royalty parley with her as an equal, at the very least. No one who is affected would dare risk the vampire's displeasure by touching her least garment, let alone her person.

Under the influence of Majesty, hearts break, power trembles, and the strong-willed shake. The wise use it with caution; the kine must keep face just as the Cainites must. Once cowed in public, a king is useless as a tool. As for the Cainites… a vampire remembers humiliation longer than even dragons do. Vengeance lives for centuries.

System: The subject must make a Courage roll (difficulty is the character's Charisma + Intimidation) if she wishes to be rude, crass or even nonservile to the vampire. A subject who fails the roll will go to absurd lengths to humble herself before the vampire. Kindred may spend a point of Willpower to overcome such feelings if the roll is failed.

•••••• Passion

This power allows the vampire to create wild passions within an individual. It is usually used either to inspire love or to incite the victim to rage. When inspiring love, the power works similar to Entrancement, but is much more compelling. This power duplicates the effects of a Blood Oath for as long as the target is in the presence of the character. Alternatively, the vampire may induce feelings of irritation and hostility in those around him. The slightest spark provokes arguments and fights.

System: Successful use of this power requires a Manipulation + Subterfuge roll (difficulty of the target's Willpower). If successful, the power allows the character an immense amount of influence over the victim. This power affects a variable number of targets depending on the number of successes.

If this power is used to incite rage, all vampires who are affected must spend a Willpower point or immediately fall into a frenzy. If the character again rolls successfully, another Willpower point must be spent each turn in the character's presence. The only way to avoid the need to spend a Willpower point is to leave the vampire's presence.

1 success	Two people
2 successes	Four people
3 successes	Eight people
4 successes	20 people
5 successes	Everyone in the character's immediate vicinity

Protean

This Discipline allows a vampire to manipulate the base element of her being — her body. Perhaps this power is a worldly reflection of the vampire's eternal mark — just as Caine's curse sets his disciples' souls apart from those of God's children, so it sets his disciples' bodies apart. A vampire can thus show the signs of the Beast and become akin to the very earth and air.

Vampires with the Protean Discipline can grow claws, assume the forms of wolves and bats, change into mist and meld into the earth. Most other Disciplines are still useful while changing form, but some clearly are not. A Cainite in wolf form can read auras and communicate with other animals, but a Cainite in mist form cannot use Dominate because no eye contact is possible. In all cases of shapechanging, clothes and personal items change along with a vampire, but other beings and large objects cannot be affected — heaven's protection of its own?

A vampire that has been staked and its soul trapped within the mortal coil cannot transform, though some Cainites claim that the truly powerful among them — those at higher levels of the Discipline — can.

• WITNESS OF DARKNESS

The Cainite is able to see normally after sunset, without torchlight, and can even perceive things hidden in the darkest caves. When this power is used, the vampire's Beast makes itself evident in his red, glowing eyes. Mortals have pronounced the effect, perhaps accurately, "the evil eye."

System: No roll is made, but it takes one full turn for the change to occur.

•• TALONS OF THE BEAST

The vampire can sprout long claws on each hand, like those of a beast. The claws can rend flesh and armor; even a doughty knight should be wary. The wounds inflicted are aggravated and cannot be healed through the expenditure of Blood Points. Some Cainites have been seen to bleed from the palms when this power is summoned, the blood pooling in the shape of a pentagram.

System: No rolls need be made; the transformation is automatic, requiring only a turn to occur. One Blood Point must be spent each time claws are grown.

••• INTERRED IN THE EARTH

This power allows a Cainite to meld with and become one with the earth. Some elders claim that because vampires defy death, they can defy the rightful order of things. Onlookers see vampires with this power actually sink into the bare ground.

Though a Cainite can wholly enter the ground, she cannot move around within it. She must also be in direct contact with bare earth. Even if the ground lies beneath a castle floor, she cannot pass through the floor to enter the soil beyond.

Outdoors, away from haven and resting place, a vampire can find full protection from daylight by interring her body. Perhaps out of respect for God's order, some vampires sleep within the earth for centuries as if attempting to find a proper death. Yet, many seem to mock death, for in sleeping below they gain power and strength. Like foolish, prattling peasants, some Cainites whisper that thousands of Ancients sleep below the ground, waiting to awaken on the night of Gehenna.

Surely the power to descend into the earth is absolute proof of Cainites' damnation — sinking into Hell to receive Lucifer's direct commands.

System: No roll is necessary and the transformation is automatic, but a Blood Point must be spent.

•••• FORM OF THE BEAST

A vampire with this power may transform into a wolf or bat. In animal form, he retains his own morals but can call upon the wiles and abilities of the beast — increased senses for wolf and flight for bat. It is rumored that other forms are possible for vampires from distant lands, and for some few among the known Cainite world. An Egyptian vampire might transform into a cat or jackal; others have been known to assume the forms of stags and vermin.

System: No roll is required, but the transformation requires the expenditure of one Blood Point. It takes three turns to complete the transformation (though the Storyteller may allow it in one turn with the expenditure of three Blood Points).

VAMPIRE: THE DARK AGES

•••• Body of Spirit

Cainites dispute the origins and meaning of this power. Many elders, often those Embraced before hearing the word of Christ, maintain that Cainites who know their true selves are able to transcend their bodies and become one with their spirits, forming a very mist in the air. Some vampires Embraced more recently, and who are still true to Church and God, insist that the Damned are not completely forsaken — that the ability to become mist is proof of a soul, whether barred from Heaven or still capable of penance.

Regardless of its source, vampires with this power can turn into mist. They may float at a brisk pace and may slip under doors, down flues and through sack-clothed windows. Furthermore, sunlight inflicts one fewer die of damage on vampires in mist form.

The vampire's ability to resist powerful winds perhaps demonstrates that mist encompasses a spirit or soul. Even storm winds flail vainly when striving to tear apart a Cainite. Yet those same winds can drive the vampire from her chosen path, like a leaf from a tree.

System: No roll is required, but the transformation requires the expenditure of one Blood Point. It takes three turns to complete the transformation (though the Storyteller may allow it to take place in only one turn with the expenditure of three Blood Points). Strong winds may buffet the vampire about; she may use Potence, and only Potence, to resist.

•••••• Blissful Slumber

Vampires of great will or conviction are able to sleep in mist form. The power offers great protection, but the vampire cannot be roused by noises or commotion surrounding her resting place. Only a breeze that disturbs her can wake her.

System: No roll is required, but the transformation requires the expenditure of five Blood Points when the vampire rests. Mist form is retained until the vampire rises again, whereupon physical form is resumed. Physical attacks cannot affect a vampire sleeping in mist form, but the vampire cannot awaken before dusk unless her mist form is physically disturbed.

Quietus

The unlife of an Assamite centers around two things: silent death and the power of blood. The clan's Discipline of Quietus embodies these, endowing the Assamite *hashashiyyin* (assassin) with mystic powers to further the clan's fanatical cause.

Storytellers and players of **Vampire: The Masquerade** will note differences in this version of Quietus. This is the Discipline as it was practiced before the Tremere laid the ritual that prevented the Assamites from committing diablerie. Storytellers running modern **Vampire** chronicles may wish to use this version for the Assamite *antitribu*.

• Silence of Death

Many Assamite *hashashiyyin* claim never to have heard their Cainite victims' final screams before their blood is released to strengthen the clan. When invoked, Silence of Death surrounds the Assamite with preternatural calm. No sound originates from the area directly around the vampire. Nothing — not footfalls, doors creaking open, bed curtains rustling or Final Death screams

can break the utter stillness that surrounds the Assamite. However, sounds originating outside the power's area of influence travel normally into the area.

System: Activation of this power evokes complete silence in the area immediately surrounding the Assamite. Generally, a small room (about 15 feet square) can be blanketed with silence. This power costs one Blood Point to create and lasts approximately an hour per activation.

•• Weakness

Assamites have developed control over mystic properties of Cainite blood. They are able to change the properties of their own blood and utilize them to create an arsenal of deleterious effects on mortals and other Cainites.

The power of Weakness allows an Assamite to transform his own blood into poison and infect the body of his victim. The Assamite simply chooses a portion of his body, usually the palm, and some of his blood instantly seeps out onto the surface of his skin and transmutes itself into the Weakness toxin. As soon as the Assamite can press the toxin to the flesh of his prey, it infects the victim and robs her of her vigor.

System: Successful use of this power requires that the Assamite touch the victim (usually via hand contact), spend one Blood Point and succeed in a Willpower roll (difficulty equal to the target's Stamina + Fortitude). If successful, the victim loses one point of Stamina. The number of successes scored on the roll determines how long the Stamina is lost.

1 success	One turn
2 successes	One hour
3 successes	One day
4 successes	One month
5 successes	Permanently (though Stamina can be bought back up with experience)

If a mortal is reduced to zero Stamina by this power, she becomes very sick and loses her immunities to disease. If a Cainite is reduced to zero Stamina by this power, she immediately enters torpor and does not recover until one of her Stamina points returns. If all a Cainite's Stamina is permanently destroyed, she may only recover from torpor through mystical means.

••• Disease

This power is similar to Weakness, only more devastating. Both mortals and Cainites may fall ill at the Assamite's touch, as their lifeblood trickles out their ears, noses and mouths. Victims become disoriented, as many in the grip of fever do, and may show signs of illness long after their afflictor leaves.

System: To use the Disease power, the attacker must expend three Blood Points, touch his foe and make a Willpower roll (difficulty of the opponent's Willpower). If successful, the victim loses one point from all three Physical Attributes. The number of successes indicates the duration of this power's effects (per Weakness, above). If either Strength or Dexterity is reduced to zero, the target cannot move until a point of one or the other is recovered. The effects on Stamina are equivalent to those of Weakness.

•••• Blood Agony

Other Cainites fear the weapons of the Assamite, and with just cause. Blood Agony allows an Assamite to poison any weapon with his own blood. This blood-turned-poison causes aggravated wounds to any Cainite struck by the coated weapon. In the midst of pitched melee, Assamites are often seen licking their own daggers, thereby cutting their tongues and bleeding onto their weapons.

Blood Agony works on almost any bladed weapon, from daggers to swords to spears, or even fingernails. Weapons like arrowheads, however, will not be able to hold the blood, especially in flight.

System: Weapons coated using Blood Agony inflict damage normally, but each wound inflicted is an aggravated one. Each extra Blood Point used on a weapon allows that weapon to inflict aggravated wounds on an additional hit. Thus if an Assamite spent two Blood Points coating his broadsword, he could hit once and inflict aggravated damage, miss and then hit again for aggravated wounds. No more hits would cause this sort of damage until he again coats the blade. Note that if a character hits but does no damage, the blood is used but no aggravated wounds are inflicted. Smaller weapons may not be able to hold more than one Blood Point at a time, at the Storyteller's discretion.

••••• Blood Essence

Blood Essence allows Assamites to diablerize their victims without themselves feeding upon and sucking out the final essence of those victims. The Assamite may bleed his victim's vitæ into any suitable container and use Blood Essence to draw out the victim's life force so that it flows with the blood into the container. Any Cainite who subsequently drinks the entire contents of the Blood Essence draught gains the benefits as if he had directly diablerized the victim. Unfortunately, the potency of Blood Essence draughts only lasts for a few days after drawn from the victim.

System: Instead of the normal Strength roll required to "bleed" the last Health Levels from a diablerized victim, the character must instead succeed in an extended Willpower roll (difficulty 9), accumulating enough successes to deplete the remaining Health Levels of the victim. Once the victim expires, the collected blood has its full potency.

•••••• Blood Sweat

The Assamite master of Quietus is able to command the blood of another vampire, causing a Cainite victim to lose large quantities of vitæ through profuse sweating. Not only does the

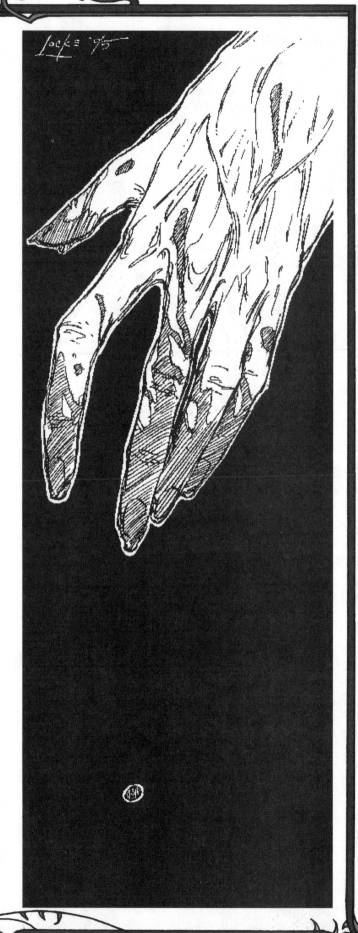

Retain the Quick Blood

Quietus 3, Celerity 3

Assamites who achieve some mastery of Quietus and Celerity are said to have developed control over the vitæ they use to give them speed. Those who master this ability are able to recover the blood spent inducing speed through Celerity.

Any blood spent by the Assamite to buy extra actions through Celerity returns to the Assamite's Blood Pool as if it had never been used. Blood Points are restored at the rate of one per hour. This power costs 15 experience points.

victim lose valuable vitæ, but sweating blood at inopportune moments can create all kinds of social difficulties in the religiously zealous Dark Ages.

System: The vampire must be able to see the target, and must successfully roll Willpower (difficulty of the target's Stamina + 3). The number of successes signifies the number of Blood Points the target loses. The blood drains from the target's body at a rate of two Blood Points per round, to the maximum indicated by the dice. A mortal target who is reduced to two or fewer Blood Points dies as a result of blood loss. A Cainite target risks frenzy or Rötschreck (the former if Self-Control/Instincts is lower than Courage, the latter if the reverse is true) from blood loss.

SERPENTIS

Serpentis is the legacy of Set, his gift to his children. The Followers of Set carefully guard this Discipline's secrets, teaching the art of corruption only to those they deem worthy (almost never outsiders). Most Cainites fear the Setites purely because of this Discipline, the way of the serpent and the tempter. Serpentis can evoke an almost primordial fear in others, particularly those who recall the tale of Eden. After all, hiss the Setites, the serpent was an evil older than even Caine himself.

• THE EYES OF THE SERPENT

This power grants the Setite the legendary hypnotic gaze of the serpent. The Setite's eyes become gold with large black irises, and mortals in the character's vicinity find themselves strangely attracted to him. A mortal who meets the vampire's beguiling gaze is immobilized. Until the character takes his eyes off his mortal victim, the person is frozen in place.

System: No roll is required, but this power can be avoided if the mortal takes care not to look into the Setite's eyes. Vampires and other supernatural creatures (Lupines, mages, et al.) can also be affected by this power if the Setite makes a Willpower roll (difficulty 9).

•• THE TONGUE OF THE ASP

The Setite may lengthen her tongue at will, splitting it into a fork like that of a serpent. The tongue may reach 18 inches and makes a terrifyingly effective weapon in close combat.

System: The tongue's razor fork opens aggravated wounds (difficulty 6, Strength damage). If the Setite wounds her enemy, she may drink blood from the target on the next turn as though she had sunk her fangs into the victim's neck. Horrifying though it is, the tongue's caress is very like the Kiss, and even strikes mortal victims helpless with fear and ecstasy.

••• BITUMENOUS FLESH

This power allows the user to mummify herself, shriveling into an almost invulnerable form. Bitumenous Flesh induces a state similar to torpor; only sunlight and fire can harm the mummified Setite. However, the character is completely immobile, and may not even employ those Disciplines that are normally active during torpor. The character can only be revived from this state by the taste of blood. Rumors speak of powerful Setite elders who took the form of Bitumenous Flesh long ago, and still wait for loyal followers to awaken their evil once again.

System: No roll is required to evoke Bitumenous Flesh, but the change takes one turn.

•••• THE FORM OF THE COBRA

The Setite may change his form into that of a huge black cobra. The serpent weighs as much as the vampire's human form, stretches over eight feet long, and is as thick as a woman's thigh. The Form of the Cobra grants several advantages, including a venomous bite, the ability to slither through small holes and a greatly enhanced sense of smell. The character may use any Disciplines while in this form save those that require hands (such as Talons of the Beast).

System: The Setite spends one Blood Point; the change is automatic, but takes three turns. The Storyteller may allow the Setite bonus dice on all Perception rolls related to smell, but the difficulties for all hearing rolls are increased by two. The cobra's bite inflicts damage equal to the vampire's, but the vampire does not need to grapple his victim; furthermore, the poison delivered is fatal to mortals.

••••• CHEAT THOTH'S SCALE

The Setite with mastery of Serpentis may pull her heart from her body. She can even use this ability on other Cainites, although this requires several hours of gruesome surgery. Only the new moon, the invisible moon, may grant this power success. If performed under any other moon, the rite fails. Upon removing her heart, the Setite places it in a small clay urn, and then carefully hides or buries the urn. She cannot be staked by any wood that pierces her breast, and finds it easier to resist frenzy. The heart is the seat of emotion, after all, and so the difficulties of all rolls to resist frenzy are two lower.

Setites are careful to keep their hearts safe from danger. If someone seizes her heart, the Setite is completely at that person's mercy. The Setite heart can only be destroyed by casting it into a fire or exposing it to sunlight. If this happens, the Setite dies where she stands, boiling away into a blistering heap of ash and blackened bone. Plunging a wooden stake into an exposed heart drives the Setite into instant torpor.

A Setite may carry her heart with her, or have several false hearts buried in different places. A Setite often avoids her heart's hiding place, to deter discovery. Those wise in Setite lore whisper that the corrupt elders of the clan often hold their underlings' hearts, the better to control the errant hatchlings. Many vampires seek out Setite hearts in order to increase their power base or keep the Serpents at bay. Needless to say, these are exceptionally hazardous quests.

System: This power requires no roll. Those who witness a Setite pull his heart from his breast (or cut the heart from another Cainite) must make Courage rolls. Failure indicates anything from strong uneasiness to complete revulsion and even Rötschreck.

•••••• BREATH OF THE BASILISK

The Setite may call on her inner corruption and spew it forth in a poisonous cloud of taint. This airborne poison is powerful enough to wither trees and even corrode stone. The breath covers an area roughly three feet across, and can catch someone's head and torso if well aimed. This power was given its current name by a horrified Toreador who watched his Lasombra patron wither and perish, eaten away by an angry Setite elder's bile.

System: The Setite spends one Blood Point to exhale a fine mist. In melee, the Setite can roll Dexterity + Brawl (difficulty 6) to catch an opponent up to six feet away. The target may attempt to dodge the cloud (the only hope for most). Each success inflicts one Health Level of aggravated damage, soakable only by Fortitude. The targets are likely poisoned as well, and mortal victims may well die within hours. This power can also be used to corrode inanimate objects; generally speaking, one breath pits and weakens an inch's depth of stone, corrodes metal blades into uselessness (if not destroying them), or thoroughly rots wood as thick as an inch.

HATCH THE VIPER

Serpentis 4, Protean 2

This rare and horrific power is known to Setites alone. The members of any other clan are hard-pressed to master Serpentis to this degree, much less find a Follower of Set willing to teach the ability. The Setite spends four Blood Points and an entire round to work the ability; no roll is needed. The following turn, the Setite may disgorge from his mouth a living poisonous serpent, formed from his blood. The serpent (which is considered a ghoul with Fortitude 1) may act independently, but follows its "parent's" commands. It must be fed one Blood Point every three nights, or else break down into a mass of tainted plasm. Drinking the venomous remains immediately causes four Health Levels of damage, soakable only by Fortitude.

The Setite may create and maintain as many serpents as he likes; the serpents must be fed their master's blood, however. Cainites with Animalism may communicate with created serpents, but the snakes always reflect too much of their master's personality to pass for natural animals. Created serpents have a distinct pattern, each one unique to the creator (gold diamonds on black skin seems to be a common motif). Acquiring this power costs 18 experience points.

THAUMATURGY

The Discipline of Thaumaturgy is one of the Tremere's most closely guarded secrets. It gives the clan an edge over other Cainites that they will not relinquish easily. Its power and unpredictability are among the reasons that this burgeoning, enemy-plagued clan has been able to survive.

Thaumaturgy combines hedge magic and older pagan arts with the high ritualistic magic practiced by the Order of Hermes. While few mortal wizards know of Thaumaturgy, those who do fear and loathe it as an aberration of true magick.

Thaumaturgy is divided into two parts — rituals and Paths. Rituals are prepared formulae and spells designed to fulfill specific purposes. Paths, on the other hand, are closer to true magick, in that they allow the vampire to create various effects, instantly, through the power of vampiric blood. Several Paths are available to the student of Thaumaturgy, offering many possibilities. It is this versatility which has proved so useful to the Tremere; one never knows what to expect from a practitioner of this Discipline.

Upon learning Thaumaturgy the character may choose one Level One Ritual and one dot in the Path of his choice.

THAUMATURGICAL PATHS

One of the powers gained from the study of Thaumaturgy is knowledge of the Via Vim or Paths of Power. The first Path a character learns is generally taught to him by his sire. During the course of a chronicle a character may learn additional Paths from a tutor or by studying a manuscript. Experience points are also necessary to acquire and progress in these Paths; the costs for such are listed in Chapter Seven.

The first Path learned is referred to as the character's primary Path; additional Paths learned are referred to as secondary Paths. A vampire can learn as many secondary Paths as he has access to, though he will always be more adept at his primary. A vampire may only choose to learn secondary Paths once he has acquired at least two dots in his primary. Furthermore, his primary Path must always be at least one level higher than any of his secondary, at least until he has achieved mastery in his primary. Only once the vampire has reached mastery (five dots) in his primary may he raise a secondary to the same level.

Each time these individual powers are employed, a Blood Point must be spent and a Willpower roll must be made against a difficulty of the power's level + 3. A failure on the roll indicates that the magic fails. A botch indicates that a permanent Willpower point is lost.

REGO VITÆ

• A TASTE FOR BLOOD

This ability was developed by the Tremere as a means of gauging the strength of their enemies — something very important to a clan whose very existence has been constantly in jeopardy. By tasting the blood of a mortal or Cainite, the vampire may determine how much blood is left in the individual, or how recently a vampire has fed and the subject's approximate generation.

System: The number of successes determines how much information is received and how accurate it is.

•• BLOOD RAGE

This power allows a vampire to cause another Cainite to use blood against her will, thus potentially weakening the opponent. The intended target must be touched — only the lightest brush is required — causing the blood to be instantly spent. A vampire so affected may feel the effects as the blood rushes through, heightening a Physical Attribute of the Thaumaturgist's choice. This power is also often used to incite frenzy in other Cainites. The expenditure of blood causes the subject to become more excitable, as well as reducing the amount of blood available, possibly causing the victim to enter a feeding frenzy.

System: Each success forces the target to spend one Blood Point immediately in a way the Thaumaturgist desires. Each success gained also adds one to the difficulty to resist frenzy for that round.

••• BLOOD OF POTENCY

This power has been vital to the spread of Tremere influence, even in the clan's infancy. The vampire may concentrate his own blood, causing it to become more potent, effectively lowering his generation.

System: Successes gained when attempting this power must be spent both to decrease the vampire's generation and to create a duration in hours. Each success equals one generation or one hour.

•••• THEFT OF VITÆ

A vampire who possesses this power may siphon the very life essence from a target. The vampire may mystically drain the blood from a mortal or Cainite without ever coming into contact with the target. The blood taken is transferred directly to the Thaumaturgist as if she had drunk from the target.

System: The number of successes determines how many Blood Points are transferred. The blood to be stolen must originate from within 50 feet and the victim must be in clear view. The source of the attack will be obvious.

••••• CAULDRON OF BLOOD

This devastating attack causes the blood of an intended victim to boil like water over a flame. The vampire must touch his target, causing the blood to simmer within the target's veins. This virtually ensures the death of any mortal, and can inflict great harm to vampires.

System: The number of successes gained determines how many Blood Points may be boiled. The victim also loses one Health Level for every Point boiled. A single success kills nearly any mortal, though not necessarily a ghoul.

CREO IGNEM

The control of flame is a powerful thing in the Dark Medieval world, particularly for a vampire. Fire is one of the few methods by which a vampire can be destroyed, and is a dangerous weapon. This Path allows the Cainite to create flames: small ones at first, but larger conflagrations may be created by those more proficient with Thaumaturgy.

The flames created by the Thaumaturgist are not natural. In fact, many believe they are demonic in origin. The flames cannot burn objects until they have been released by the Cainite. Therefore, a "palm of flame" does not burn the vampire's hand and create an aggravated wound — it only produces light. Once the fire has been released, however, it burns normally and the character has no control over it.

System: The number of successes determines how long the fire may be "held" before being released — one minute for each success gained. The Storyteller may require a Perception + Alertness roll to place the flame in the desired spot.

Individual descriptions are not provided for each level of this Path as each level is fairly self-explanatory. The chart below describes the Path level required to create a certain amount of flame.

- •   Candle
- ••   Palm of flame
- •••   Campfire
- ••••   Bonfire
- •••••   Conflagration

REGO MOTUS

Thaumaturgists who choose this Path may control the movement of objects through the power of their blood. At greater levels, Rego Motus even confers the power of flight. Objects under the character's control may be manipulated as he wishes; they may be lifted into the air or spun in circles. Even living creatures may be affected. Objects cannot be moved faster than

the character can move himself, so objects cannot be "thrown" with any great ability. However, objects may be manipulated as if by the vampire's own hands; an axe can chop at people or trees, assuming the Cainite is advanced enough to lift the object.

This Path is extremely useful for frightening mortals without directly confronting them. Some people become quite cowed when objects begin moving about on their own.

System: The number of successes determines how long a particular object may be manipulated — generally one turn for each success gained. At the end of the duration the vampire may attempt to maintain control by making a new test. If the test is successful, the control is maintained.

If this Path is practiced on a living creature, the subject can attempt to resist; the caster and the subject match Willpower in an opposed roll.

Individual descriptions are not provided for each level of this Path as each level is fairly self-explanatory. The weight of the object moved is very important; a certain rating is necessary even to attempt to move certain objects. Once a vampire achieves a rating of 3, he is able to levitate himself, no matter how much he weighs. Otherwise, weight restrictions apply.

•	One pound
••	20 pounds
•••	200 pounds
••••	500 pounds
•••••	1000 pounds

Rego Tempestas

This Path places the forces of the weather under the Thaumaturgist's control. The character can affect the elements as she desires, causing the weather to become suddenly dark and stormy on a bright and sunny day. This can be a most useful talent for any Cainite, particularly advantageous if one needs to move about during the day.

System: The number of successes gained determines how long it takes to effect the desired changes in the weather. One success generally means an entire day, while five indicates an almost immediate change.

The difficulty for affecting weather may vary depending upon the degree of variance the character is trying to create. The Storyteller may add or subtract from the difficulty depending upon the current weather conditions. For example, it is easier to summon a lightning bolt during a thunderstorm than to summon a rainstorm in the middle of the desert.

When summoning a lightning strike the player must roll Perception + Archery to attempt to hit a specific target.

Individual descriptions are not provided for each level of this Path as each level is fairly self-explanatory.

•	Fog
••	Rain
•••	Wind
••••	Storm
•••••	Lightning strike (roll 10 damage dice)

Rego Aquam

The control of water was one of the first Paths discovered by the Tremere. This Path, perhaps more than any other, has taken unwary Cainites by surprise. Traditionally, vampires do not have much to do with water; they have very little use for it as they do not need to bathe or drink. It is rumored that the very spirits of water commune with the vampires who follow this Path, granting them great power over water in its many forms. Some say that the spirits of water favor these Thaumaturgists, and at times will perform favors for them. Others say that they are coerced into performing these services.

Vampires who specialize in this Path and Rego Elementum are often known as Elementalists.

• Eyes of the Sea

By peering into a body of water, the Thaumaturgist can view events that have transpired in the surrounding area as if she were that body of water. This power grants credence to the belief that the Thaumaturgist is in direct contact with the spirits of the water.

System: The number of successes determines how far into the past the Thaumaturgist can look.

1 success	One day
2 successes	One week
3 successes	One month
4 successes	One year
5 successes	10 years

A body of water can be anything from a lake to a puddle. Obviously, oceans and rivers are not standing bodies.

•• Prison of Water

At the command of the Thaumaturgist, water rises up and imprisons the intended target. A substantial amount of water must be present for this power to be effective, although a small amount of water can be formed into manacles stronger than forged steel. Mortals caught within this watery prison will soon drown. Vampires cannot drown, but can be crushed if the water pressure is great enough.

System: The number of successes scored is the number of successes the trapped being must score on a Strength roll (difficulty 8; Potence adds successes) to break free. The target can only be held in one prison at a time. The Thaumaturgist can dissolve it at will.

••• Dehydrate

This power allows the vampire to remove water directly from a living body, causing the victim horrible internal wounds as the body slowly withers to a desiccated husk. Victims of this power are often believed to have succumbed to some horrible plague.

System: The target can resist this power by rolling Stamina + Survival (difficulty 9). Each success scored by the Tremere over the target's total number of successes causes the target to lose one Health Level. These wounds can be healed normally. Vampires lose Blood Points instead of Health Levels, though Health Levels are removed once all blood is gone. The victim, mortal or immortal, must also make a Courage roll (difficulty of the number of successes that the Tremere scored + 3) to take any action the next turn. Failure means the victim has been incapacitated by the pain.

•••• Flowing Wall

By touching the surface of a standing body of water, the Thaumaturgist may cause the water to rise up into a wall, impassable by supernatural creatures, including vampires, werewolves, faeries and even ghosts. The wall remains standing until the next sunrise or sunset, at which time it collapses into its natural state. The wall cannot be climbed in any manner, though it may be flown over.

System: The number of successes gained limits the height of the wall — 10 feet for each success gained.

When creating a wall, the Thaumaturgist must spend three Willpower points. To break the barrier, an intruder must make a Strength + Courage roll (difficulty 9). At least three successes are required, and they cannot be accumulated. Note that the Flowing Wall also blocks its creator, though he can remove it at will.

••••• Blood to Water

At this level the Thaumaturgist's power over water has become so great that he can create water from other substances. The most widespread use of this power is to transform a victim's blood into water with but a touch. It is rumored that some Tremere can transform other liquids into water, though certainly the transformation of blood is the most useful, at least as an attack.

System: Each success converts a Blood Point to water. This is almost immediately fatal to mortals. Besides destroying a vampire's vitæ, such an attack inflicts wound penalties to Dice Pools just as if the vampire had actually suffered an equivalent number of wounds. The water evaporates after the vampire sleeps, but the blood does not return.

The Storyteller may allow characters to transform other liquids into water (difficulty fewer by one). Of course, the liquid must still be touched.

Rego Elementum

Thaumaturgists who follow this Path learn to unlock the secrets of the inanimate world, giving them closer ties with all things natural. This is considered anathema by many Cainites because of its ties to the world of the living. After all, vampires are the undead and should have nothing to do with the living world. As with Rego Aquam, most view this Path as a means of communion with elemental spirits.

• Elemental Strength

This power allows the vampire to draw upon the spirits of the Earth to increase his physical attributes without the need for blood. A very potent power indeed, especially for those of higher generation.

System: The vampire spends two Willpower points to increase Strength, Dexterity and Stamina by one dot each. The number of successes gained indicates the number of turns the effect lasts. For each turn the heightened Attributes are maintained, however, the vampire must spend another Willpower point.

•• Wooden Tongues

A vampire employing this power may speak, at least in a limited fashion, with the spirit of any inanimate object. While inanimate objects have only a limited concern for what goes on around them, Wooden Tongues allows a vampire to get at least the impression of what an object has experienced. The memories

of such objects are limited and may seem extremely strange and foreign to the character. What is important to a vampire may not necessarily be of importance to a stone.

System: The number of successes gained determines the amount of information received.

••• Animate the Unmoving

Chairs grab their occupants, doors swing open and closed, and swords leap out of their owners' hands when this power is used. An object cannot take actions impossible for its form (a door can't pick someone up and carry her across a street), but objects with legs can run, wooden stakes can twist out of hands, and statues can mimic human life.

System: Use of this power requires the expenditure of a Willpower point. Each use makes one object within the character's line of sight come to life. The object remains animated as long as the caster keeps it in line of sight.

•••• Elemental Form

With this power, the character can take the form of some inanimate object of equal size and weight.

System: The number of successes gained determines how accurate the change is. At least three successes are required to allow the character to use any senses or Disciplines while in this form.

••••• Summon Elemental

Summon Elemental allows the character to summon one of the traditional elementals of myth and legend. Beings of water, earth, fire and air appear within five feet of the character. The Thaumaturgist may choose what type of elemental he wishes to summon.

System: These beings require the presence of some amount of their natural element to be invoked, and may or may not follow their summoner's instructions. The number of successes gained determines the general power of the elemental summoned and what degree of control the character has over the summoned elemental.

The exact abilities of the summoned elemental are determined by the Storyteller. Assume 3 in all Physical Attributes. One point may be added to the elemental's Attributes for each success gained by the caster (the caster determines where these points are assigned). Damage and special attacks relating to the element should be determined by the Storyteller.

Once the elemental has been summoned, the caster must try to gain control over it. The more powerful the summoned elemental, the more difficult it will be to control. The caster must roll Wits + Occult (difficulty equal to the number of successes gained when the elemental was summoned + 4). If no successes are gained, the caster has no control over the elemental.

1 success	The elemental will probably not attack the caster.
2 successes	The elemental will behave favorably toward the caster and may perform a favor in exchange for payment (the form of payment should be determined by the Storyteller).
3 successes	The elemental will usually perform one favor.
4 successes	The elemental will serve the caster in any way that does not risk its own existence.
5 successes	The elemental will perform any task the caster desires.

Rituals

Akin to the formulae prepared by hedge wizards, rituals are rigid, meticulously prepared, but powerful spells which must be performed under a specific set of circumstances and according to exacting procedures. All Tremere who know Thaumaturgy have the ability to cast rituals. By learning the basic concepts of Thaumaturgy, an apprentice acquires a familiarity with the magical formulae required to perform such castings.

Each Thaumaturgical ritual in **Vampire: The Dark Ages** is rated in power from one to five (or higher, in some cases). A character must have a Thaumaturgy rating at least equal to the power level of the ritual in order to perform it successfully. Unless stated otherwise, rituals take at least five minutes per level to cast.

Sometimes material components are required, as stipulated by the ritual itself. These could include such things as feathers, wood splinters, mud, herbs, bones, eye of newt and frogs' toes. Blood is used in many rituals.

At the first level of Thaumaturgy, the vampire automatically gains a single Level One ritual. In order to learn further rituals, a character must find a teacher (or discover the ritual in a scroll or manuscript) to instruct him in the proper procedures and incantations. Learning how to perform a ritual properly can take anywhere from a few days (Level One ritual) to many years (Level Five ritual).

In order to cast a ritual successfully, the caster must make a successful Intelligence + Occult roll (difficulty 4 + the level of the ritual). Generally, only one success is needed for the ritual to be successful.

In later centuries, the Tremere are able to cast rituals without the risk of failure. However, during the Dark Ages Thaumaturgy is a relatively new practice, its ways still largely unknown. It is because of this uncertainty that a roll is required to determine the success or failure of a ritual. Should the roll to cast a ritual fail, the Storyteller should feel free to ad-lib strange occurrences or even make it appear that a ritual was a success, only to reveal a fatal flaw at a later date. A botch might indicate a catastrophic side effect, possibly even a demonic manifestation.

Level One Rituals

Defense of the Sacred Haven

This ritual blankets an area in utter darkness, providing a secure haven in which a vampire may spend the daylight hours. It has proved extremely useful for Tremere on the run from others of their kind. Once the ritual is cast, no sunlight may pass through any window within 20 feet of where the ritual is performed. The caster must use his own blood to draw an appropriate sigil on each window in the ritual's area of effect. The ritual lasts for only as long as the Tremere stays within the area effect.

System: This ritual takes an hour to perform, during which time the proper sigils must be drawn on every window of the chamber. These sigils are commonly drawn on the shutters or just above the windowpanes, or directly on the glass if such exists. At least one Blood Point is expended in the casting of this ritual.

Wake with Evening's Freshness

Another ritual popular with Tremere who fear that enemies may come for them during the day, this allows the protected Cainite to awaken immediately at any sign of danger during the next day. The caster of this ritual must spread the ashes of burned goose feathers over the area he intends to sleep in.

System: This half-hour ritual must be performed immediately before a vampire prepares to sleep through the coming day. A period of complete meditation is required. Any interruption or performance of other activities after the ritual, but before sleep, renders the magic ineffective. The rule regarding how the vampire's Via restricts the number of dice usable during the day is waived for the first two turns of action. Thereafter, it is once again effective, but no matter what the character's condition, he will awaken in time to (hopefully) alleviate the danger.

Communicate with Sire

By casting this ritual the Tremere may join minds with his sire, allowing them to speak telepathically at any distance. This conversation lasts until either party decides to terminate the connection. The caster must possess an item that once belonged to his sire.

System: The caster must maintain a state of meditation for at least 30 minutes to achieve the connection. The conversation may be maintained for up to 10 minutes per success gained.

Deflection of Wooden Doom

The possibility of being staked and rendered immobile is perhaps the greatest fear of any Cainite. This ritual protects the Thaumaturgist from this possibility. The first stake that would pierce the vampire's heart is deflected, and the stake disintegrates in the attacker's hand. A stake merely held near the Cainite's heart is not affected. The stake must actually be used to penetrate the vampire.

System: In order to cast this ritual, the Thaumaturgist must be completely surrounded by a circle of wood for a full hour. Anything wooden, even furniture or wood shavings works, but the circle must remain unbroken. A wooden splinter must be placed in the caster's mouth at the end of the ritual (if the splinter is taken out, the ritual is nullified). The ritual lasts until the following dawn or dusk.

Devil's Touch

This ritual is used by the Tremere to curse any mortal who has earned their displeasure. The casting of the ritual places an invisible mark on the afflicted mortal, causing all who encounter him to react with extreme dislike. The mortal is treated as if he is the most despicable form of life; he is spat upon by beggars, and small children curse his name.

System: This effect lasts for one night only, disappearing with the first light of day. The mortal needs to be present for the ritual to be effective, and a copper coin must be placed somewhere upon the mortal's person (such as in a pocket). The ritual requires 15 minutes to enact.

Level Two Rituals

Blood Walk

This ritual allows the caster to trace the lineage of another Cainite.

System: Successful casting requires a full three hours and a Blood Point from the subject being traced. While the caster is in a deep trance, the blood must be tasted. This gives the caster knowledge not only of the subject's immediate sire, but of successively older generations. A Perception + Empathy roll (difficulty 6) is required; each success discovers a lower generation. Also, the caster automatically becomes aware of any Blood Oaths the subject has, either as Regnant or Thrall. Specific knowledge of each Oath-bonded vampire is also obtained, including the vampire's true name, personality and relation to the subject.

Ward Versus Ghouls

This ritual allows the vampire to create a potent ward against any ghoul — human or animal. Any ghoul that comes into contact with this ward suffers a burning jolt of mystical energy for as long as contact is maintained. This ward is formed by tracing an arcane sigil on the desired object, using mortal blood as the ink.

The Tremere use this ward in a variety of fashions, often placing it on pieces of jewelry, coins or other small objects. A potent weapon can be created by placing the ward on a weapon, such as a sword, dagger or even an arrow.

One of the restrictions of the ritual is that the mystic symbol only wards one object. For example, if the caster places a ward on a door to a room, the ward affects that door, not the whole room. The room could easily be entered through another door.

A final note: wards can be placed on arrowheads. As long as the arrowhead remains within the body, the ghoul continues to take damage. Often the arrowhead will pass through a portion of the body, in which case the sigil is destroyed on the entry. In order to ensure that the arrowhead remains lodged within the body, the person firing must score at least three successes with an Archery roll.

This ward can be destroyed by any normal means, though not by the creature it is dedicated to.

System: At least one point of mortal blood is required to cast this ritual. In 10 hours, the ritual is complete, and the strange symbol appears on the object. Any ghoul who touches the warded object immediately suffers a burning jolt (causing three dice of damage).

Once a ghoul has touched the ward, he must spend a Willpower point to willingly touch it again. It is rumored that some of the mightiest composite ghouls of the Tzimisce are immune to this ritual.

Donning the Mask of Shadows

Darkness seems to envelop the caster as her body appears to fade into inky blackness. This ritual transforms the vampire into a ghost-like state, rendering her nearly invisible in darkness and striking fear into the hearts of mortals who witness her change. This ritual only affects the character's appearance. Even though a character may appear shadowy and transparent, she is still physically present.

System: Casting requires a 20-minute chant, after which the caster can only be seen with an Intelligence + Alertness roll (difficulty of the caster's Wits + Stealth). Auspex subtracts three from the difficulty of a person's chance to see the shady warlock, but animals can automatically sense the caster. The effects of this ritual last for a number of hours equal to the number of successes rolled on the Intelligence + Occult roll made to cast the spell.

Principal Focus of Vitae Infusion

This ritual allows the caster to imbue a physical object with a portion of his blood, creating a convenient means of storing blood for later use. The blood may be consumed at any time in the future by swallowing the infused item. Many Tremere wear several pieces of infused jewelry as a precaution.

System: The object must be of a size that the vampire can easily hold in both hands, and can be as small as a pea. One of the caster's own Blood Points must be used, and the proper incantations require four hours to complete. Afterward, the object takes on a slightly ruddy hue and is oddly slick to the touch. By touching the object, the original caster may release the blood from its enchantment, causing the object to disintegrate. In moments, it completely breaks down into a puddle of blood (one Blood Point's worth), which can then be used in many ways.

Such an "infused focus" can be made for another Cainite, though the other vampire must be present at the initial ritual (the Blood Point must still be the caster's).

Level Three Rituals

Ward Versus Lupines

This ritual functions exactly as Ward Versus Ghouls, (Level Two ritual, above), but affects werewolves.

System: The requirements for this ward are exactly the same as for Ward Versus Ghouls, except that silver dust is required in the place of mortal blood

Shaft of Belated Quiescence

This vicious ritual is cast on a stake that is meant for the heart of a vampire. The intended shaft is carved with ornate symbols and blackened in an oakwood fire. The darkened shard then becomes one of the most feared vampire-slaying weapons known. A simple hit with the stake, even in the leg or arm, causes the tip to break off inside the victim and begin burrowing into the victim's body. The point slowly works its way to the heart. The victim of this attack may not even know what is occurring until it is too late. This ritual is also commonly cast on arrows.

System: During a five-hour ritual, the caster must carve an ornate series of symbols onto a sharpened shaft of rowan wood, coat the stake with her blood and blacken it in an oakwood fire. The point reaches the heart in one to 10 days (roll a die). During the time of the splinter's journey, the sufferer occasionally feels sharp pains. These pains grow closer together and more unbearable as the tip nears its target. Damage caused on the splinter's journey isn't enough to remove Health Levels from a vampire, but will harm a mortal or ghoul. One of the only ways to remove the thing is to dig for it — a very grisly process that may not necessarily work. The vile thing may actually try to elude the surgeon by burrowing away from the open wound. The "surgeon" does more and more damage as he digs deeper after it. Needless to say, this weapon is a death sentence for a mortal, and may well destroy a Cainite — who knows where the vampire might be when he is immobilized….

Flesh of Fiery Touch

This ritual causes the caster's very flesh to burn any Cainite who comes into contact with him. Most Tremere cast this ritual with some degree of caution, for it is commonly believed that its power comes directly from the abyss.

System: After the ritual is completed, any Cainite who touches the bespelled Tremere's flesh receives a single Health Level of aggravated damage in the form of a searing burn. The damage can be resisted with Fortitude, but if the vampire continues to hold the caster, the victim continues to take damage. However, the caster cannot inflict this damage by touching someone; he must himself be touched. Although this effect lasts until dusk of the next day, it is not without its price. During the two- or three-hour ritual, the casting vampire must consume a small burning coal, causing an aggravated wound (again, resist with Fortitude) and costing a Willpower point (to bring himself to do it). While the enchantment is in effect, the Cainite's skin takes on a subtle bronze tint. This hue can be noticed with a straight Perception roll (difficulty 8) by a character who closely inspects the warlock. The caster is also unnaturally hot to the touch.

Incorporeal Passage

This ritual allows the vampire to become as intangible as a ghost. All that remains visible of the warlock is a hazy outline. While in this form the Cainite can travel unhindered through all obstacles, even walls, as if they do not exist. The caster is impervious to most attacks, just as if she were utilizing the Protean power Body of Spirit. While assuming this form, the caster must walk in a straight line through objects; once she begins, she must continue through — she cannot draw back. However, the vampire may not travel downward into solid ground, for it would be an impossible walk. Certain Tremere whisper that the use of this ritual brings the caster closer to the world of the dead — and thus subjects him to the power of the restless dead.

System: The ritual takes about an hour to prepare, and lasts a number of hours equal to the number of successes scored on a Wits + Survival roll (difficulty 6). During the ritual, the vampire must break a mirror holding her reflection. One of the pieces is used later to hold her image as she moves incorporeally. She need not look into the mirror, only make certain that it reflects her. The ritual can be canceled by shifting the mirror so that the caster can no longer see her reflection in it.

Level Four Rituals

Ward Versus Cainites

This ritual works in a manner similar to Ward Versus Ghouls (Level Two ritual), but affects vampires.

System: All requirements are the same as Ward Versus Ghouls, except that a point of vampire blood is required instead of mortal blood.

Binding the Beast

Through use of this ritual the warlock can temporarily separate the Beast from the soul of another Cainite. The ritual is often attempted to subdue a frenzied character, though it can be attempted at any time. The subject of this ritual often languishes in a state of utter despair, not even having the will to live; along

with the Beast, the instinct for survival is removed. The desire for blood is also mostly removed, causing the very act of feeding to become repugnant to many vampires. Some Cainites have starved into torpor after having been subjected to this ritual.

System: The ritual takes only 10 minutes to perform. The caster does not have to see the subject, but must imbibe a full Blood Point of the frenzied character's blood (it can have been drawn earlier), and must push an iron spike through his own hand (causing two Health Levels of damage that can't be soaked). Upon completion of these acts, the subject suddenly emerges from frenzy, and often becomes uncharacteristically passive.

In truth, the subject's bestial side has been separated from his psyche for a number of nights equal to the number of successes the caster scores on a Manipulation + Empathy roll (difficulty of 10 minus the subject's Road or Via). During this time, the subject cannot frenzy, cannot regain Willpower, can only use one Blood Point per turn regardless of generation, and cannot feed without making a Courage roll. In addition, the vampire must make a Willpower roll (difficulty 7) to use any Discipline. The caster may never perform this ritual on himself.

HEART OF STONE

By casting this ritual the caster causes her heart to become solid stone — completely "stakeproof." It is said that Tremere who regularly perform this ritual become emotionless automatons, without a shred of conscience or humanity.

System: The caster must mold a three-inch-high, two-meter-wide earthen circle on a stone surface (solid stone is preferred, flagstone is acceptable) and must then lie naked on her back in the center. A candle is placed directly above her heart, and allowed to burn until the wick is gone and the flame is smothered by the candle's wax. The wax melts all over the caster's chest, causing one aggravated wound, which can be soaked with Fortitude. The ritual takes seven to nine hours to complete, but its effects last as long as the caster wishes. While under this ritual's effects, the caster suffers the following drawbacks and limitations: she cannot use Willpower, and if forced to spend a Willpower point, the spell is immediately canceled; the caster's Conscience/Conviction rating drops to 1 (or zero if the Trait was already 1); and the caster loses half her Dice Pool on all Empathy rolls, most Social rolls and nearly all rolls when she is trying to be compassionate or friendly.

LEVEL FIVE RITUALS

ESCAPE TO A TRUE FRIEND

More than one Tremere has escaped the clutches of certain death through the use of this ritual. This ritual must be prepared ahead of time, but can be of great use in a tight situation. The ritual allows the caster to vanish suddenly by stepping into a previously prepared circle. The warlock is instantly transported into the vicinity of a previously designated person, generally a close friend or ally of the Tremere. The character does not suddenly appear before his friend, but materializes someplace nearby and out of sight (usually within earshot of the friend's location). The enchantment may be reused until the circle is broken or the symbols are marred.

System: A one-meter circle must be burned into the ground, and many arcane symbols must be precisely placed about it. The entire process takes three to four nights and costs five of the caster's own Blood Points. Once this is accomplished, the caster (and only the caster) may at any time step into the circle while repeating a friend's true name and be mystically transported to that friend.

WARD VERSUS SPIRITS

This ritual works in a manner similar to Ward Versus Ghouls (Level Two ritual), but affects ghosts and spirits.

System: The requirements for this ritual are the same as for Ward Versus Ghouls, except the required component is pure sea salt instead of mortal blood.

BLOOD CONTRACT

This ritual creates an unbreakable oath between two parties. The contract must be written in the caster's blood and takes about three days to complete. The ritual is finished when both parties sign the agreement in their own blood, after which they are compelled to abide by the terms as stated. The only way out is to complete one's part of the bargain or burn the contract.

System: If one of the parties breaks the contract, she receives enough aggravated damage to fall into torpor. Storytellers may feel free to adjust the punishment as they see fit.

VICISSITUDE

Vicissitude is the signature power of the Tzimisce and is almost unknown outside the clan. Not that the Fiends have too many would-be pupils; some things are beyond the pale even for the rest of the Damned.

Vicissitude is similar in some respects to Protean, but springs from a much darker source. Whereas Protean merely enables a Cainite to emulate God's creatures, this twisted power allows a Tzimisce to defile and deform those creatures (or herself) for all manner of perverse ends. The most beautiful maiden or noble stallion can, with but a knead of the fingers and a flick of the wrist, be reduced to a hideous freak or a blob of deliquescent pus. The Fiends have certainly used Vicissitude's more grotesque side effects to cement their infamous reputation.

Note that while this Discipline permits powerful and horrific effects, the wielder must obtain skin-to-skin contact and must often physically sculpt the desired result. This even applies to the use of the power on oneself. Tzimisce skilled in Vicissitude are often inhumanly beautiful; those less skilled are simply inhuman.

BODY CRAFTS

The sub-Skill of Crafts required to use Vicissitude properly is known as Body Crafts. This Skill enables its possessor to make all manner of alterations to living and dead flesh and bone. The Skill also gives insight into more mundane techniques: many Tzimisce are fiendishly skilled at flaying, tanning, carving, embalming, taxidermy, tattooing and piercing (for earrings and the like).

• MALLEABLE VISAGE

A vampire with this power may alter her bodily parameters: height, build, voice, facial features and skin tone, among other things. Such changes are cosmetic and minor in scope. She might, for example, resume her mortal coloration; make herself resemble a Moor, Viking or Saracen; or even copy the form of a web-fingered naiad or faerie noble.

System: The vampire must spend a Blood Point for each body part to be changed. Then she must roll Intelligence + Body Crafts (difficulty 6). To duplicate another person or voice requires a Perception + Body Crafts roll (difficulty 8), and five successes are required for a flawless copy (fewer successes leave minute, or not-so-minute, flaws). Increasing one's Appearance Trait is difficulty 10 (thus usually requiring Willpower expenditure for even minimal success), and a botch permanently reduces the Attribute by one.

•• TRANSMOGRIFY THE MORTAL CLAY

This power is similar to Malleable Visage, above, but allows the vampire to perform drastic, grotesque alterations on other creatures. Tzimisce often use this power to transform their servitors into monstrous guards, the better to frighten foes. Only flesh (including muscle, fat and cartilage, but not bone) may be transformed. The power is permanent on mortals, though vampires may spend Blood Points to "heal" the transformation.

System: The vampire must grapple the intended victim and make a successful Dexterity + Body Crafts roll (difficulty variable: 5 for a crude yank-and-tuck, up to 9 for transforming a Toreador popinjay's perfect aquiline nose into a grotesque replica of a tapir's snout). A vampire who wishes to increase another's Appearance Trait does so as described under Malleable Visage, above; reducing the Attribute is considerably easier (difficulty 5), though truly inspired disfigurement may dictate a higher difficulty. In either case, each success increases/reduces the Attribute by one.

A vampire may use this power to move clumps of skin, fat and muscle tissue to provide additional padding where needed. For each success scored on a Dexterity + Body Crafts roll (difficulty 8), the vampire may increase the subject's soak Dice Pool by one, at the expense of either a point of Strength or a Health Level (vampire's choice).

••• REND THE OSSEOUS FRAME

This terrible power allows a vampire to manipulate bone in the same manner that flesh is shaped. In conjunction with Transmogrify the Mortal Clay, above, this power enables a Vicissitude practitioner to deform a victim (or herself) beyond recognition. This power should be used in conjunction with the flesh-shaping arts, unless the vampire wants to inflict injury on the victim (see below).

System: The vampire must make a Strength + Body Crafts roll (difficulties as above). Rend the Osseous Frame may be used without the flesh-shaping arts, as an offensive weapon. Each success scored on the Strength + Body Crafts roll (difficulty 7) inflicts one Health Level of damage to the victim, as his bones rip, puncture and slice their way out of his skin.

The vampire may utilize this power (on herself or others) to form spikes or talons of bone, either on the knuckles as an offensive weapon or all over the body as defensive "quills." In the former case, the vampire or victim takes one Health Level of normal damage; in the latter, the subject takes a number of Health Levels equal to five minus the number of successes (a botch kills the subject or sends the vampire into torpor). These Health Levels may be healed normally. Knuckle spikes inflict Strength + 2 nonaggravated damage, while defensive quills inflict a hand-to-hand attacker's Strength in nonaggravated damage unless the attacker scores three or more successes on the attack roll (the defender still takes damage normally). Quills also enable the vampire or altered subject to add two to all damage inflicted via grapples or body slams.

A vampire who scores five or more successes on the Strength + Body Crafts roll may cause a rival vampire's rib cage to curve inward and pierce the heart. While this does not send a vampire into torpor, it does cause the affected vampire to lose half his Blood Points, as the seat of his vitæ ruptures in a shower of gore.

•••• AWAKEN THE *ZULO* SHAPE

The Tzimisce who employs this fell power becomes the veriest monster, the dread *zulo* of Balkan peasants' terrified whispers. The vampire's stature increases to a full eight feet; the skin becomes a sickly greenish-gray or grayish-black chitin; the arms become apelike and ropy, tipped with ragged black nails; and the face warps into something out of a nightmare. A row of spines sprouts from the vertebrae, and the external carapace exudes a foul-smelling grease.

System: The *zulo* shape costs two Blood Points to awaken. All Physical Attributes (Strength, Dexterity, Stamina) increase by three, but all Social Attributes drop to zero, save when dealing with others also in *zulo* form. (However, a *zulo*-transformed vampire trying to intimidate someone may substitute Strength for a Social Attribute!) Damage inflicted in brawling combat increases by one due to the jagged ridges and bony knobs creasing the *zulo*'s hands.

••••• ASCENDANCY OF THE SANGUINE HUMOR

The blood is more than life to a vampire with this power, for she can physically transform all or part of her body into sentient vitæ. This blood is in all respects identical to the vampire's normal vitæ: she can use it to nourish herself or others, create ghouls and establish Blood Oaths. If all this blood is imbibed or otherwise destroyed, the vampire meets Final Death.

Vampires who assume this shape often act giddy and fey for several hours afterward, as the sanguine aspect of their nature imposes itself over their choleric, phlegmatic and melancholy humors.

System: The vampire may transform all or part of herself as she deems fit. Each leg can turn into two Blood Points worth of vitæ, as can the torso; each arm, the head and the abdomen convert to one Blood Point (though turning one's head to blood is somewhat foolish). The blood can be reconverted to the body part, provided it is in contact with the vampire. If the blood has been utilized or destroyed, the vampire must spend a number of Blood Points equal to what was originally created to regrow the missing body part.

A vampire entirely in this form may not be staked, cut, bludgeoned or pierced, but can be burned or exposed to the sun. The vampire may not physically attack or move in this form, but her fluid body acts in ways normal for a puddle of gore (so she can splash free from manacles or ooze through a dungeon grate beneath her).

Mental Disciplines may be used, provided no eye contact or vocal utterance is necessary — and if a vampire in this form "washes" over a mortal or animal beneath her, that mortal must make a Courage roll (difficulty 8) or fly into a panic.

•••••• CHIROPTERAN MARAUDER

This power is similar to Awaken the *Zulo* Shape, but even more potent. The vampire assumes a form similar to the *zulo* (and gains all the benefits and drawbacks thereof), but gains several additional advantages. A vampire in this shape resembles nothing so much as a great bipedal bat.

The vampire's arms sprout fluted, leathery wings enabling flight at 25 mph (objects can be carried but not manipulated while the vampire is airborne). Additionally, the vampire may make a Strength + Body Crafts roll (difficulty 6) to extend talons on the ends of the wings (where the hands are); these talons inflict Strength + 2 aggravated damage.

Finally, the vampire subtracts two from the difficulties of all hearing rolls, but adds one to visual difficulties (bats, as everyone of learning knows, are blind — and even bat-monsters are somewhat myopic).

System: The vampire must spend three Blood Points to assume the shape and must make a separate roll to form the talons.

SPECIAL POWER: BODY ARMORY

The vampire must have ratings of 3 in both Vicissitude and Protean and must spend 20 experience points. This power enables the vampire to form weapons from the very stuff of her body. Each weapon created costs two Blood Points.

Any sort of hand-to-hand weapon can be created, though two-handed ones (polearms, great axes and the like) cost double the normal Blood Point expenditure. These weapons inflict damage per their type, but this damage is aggravated.

Chapter Six: Rules

Wrest once the law to your authority
To do a great right, do a little wrong
And curb this cruel devil of his will.
—William Shakespeare, The Merchant of Venice

There is always chance in life. There's a chance you'll win the lottery, a chance you'll be audited and a chance you'll die in a plane crash. Chance plays a role in Vampire: The Dark Ages as well. However, we use dice to simulate the duplicity of Lady Luck

The Storyteller game system consists of rolling 10-sided dice, which you can buy in any game store. If you are the Storyteller, you will want a lot of dice, at least 10, all to yourself. As a player, you'll want dice as well, but sharing dice with other players will work.

Whenever the success of an action is in doubt, or the Storyteller thinks that there is a chance you might fail, you will have to roll dice. This gives your character an opportunity to let both weaknesses and strengths exhibit themselves, thereby revealing something of the character's true nature to both you and the other players.

GAME TERMS

These are a number of terms used in the rules that first-time players and new Storytellers might not be familiar with. They'll be described further throughout the chapter.

• **Ability:** These are Traits that describe what a character knows and has learned, rather than her physical and psychological make-up. Abilities are Traits such as Intimidation, Archery and Occult.

• **Action:** An action is the performance of a deed, which is a consciously-willed, physical, social or mental activity. When players announce that their characters are doing something, they are taking an action.

• **Advantage:** This is a catch-all category that describes the mystical Disciplines and Backgrounds of a character.

• **Attribute:** These are Traits that describe what a character inherently is. Attributes are such things as Strength, Charisma and Intelligence.

• **Botch:** A disastrous failure, indicated by rolling more ones than successes on the 10-sided dice rolled for an action.

• **Character:** Each player creates a character, an individual they roleplay over the course of the chronicle. Though "character" could imply any individual, in **Vampire: The Dark Ages** it is always used to describe the players' characters.

• **Dice Pool:** This describes the dice you have in your hand after adding together your different Traits. It is the maximum number of dice you can roll in one turn, though you can divide them among different actions.

• **Difficulty:** This is a number from 2-10 measuring the difficulty of an action a character takes. The player needs to roll that number or higher on at least one of the dice rolled.

• **Downtime:** The time spent between scenes, where no roleplaying is done and turns are not used. Actions might be made, and the Storyteller might give some descriptions, but generally time passes quickly.

• **Extended Action:** An action that requires a certain number of successes for the character to actually succeed.

• **Health:** This is a measure of the degree to which a character is wounded or injured.

• **Point:** The temporary score of a primary trait such as Willpower, Humanity and Health — the squares, not the circles.

• **Refresh:** When points are regained in a dice pool, it is said that they are being "refreshed."

• **Rating:** A number describing the permanent value of a Trait, most often a number from 1-5, though sometimes a number from 1-10.

• **Resisted Action:** An action that two different characters take against each other. Both compare their number of successes, and the character with the most wins.

• **Scene:** A single episode of the story; a time when and place where actions and events take place moment by moment. A scene is often a dramatic high point of the story.

• **Score:** The temporary value of a Trait or combination of Traits used in a single roll.

- **Simple Action:** An action that requires the player to get only one success to succeed, though more successes indicate a better job or result.

- **Storyteller:** The person who creates and guides the story by assuming the roles of all characters not taken by the players and determining all events beyond the control of the players.

- **System:** A specific set of complications used in a certain situation; rules to help guide the rolling of dice to create dramatic action.

- **Trait:** A Trait is any Attribute, Ability, Advantage or other character index that can be described as a number (in terms of dots).

- **Troupe:** The group of players, including the Storyteller, who play **Vampire: The Dark Ages**, usually on a regular basis.

- **Willpower:** One of the most important Traits is Willpower. It measures the self-confidence and internal control of a character. However, Willpower works differently than most Traits — it is usually used up, rather than rolled.

Ratings

A character is described by her Traits — the innate and learned abilities and aptitudes she possesses. Traits are defined by numbers; each Trait has a rating from 1 to 5, which describes how good the character is in that particular Trait, with 1 as "poor" and 5 as "superb." This scale of 1 to 5 is the "star" rating system made famous by movie and restaurant critics.

You should consider the normal human range to be from one to three, with two being average. However, exceptional people can have Traits of 4 (exceptional) or 5 (superb), or even have a zero in a Trait (which is extremely rare, but not unheard of). Vampires of particularly low generations can exceed the normal human maximum as well.

x	Abysmal
•	Poor
••	Average
•••	Good
••••	Exceptional
•••••	Superb

For every dot your character has in a particular Trait, you get to roll one die. Thus, if you had four dots on Strength, you would get to roll four dice. If you had a 1 Perception, you would get to roll only one die. However, you almost never simply roll the number of dice you have in an Attribute, which are your intrinsic capabilities. Usually you get to add the number of dice you have in an Attribute with the number of dice you have in an Ability — things which you know and have learned.

So if you wanted the players to roll to see if they notice the bandits creeping up behind them, you would have them roll their Perception + Alertness — an Attribute + an Ability. They would take as many dice as they had points of Perception, put them in their hands, and then they would take as many dice as they had points of Alertness, and put those in their hands also. They get to roll as many dice as they have total points in their Attribute and Ability.

These dice are called the Dice Pool, which is a description of the total number of dice you roll in a single turn — usually for a single action, though you can divide up your Dice Pool in order

to be able to perform more than one action. You almost always roll the number of dice equal to a Trait's permanent rating (the circles), not its current score (the squares).

There are many actions that don't require or even have an appropriate Ability, such as when you want to break down a door. In such cases, you would only use an Attribute, rolling the number of dice you have listed for that Attribute — in this case, Strength.

There is absolutely no situation where more than two Traits can add to a Dice Pool. Only one Trait can be used if it has a potential value of 10 (such as Humanity or Willpower). It is generally impossible for a normal human being to have more than 10 dice in a Dice Pool (though vampires are a different story).

Difficulties

Now you've got to figure out what you need to look for when you roll the dice. The Storyteller will give you a difficulty number, which is the number that you need to obtain in order to succeed in whatever you are attempting. A difficulty is always a number between 2 and 10. You need to get that number or higher on at least one of the dice you roll in order to succeed. Every time you do so, it's called a success. If the difficulty is a 6 and you roll a 2, 3, 6, 5 and 9, you have scored two successes. Though you need only one success to actually succeed, the more successes you get, the better you do. Getting only one success is considered a marginal success, while getting three is considered a complete success, and getting five is a momentous event.

You can see that if the difficulty is lower, it becomes easier to get a success, and if it is higher, it is more difficult. The Storyteller will assign high difficulties whenever the action you have decided to take would be tough or challenging, and will either let you do something automatically (because your Attributes and Abilities are so high) or give you a low difficulty if it is particularly easy.

Though they are not on the list above, the Storyteller can also assign a difficulty of two or 10. However, these should almost never be used. Difficulty two is so pathetically easy that you might as well let the player succeed without wasting time on a roll. Difficulty 10 is so difficult that there is an equal chance to botch

DIFFICULTIES	
Three	Easy
Four	Routine
Five	Straightforward
Six	Standard
Seven	Challenging
Eight	Difficult
Nine	Extremely Difficult

DEGREES OF SUCCESS	
One Success	Marginal
Two Successes	Moderate
Three Successes	Complete
Four Successes	Exceptional
Five Successes	Phenomenal

(described below) as there is to succeed, no matter how many dice the player is rolling. A 10 is pretty near impossible. On the rare occasions when you do announce a difficulty of 10, be sure you realize how impossible you are making the chance of success. If a player ever rolls a 10, it is automatically a success, no matter what.

Unless the Storyteller says otherwise, the difficulty for a particular task is always a six. This is the standard, assumed difficulty.

THE RULE OF ONE

The final thing you need to know about rolling dice is the "rule of one." Whenever you roll a "1," it cancels out a success. It completely takes it away. You remove both the "success" die and the "1" die and ignore them. If you roll more "1s" than you do successes, a disaster occurs, and something called a "botch" takes place. Don't count the "1s" that canceled out successes, but if even a single "1" is left after all the successes have been canceled, a botch occurs. Getting a single "1" or five "1s" has about the same result in most cases; the circumstances surrounding the botch determine if it is catastrophic or a minor mishap. If there are no "1s" or successes left, you've simply failed.

AUTOMATIC SUCCESSES

You don't want to be rolling dice all the time; it can get in the way of the roleplaying. **Vampire: The Dark Ages** employs a very simple system for automatic successes, allowing players to avoid making rolls for actions their characters could perform in their sleep.

Thus, if the number of dice in your Dice Pool equals or exceeds the assigned difficulty, your character succeeds automatically. Such a success is considered marginal (the equivalent of scoring only one success), so a player will sometimes want to roll anyway in an attempt to gain even more successes. For very simple and often-repeated actions, however, automatic successes can eliminate a lot of wasted time. (Note that certain actions, such as combat, are always problematic and should not be handled with this system.)

The automatic success rules can be used to eliminate dice completely. In such situations, automatic successes aren't a matter of choice. Either you are good enough to succeed or you are not. It's simple, but so was Cops 'n' Robbers, and we liked it just fine. The story was what was important; the rules didn't matter.

This simple system even has a twist, making it not quite so black-and-white. A Willpower point (see pg. 135) can be spent to earn an automatic success. You won't want to do this often, but for certain actions it can be very advantageous to do so. Of course, the Willpower expenditure only counts for one success if multiple successes are required.

COMPLICATIONS

You may have already realized that it is quite easy to score a single success, even when you roll only one or two dice. You have a 75% chance for a marginal success when you roll only two dice and the difficulty is 6. While that may sound too easy, there are various ways to complicate matters, some of which are discussed below.

For troupes heavily into roleplaying, simple rolls and automatic successes are enough. Generally, complications are needed only if the players or you want a break from the roleplaying, if you want a

realistic result or if you want to make a game out of the scene. Complications add drama to the story, evoking passion and focusing events.

EXTENDED ACTIONS

In order to succeed fully, you will sometimes need more than one success — you will need to accumulate three, seven or even (rarely) 20 successes. An action that requires only one success is called a simple action. An action that requires more than one success is called an extended action.

An extended action allows you to roll over and over on subsequent turns in an attempt to collect enough successes to succeed. For instance, suppose your character is climbing a tree. The Storyteller announces that when you roll a total of seven successes, your character has climbed to the top. She'll get there eventually, but the more times you roll, the more chances your character has to botch and injure herself. If she is attempting to climb down the tree because it is on fire, the amount of time it takes becomes exceedingly important.

During an extended action, you can keep trying to obtain successes for as long as you want, or at least until you fail to score even one success. If you botch, your character may have to start over from scratch, with no accumulated successes. The Storyteller may decide not to let the character try again at all.

This type of action is more complicated than a simple action, and should not often be employed in the middle of intense roleplaying. As the Storyteller, you decide what type of action is appropriate. A little bit of experience will serve you well when employing these rules.

RESISTED ACTIONS

Sometimes you will act in opposition to another character. Both of you make rolls against a difficulty often indicated by a Trait of the other character, and the person who scores the most successes succeeds. However, you are considered to score only as many successes as the amount by which you exceed your opponent's successes. The opponent's successes eliminate your own, just as "1s" do. Therefore, it is very difficult, and rare, to achieve an outstanding success on a resisted action. Even if your opponent cannot beat you, she can diminish the effect of your efforts. During actions that are both extended and resisted, one of the opponents must collect a certain number of successes in order to succeed completely. Each success above the opponent's total number of successes in a single turn is added to a success total. The first opponent to collect the designated number of successes wins the contest.

TEAMWORK

Sometimes characters can work together to collect successes, most often during an extended action. At the Storyteller's discretion, two or more characters can make rolls separately and combine their successes (though they may never combine their separate Traits for one roll). Teamwork is effective in some circumstances, such as when characters are engaging in combat, shadowing prey, collecting information or repairing devices. During others, it can actually be a hindrance, such as in many social actions (where it can confuse the subject).

TRYING IT AGAIN

It can often be annoying to fail. If you're trying to hit a target while jousting and you keep missing as you go by, it can get frustrating. This is reflected in the Storyteller system by increasing the difficulty of any action if it is tried again after it's already been failed.

Whenever a character attempts an action she has previously failed, the Storyteller has the option of increasing the difficulty of the action. Consider a character who tries to intimidate someone. If the first attempt fails, it's going be harder the second time around, so the difficulty is one greater. If tried a third time, then the difficulty is two greater. In cases like this, though, the Storyteller might simply rule that the character cannot even make another try — how do you intimidate someone who has already called your bluff?

Other examples of when to use the rule are picking a lock (Larceny), scaling a wall (Athletics) and remembering a word in a foreign language (Linguistics).

Sometimes the Storyteller shouldn't invoke this rule. A notable example is during combat. Missing someone with a first arrow doesn't necessarily mean that the archer is frustrated and has a better chance of missing again. Though after the archer has missed a couple of times, especially if they are easy, close-range shots…

Other examples of when not to use the rule are seeing something out of the corner of the eye (Alertness) and dodging an attack (Dodge).

TRY IT OUT

Well, that's it. These are the rules. This system for dice is all you really need to know in order to play this game. All the other rules are just clarifications and exceptions. So long as you understand what's been discussed here, you won't have any difficulty understanding anything else. If you don't think you've caught everything, just read this chapter again; you'll find it makes more sense the second time around.

Now go ahead and make a few rolls, using the example character from Chapter Four. Anatole is attempting to escape a group of enraged townsfolk. He crouches down behind a low wall, hoping that they will run past without seeing him. The Storyteller

THE GOLDEN RULE

Remember that in the end there is only one real rule in any game in the Storyteller series, including **Vampire: The Dark Ages**: *there are no rules.* You should fashion this game into whatever you need it to be — if the rules get in your way, then ignore or change them. The true complexity and beauty of the real world cannot be captured by rules; it takes storytelling and imagination to do that. These rules are designed to be guidelines, and you are free to use, abuse, ignore and change them as you wish. Players take note: the Storyteller is the final arbiter of any rules question.

assigns a difficulty of 7 to this feat and decides that the appropriate roll is Dexterity + Stealth. Take four dice because of Anatole's Dexterity Attribute of 4, and three extra dice because of his Stealth Ability of 3. You should now have seven dice in your hand — a good number, reflecting Anatole's aptitude for stealth. Roll the dice and look to see how many successes you have, making sure to subtract a success for every "1" you roll. Did you make it, did you fail, or did you botch? The more successes you get, the better you hide. Only one success might mean that you barely make it under cover in time. Two might mean that you manage to crouch under a little overhang. Three might mean that you are completely silent, and that the mob doesn't even get an opposed Perception roll.

Next, try out an extended and resisted action. An example of this is a drinking contest (not common among vampires, but possible given the presence of inebriated vessels...). It requires an indefinite series of rolls, each with a different difficulty. You need to accumulate five successes more than your opponent in order to win. A botch eliminates all your accumulated successes.

• First roll: Each player rolls Stamina; the difficulty is the opponent's Manipulation + 3 (don't let him intimidate you).

• Second and third rolls: Each player rolls Stamina; the difficulty is the opponent's Stamina + 3.

• Fourth roll (and all subsequent ones): Each player rolls Stamina; the difficulty is the opponent's Willpower.

EXAMPLES OF ROLLS

Each Attribute can be combined with each Ability, allowing for 270 types of simple rolls. Admittedly, you will not often have cause to roll Strength + Academics, but it might come up. The following are some examples of rolls that may come up during the course of a story.

• You attempt to impress the lord of a manor by singing a ballad. Roll Charisma + Music (difficulty 7).

• You're trying to locate a rare herb which might save the life of a valuable mortal ally. Roll Perception + Herbalism (difficulty 8).

• You attempt to frighten an enemy with a display of physical prowess. Roll Strength + Intimidation (difficulty 7).

• While trying to escape from the castle guard, you must dive off the highest tower into the moat. Roll Dexterity + Athletics (difficulty 5).

• Do you notice the archer hiding in the trees above the road? Roll Perception + Alertness (difficulty 9).

• You wish to rally the peasantry to revolt against the local lord. Roll Charisma + Leadership (difficulty 8).

• A beautiful young maiden catches your eye, and you attempt to make an impression during the feast. Roll Appearance + Etiquette (difficulty 8).

VAMPIRE: THE DARK AGES

• When galloping down a path, you see a log in front of you. Roll Manipulation + Ride (difficulty 7) to get your horse to leap over the log.

• While you're walking through the courtyard, a shadowy figure springs up from behind a bush and shoots a crossbow at you. Roll Wits + Dodge (difficulty 6) to avoid being hit by the bolt.

• While traveling, you come across a glade in the middle of the forest. Roll Perception + Occult (difficulty 8) to recognize it as a faerie glade.

• You find an ancient-looking manuscript on the body of a monk. Roll Intelligence + Academics (difficulty 6) to translate it.

• You're attempting to slip a poison into the drink of the person sitting next to you. Roll Dexterity + Larceny (difficulty 8).

• A neighboring noble seizes one of your fiefs. Roll Manipulation + Law (difficulty 6) to plead your case successfully to the duke and convince him that the land is rightfully yours.

• You wish to ride a horse that is unfamiliar with you. Roll Manipulation + Animal Ken (difficulty 7) to overcome the beast's natural fear of the undead.

• You are hanged for a petty crime. Though this does you no harm, you wish to fool the mortals into thinking that you are in fact dead. Roll Stamina + Acting (difficulty 7) to fake your death and remain still until all the mortals have left.

• You're attempting to quietly enter the home of your intended victim. Roll Dexterity + Stealth (difficulty 6).

• How well do you understand an emissary with a strong native accent? Roll Perception + Linguistics (difficulty 9). Three successes allows you to understand the complete message.

• You discover a man, impaled by an arrow, lying in a field. Roll Perception + Investigation (difficulty 9) to notice that the wound was originally made by a knife, not an arrow.

• You wish to persuade a group of nobles that it would be in their best interests to join you in a campaign against a neighboring lord. Roll Manipulation + Politics (difficulty 7). One success means that they support you but will not commit men; five or more mean that they will personally join the field.

BOOK THREE: CRUSADER

My flesh is cold as the metal I wear, but I feel no true discomfort. Some say it's death to be out here at night, away from the safety of the cities. I've traveled too many leagues on far too many nights to feel true worry. I should be too weary to live, but I cannot force myself to lie down.

The wind churns dark clouds above me, wailing paganlike through the lightless valleys. Miles from here, they are no doubt laughing in torch-lit rooms, drumming taloned fingers on stone sills, sipping nectar from torn throats.

I have earned a name from the children of Cain. Autarkis. Lawless among the lawless. A damned thing, but one who seeks to redeem himself before the Judgment. With God's will, I may yet pull myself into Heaven.

There. The pinprick of light must be leagues and leagues away, over the black hills. My dead eyes serve me far better that they ever did while I drew breath. The remembered taste of blood surges behind my teeth, floods my brain. I taste the wind, and will my heart to beat again for the pleasure of it.

I begin to run.

Chapter Seven: Systems

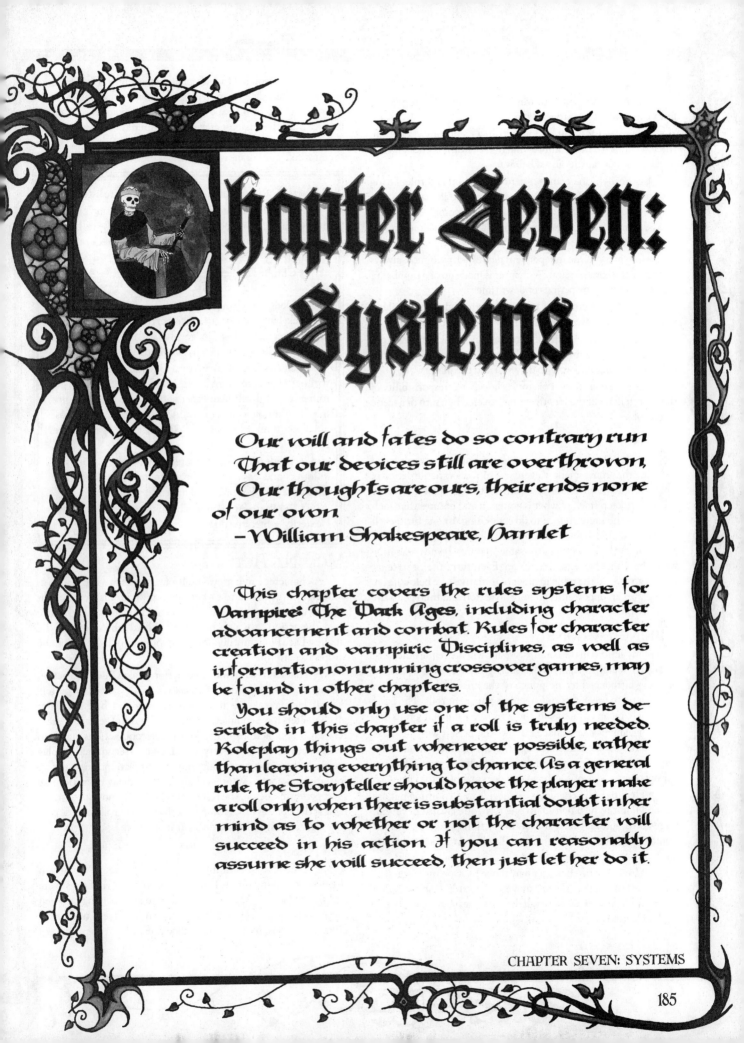

*Our will and fates do so contrary run
That our devices still are overthrown,
Our thoughts are ours, their ends none
of our own.*
— William Shakespeare, Hamlet

This chapter covers the rules systems for Vampire: The Dark Ages, including character advancement and combat. Rules for character creation and vampiric Disciplines, as well as information on running crossover games, may be found in other chapters.

You should only use one of the systems described in this chapter if a roll is truly needed. Roleplay things out whenever possible, rather than leaving everything to chance. As a general rule, the Storyteller should have the player make a roll only when there is substantial doubt in her mind as to whether or not the character will succeed in his action. If you can reasonably assume she will succeed, then just let her do it.

TIME

There are five different ways to describe time, progressing from the smallest unit to the largest.

• Turn — One unit of time within a scene, anywhere from three seconds to three minutes in length. A turn is enough time to take one action (discussed below).

• Scene — One compact period of action and roleplaying that takes place in a single location. A scene is made up of a variable number of turns (as many as it takes to complete it); it can also be completed strictly through roleplaying, which requires no use of turns.

• Chapter — One independent part of a story, almost always played in one game session. A chapter is made up of a number of scenes connected by periods of downtime.

• Story — A complete tale, with an introduction, buildup and climax, that often takes several chapters to complete.

• Chronicle — A series of stories connected by the lives of the characters and perhaps by a broadly conceived theme and plot. It is simply the ongoing story told by you and the players.

The pace of a chapter or story is largely the responsibility of the Storyteller, but the length of time covered by a turn or a scene is less subjective.

TURNS

A scene is divided into turns in order to organize and structure the arrangement of events. A turn is a variable period of time during which characters can do things. This helps the Storyteller keep track of what is going on and ensures that each player gets the same chance to do something. In one turn, each character should be able to do one thing. Additionally, each player should be given about the same amount of time to describe what she wants her character to do. Each turn, the Storyteller should go around the table in order of initiative (see below), give each player an opportunity to state an action and then go to the next person.

TAKING ACTIONS

Many actions in the course of a game will not require die rolls, and can be simply roleplayed out, such as interrogating a prisoner or being introduced to the prince of the area. However, action scenes tend to break this rule, requiring frequent rolls. The basic actions characters can take in one turn without making rolls are:

• **Yielding:** The character allows the person with the next highest initiative to take his action, thereby yielding her turn. She can still take her action at the end of the turn. If everyone, including her opponents, yields as well, no one does anything that turn.

• **Healing:** The character can decide to do nothing but use a Blood Point to heal herself. In one turn, one Health Level can be restored automatically if no other action is taken. A Blood Point can also be used to enhance a Physical Attribute while the character performs other actions.

• **Moving:** The character may move by walking, jogging or running. If she walks, she may move seven yards. If she jogs, she may move 12 yards + Dexterity. If she runs, she may move 20 yards + (3 x Dexterity).

No roll is required to move, but movement is the only action allowed to the character in that turn. In some situations, it can be hazardous to jog or run, and a roll might be required to maintain balance when there is loose gravel on the ground or arrows are raining down. If a character wants to run away from a conflict or encounter, she must dodge unless she is not in melee range or otherwise hindered.

All sorts of other actions require rolls. Some are listed here:

• **Attack:** A character may decide to attack with a melee or ranged weapon or strike someone. The roll made depends on the attack; for instance, a melee attack requires a Dexterity + Melee roll.

• **Climb:** This action requires a Dexterity + Athletics roll.

• **Dodge:** Dodging not only allows a character to avoid an attack, but removes him altogether from the line of attack. A character can make a Dodge roll right after someone tries to hit him, thereby (hopefully) avoiding the blow.

• **Get to Feet:** It takes a turn to get up from the ground without having to make a roll. If a character wants to get to her feet and still take other actions, she can take dice from her announced action and attempt to score at least one success on a Dexterity + Athletics roll (difficulty at least 4).

• **Leadership:** A character may give commands to followers and have them obeyed by making appropriate Charisma (or Manipulation) + Leadership rolls.

• **Sneak up on Enemy:** This action usually requires a Dexterity + Stealth roll.

MULTIPLE ACTIONS

A character can perform multiple actions in a turn (such as dodging and firing an arrow), but he has to divide his dice. To split a Dice Pool among different actions, the character takes the dice from the action at which he is least skilled (the one with the smallest Dice Pool) and divides that Pool among all the actions he wishes to perform.

A character with multiple actions takes his first action during the normal order of initiative (unless he deliberately delays). He may take no more than one action at this time. After all characters have completed their first (or only) action, characters with more actions may take their second actions, again in order of initiative. After everyone has taken a second action, play proceeds with the third and subsequent actions in order of initiative, as above. While a character may delay his action, he must perform it before the rest of the characters move on to their next action, or it is lost. However, a character can always use dice to dodge, as long as he has dice left in his Pool.

SCENES

A scene is a moment in a story when the troupe focuses on the events at hand and roleplays through them as if they were actually occurring. A scene may only need roleplaying between the players and the Storyteller, or it may involve a number of different actions, some requiring dice rolls.

A scene is like a series of shots taken in a movie, in the same location and at the same moment in the story. It is the essence of roleplaying, when players describe their characters' reactions to events rather than explaining what they intend to do.

Time in the story not spent in a scene is called downtime. This can be when characters travel or conduct extensive research, or it can simply be a period during which it isn't necessary to roleplay every moment. Downtime is a break from the intensity of the scene. Though it should not be overused (it can be relatively boring), you shouldn't avoid it altogether. Use downtime to organize players, direct the story more precisely and progress the plot more quickly.

The story can turn into a scene at almost any time. Often it does so quite naturally, without anyone realizing it has happened. For instance, while the Storyteller and the players discuss how the characters intend to make a journey to a neighboring vampire's castle, you may begin to describe what they see along the way. You have gone from downtime to a scene.

Combat

Of course he has a knife. We all have knives. It's 1183, and we're all barbarians.

—James Goldman, *The Lion in Winter*

Combat in the Storyteller system attempts to capture the drama of violent conflict without downplaying the grim reality of what is going on. We have made every effort to create a system true to the dynamics, limitations and viciousness of real combat while still leaving room for the unique elements vampires bring to it.

There are three types of combat, all of which use the same basic system yet have some minor differences. They are: missile combat, melee and brawl.

• Missile combat is any type of armed combat using missile weapons, usually bows and crossbows. Opponents normally need to be within sight of each other to engage in missile combat.

• Melee refers to fighting with hand weapons, anything from table legs to broadswords. Opponents need to be within one or two yards of each other to engage in melee.

• A brawl describes a hand-to-hand battle fought with bare hands, unarmed combat. Opponents need to be within touching distance to engage in a brawl.

The rolls made in combat determine whether or not an attack succeeds, whether the target dodges and how much damage the target suffers. Almost all combat turns are measured to be around three seconds long, though they take somewhat longer than that to resolve.

There should only be two dice rolls involved on the part of the attacker in any combat maneuver: an attack roll and a damage (or effect) roll. All effects from the maneuver should be figured through these two rolls. An exception to this rule is a movement-based maneuver (see page 193).

As with all action scenes, combat turns begin with an initiative roll. However, because combat can sometimes get a little sticky, divide the turn into three stages — initiative, attack and resolution — to make it easier to keep track of things.

DESCRIBING THE SCENE

At the beginning of each turn, the Storyteller should describe the scene from each character's perspective. Sometimes this will be a wrap-up of the last turn, making it clear to all players what occurred. This sort of constant description is essential to avoid confusion.

This is the Storyteller's chance to organize and arrange things so that all goes smoothly when the players begin to interact with the environment he has created. The Storyteller should make his description as interesting as possible, leaving open all sorts of possibilities for characters' actions.

STAGE ONE: INITIATIVE

This stage is when characters declare their actions, and organizes the turn. Characters can take a number of different actions, from leaping behind a wall to shouting a warning. Each player must declare what his character is doing in as much detail as the Storyteller requires. At this point, everyone needs to decide what weapon to use, if any.

Players make initiative rolls using Wits + Alertness (difficulty 4, though Storytellers can vary this roll if they so desire), and the Storyteller rolls for any non-player characters involved in the scene. The character with the most successes acts first (or, if the Storyteller chooses, the one with the highest Dexterity goes first), while characters who rolled fewer successes take their actions in descending order of successes. Some characters will act simultaneously because they rolled the same number of successes. Those who gain no successes at all on this roll go last, and a botch means the character does not get to act that turn — his bowstring breaks, or he stumbles and cannot punch or dodge.

Remember to have players declare what actions they want their characters to take during the combat turn before going to the attack stage. A player splitting his character's Dice Pool must declare how many dice he is allocating to each action.

A character's actions happen when it is her turn to act. The only exception to this is the dodge, which a character can perform at any time as long as she has dice left in her Dice Pool.

AMBUSHES

Sometimes it will be obvious who goes first, such as when an ambush was set or when one combatant is clearly caught by surprise. In combat, however, if the Storyteller intends to let the opponents have a free shot at the characters, he should allow the players to make Perception rolls (difficult ones) to see if they notice something just before the bad guys spring. The difficulty depends on how well the ambush was set (usually 8). The number of successes the players score indicates the number of dice they can roll on their first actions (usually dodges).

STAGE TWO: ATTACK

The attack is the meat of the combat turn. This stage is where the success or failure of an action is determined, as well as something of its potential impact on the target.

There are three different types of attack rolls; the type of combat determines which one to use.

- For missile combat, roll Dexterity + Archery.
- For melee (with weapons) combat, roll Dexterity + Melee.
- For hand-to-hand (without weapons) combat, roll Dexterity + Brawl.

The weapon or attack used by the attacker determines the base difficulty of the roll. The number of dice rolled might be modified by the bow's rate of fire, but the difficulty is usually modified only by the circumstances of the attack. If no successes are rolled, the character fails his attack and inflicts no damage. If the player rolls a botch, then not only does the attack fail, but something nasty happens to the attacker; the Storyteller needs to invent something truly awful.

OPTIONAL INITIATIVE FOR MELEE

If one opponent has a significantly longer weapon than the other (dagger vs. bastard sword, for example), and neither opponent is using a shield or parrying weapon, it is virtually impossible for the person with the shorter weapon to gain the initiative. In order to place himself in a position where he can attack, he must get inside the range of his opponent's weapon. If the Storyteller desires, she may rule that in one-on-one combat, the person with the longer weapon will always go first. It is entirely possible for the person with the short weapon to dodge (or parry) the attack successfully and then make an attack of his own, but that is about the only way he can close the distance.

DODGING

Any time someone attacks a character, she has the option of dodging. In fact, a player may announce at any time that her character is using an action (or part of one, by dividing her Dice Pool) to dodge, simply by declaring "Dodge!" before the opponent makes an attack roll. Some situations may prohibit a dodge, such as confined quarters or when the character has been surprised. The required roll is Dexterity + Dodge; each success subtracts one success from the attacker's roll. A character can even subtract successes from different opponents, though this means dividing successes between (or among) them.

The difficulty to dodge melee or brawling attacks is a base 6, increased by one for each opponent after the first.

Difficulty	Terrain
2	By moving back half a step, the character is back under full cover.
4	Full cover within diving distance (one yard)
6	Full cover within running distance (three yards)
7	Partial cover within running distance (three yards)
8	Flat and featureless, no cover (the character dives to the ground)

In missile combat, the difficulty depends on the availability of nearby cover a character can dive behind to avoid getting hit. Each success removes one of the opponent's successes. After such a dodge attempt, the character usually ends up behind some sort of cover or, at the very least, lying on the ground (if there is no cover to be found).

The difficulty to dodge during missile combat is determined by the proximity of cover.

Stage Three: Resolution

During this stage, characters determine the damage inflicted by their attacks, and the Storyteller describes what occurs in the turn. The Resolution Stage is a mixture of game and story, for though the dice never lie, the Storyteller must interpret what luck has decreed.

Damage: Each weapon or attack allows the wielder to roll a certain number of dice in order to inflict damage (difficulty 6). Each success causes the target to lose one Health Level. Melee and brawling successes do not add to the damage.

Soak: A target may make a roll to see how much damage she "soaks" because of her natural hardiness. The target rolls Stamina (difficulty 6); each success reduces inflicted damage by one. Fortitude and armor may both add to the number of dice in the soak pool.

Note: Damage and soak rolls are two rolls in **Vampire: The Dark Ages** that cannot be botched.

Combat Summary Chart
Stage One: Initiative

• Roll Wits + Initiative (difficulty 4). The winner declares her action *last* (after she has heard everyone else's actions) and performs it *first*.

• Declare Dice Pool division if performing multiple actions.

Stage Two: Attack

• For missile combat, roll Dexterity + Archery.

• For melee (with weapons) combat, roll Dexterity + Melee.

• For hand-to-hand (without weapons) combat, roll Dexterity + Brawl.

• Dodge: roll Dexterity + Dodge. A character can forfeit some or all of his Dice Pool to dodge at any time; each success subtracts one from the opponent's successes. (However, remember that straying from your declared action will still remove one die from your Dice Pool.)

Stage Three: Resolution

• Roll damage, determined by weapon or maneuver (difficulty 6).

• Soak damage: roll Stamina (difficulty 6).

Freeform Combat (Optional)

The Storyteller should be flexible when arbitrating combat situations; no rules can fully reflect the variety of situations encountered on the battlefield. The Storyteller should feel free to let the players devise rules for special situations not covered by any of the existing combat maneuvers. For their part, players should remember that the Storyteller is the ultimate arbiter in such situations, and her word is final.

If bickering or slowed combat results, go back to the standard maneuvers. They are broad enough to handle most situations. Freeform combat is meant to add depth to the game, not create conflict between the players and the Storyteller.

Medieval Weaponry

Most of these weapons should be familiar, though one or two might be new to you.

A **knife** is a small tool, no more than six or eight inches long, designed for eating, hunting or some manual craft. A **dagger** may be longer, up to 12 inches or even more, and is specifically designed for stabbing.

A **broadsword** is a standard one-handed sword, a couple of feet long, designed for hacking. A **bastard sword** is slightly longer (around three feet), typically used with two hands; a strong person (Strength rating 4 or more) may use a bastard sword in one hand. A **great sword** is anything up to six feet in length, it is two-handed and cannot be used from horseback (Note: few great swords are in use during this period; stats are included for Storytellers wishing to run chronicles in later periods).

A **spear** is a standard peasant weapon, because it is so cheap. It is simply a shaft of wood with a sharp metal point, in total around five to eight feet long. A **lance** is simply a longer spear, used exclusively by mounted knights. A **pitchfork** is used by farmers to move hay and straw; it is a six-foot wooden shaft, splayed into a fork at one end, with sharpened points, and besides a club is the only "weapon" available to most impoverished peasants.

A **battle axe** resembles a modern wood axe and requires two hands to wield. A **hand axe** is a slightly smaller, one-handed weapon. A **poleaxe** is a longer two-handed weapon, usually around six or seven feet long (Note: few, if any, poleaxes are in use during this period; stats are included for Storytellers wishing to run chronicles in later periods).

A **mace** is a wooden haft with a metal head (perhaps spiked or ribbed). A **morning star** is like a mace, except that a chain connects the head to the haft.

A **short bow** is a hunting weapon, three or four feet long, which may be fired from horseback. A **long bow** is around six feet long, and may not be fired from horseback. A **crossbow** is a mechanical device resembling a modern rifle, with a horizontal bow attached to the front end; the bow is drawn by a winch or by hand, and the arrow (called a bolt or quarrel) is placed in the bow. The bowman squeezes a large trigger to release the bow and so shoot the arrow.

A traditional **quarterstaff** is "as tall as the wielder, and as big around as her fist," but any pole, pipe or board that is long enough will suffice. In general, the heavier the object, the more damage it does.

Melee Weapons

Weapon	Difficulty	Damage	Concealment	Strength Required
Knife	5	Strength + 1	P	1
Dagger	4	Strength + 1	C	1
Broadsword	6	Strength + 4	L	2
Bastard Sword	6	Strength + 5	L	3
Great Sword	5	Strength + 6	N	4
Quarterstaff	4	Strength +1 to +3	N	1
Spear, one hand (*1)	7	Strength + 1	N	2
Spear, both hands (*1)	6	Strength + 3	N	1
Lance (*2)	8	Strength + 6	N	2
Pitchfork(2 hands)	6	Strength + 1	N	1
Hand Axe	7	Strength + 5	L	3
Battle Axe	7	Strength + 6	N	3
Poleaxe (*3)	7	Strength + 6	N	3
Mace	6	Strength + 4	T	1
Morning Star	7	Strength + 6	L	1

Ranged Weapons

Weapon	Difficulty	Damage	Rate	Concealment	Strength Required	Range
Short Bow	variable	2	1/2	T	2	60 yards
Long Bow	variable	4	1/2	N	4	120 yards
Crossbow (*4)	variable	3	1/4	N	2	90 yards
Spear (thrown)	variable	Strength + 2	N/A	N	2	N/A
Knife (thrown)	variable	Strength	N/A	N	2	10 yards
Rocks	variable	Strength-1	N/A	P	2	10 yards
Hatchets	+1	Strength + 1	N/A	C	2	12 yards

Concealment: P = may be hidden in a pouch (medieval tailors do not make garments with pockets!); C = can be hidden in the folds of clothing such as a tunic or short cloak; L = may be hidden in a long cloak, coat or monk's robes; N = may not be concealed on your person.

Rate: 1/3 = requires three full turns to reload. A bow usually fires every other turn, as it takes one turn to prepare an arrow and another to aim and fire. A quick shot may be taken with a short bow or long bow, but to do so the archer may only roll half her usual Dice Pool for the roll.

Range: You may shoot up to double the range listed, but it will be considered a long-range shot (with a higher difficulty).

Weapon Notes

*1: Spears are usually six to eight feet long, and are held out leveled toward the target before an attack.

*2: Lances are cavalry weapons. Damage if used on foot is only Strength. If used at a full gallop it inflicts Strength + 6 and automatically gains the wielder the first attack if used against opponents with normal hand weapons. Used from the back of a horse moving at a slower rate, the lance does less damage (Strength + 3, for example) at the Storyteller's discretion.

*3: A **poleaxe** usually has a point set above the axe head, and can also be used as a spear. The heads of some poleaxes also have additional features, such a hook used to drag a mounted opponent off his horse.

*4: Botches with morning stars are always particularly bad. Either the ball and chain become entangled in some inconvenient object, or the character loses control of the weapon and strikes herself.

Thrown Weapons

Many weapons can be thrown, including knives, hatchets, spears and rocks. The difficulty of hitting with a thrown object or weapon is determined by dividing the range in yards to the target by the Strength of the character (yards/Strength). Thus, if a character with a Strength of 3 throws a rock at a doorway 16 yards away, the difficulty of the attack is six (always round up).

The maximum range a character can throw a small object is Strength x 10 in yards. The weight that can be thrown is two pounds per point of Strength (or more if the thrown object is aerodynamic). The Dice Pool to hit is made up of Dexterity + Athletics. Strength determines the difficulty and, of course, the number of dice in the damage Pool. The number of successes on the attack roll does not increase the damage.

At the Storyteller's discretion, a character can make one-for-one trade-offs between range and weight. Thus a character with a Strength of 5 could throw an eight-pound object as though his Strength were 6, or a 12-pound object as though his Strength were 4.

Also at the Storyteller's discretion, if a character misses a knife or hatchet attack by one success, the weapon strikes the target with the handle or haft. The Dice Pool for damage should be reduced by five dice, very possibly causing no damage.

Rocks

Rocks are found almost everywhere; they are the basis of the thrown weapon system. They do Strength damage.

Knives

Knives use the throwing rules above, with one exception. Always treat a thrown knife as being one pound heavier than it really is; this represents the control required to strike the target blade-first. Throwing knives do Strength + 1 damage.

An Arrow Through the Heart

In order to shoot an arrow through the heart of a vampire, and so stake him, raise the difficulty of the shot by two (to a maximum of 10). Remember, in order to stake a vampire, the character must achieve at least five successes and inflict three Health Levels of damage.

Hatchets

Hatchets use the throwing rules above; however, a hatchet is a natural lever for multiplying force. Add one to the Strength of a thrown hatchet attack made by someone with an appropriate specialty. However, hatchets are harder to control than knives, so always increase the difficulty of a thrown hatchet attack by one in addition to all other modifiers.

Spears and Javelins

A javelin is a short spear about four feet in length. Spears meant for throwing are also generally around this length.

Armor

Soldiers in the Dark Medieval world typically wear leather or metal armor to protect themselves. Leather of different thicknesses could be used, quilted or with rings or studs attached, layered, reinforced or hardened. Several different varieties of chainmail could be combined with shaped metal plates; there are dozens of possible combinations.

However, to keep these systems nice and simple, let's assume that there are four different classifications for medieval armor.

• **Light Armor:** Pieces of leather, perhaps hardened or quilted, perhaps with a hood. These leathers are clearly different from the normal woolen clothes worn by ordinary folk. This category includes armor worn by gate guards, outlaws, city watchmen and by soldiers in garrisons during peacetime. It also includes the padding worn by knights and soldiers beneath their metal armor.

VAMPIRE: THE DARK AGES

- **Composite Armor:** A mish-mash of different armor types, made up primarily of pieces of leather reinforced by studs and rings, maybe including a battered helmet and scraps of rusty chainmail. Composite armor has usually been assembled by looting the dead after battles and buying or improvising odd bits piecemeal. This is usually worn by mercenary bands or well-established bandits.

- **Heavy Armor:** Chainmail or heavily reinforced leathers, usually worn with a helmet like a metal cap, with proper quilted padding underneath. The face remains exposed, and sometimes the neck and hands are also vulnerable. This is worn by men-at-arms and impoverished noblemen when they are expecting a fight. It weighs at least 50 pounds, so it is only worn when danger is thought to be near.

- **Knight's Armor:** Chainmail covers the body, including the neck, with bulky gauntlets on the hands and a large, heavy helmet over the head. (The helmet looks like a bucket with slits to see out of.) It can weigh over 100 pounds, and only the wealthier nobles can afford to buy or maintain such suits.

Note that the typical "plate mail" armor many people think of as belonging to this period came along several centuries later, and was not in use very long. Around the same time full plate armor came into vogue, early firearms also came into use, making said armor all but useless. Great weapons (great swords, great axes, poleaxes, etc.) were also from this period and were developed partially to serve as can openers against opponents in plate armor.

The exact effects of wearing armor are described on the chart below.

The Protection rating indicates the number of dice added to the character's Dice Pool to "soak" damage. Normal mortals may roll this number of dice to resist damage inflicted against them; vampires add this rating to their normal "soak" rolls, by rolling Stamina + Fortitude (if any) + Armor Protection.

The Dexterity and Perception modifications apply for as long as the person wears the armor (though neither Attribute may be reduced below a rating of 1 by these penalties).

Minimum Strength denotes the minimum Strength rating a character must have to wear the armor.

USING SHIELDS

A character using a shield is more difficult to strike in combat than a character without a shield. However, shields are heavy, bulky objects, made of wood, leather and metal. Shields are only carried in time of war or serious civil unrest, and are not concealable. There are two main varieties of medieval shields:

Footmen's Shields are round or triangular, and one to three feet across. Anyone fighting a character who is using a footman's shield has the difficulties of his or her Melee attack rolls increased by one. (So the difficulty of striking her with a battle axe rises from 7 to 8.)

Cavalry Shields are long, thin shields, often kite-shaped. They are usually only used by cavalrymen; leather straps from the horseman's shoulders bear the shield's considerable weight.

If used by a dismounted character, the cavalry shield increases enemies' Melee attack difficulties by two (e.g., the difficulty of striking her with a battle axe rises from 7 to 9). If used by a mounted character, the effectiveness of the shield depends upon the side from which he or she is being attacked. As the shield covers the character's left side, enemies to the left have their Melee difficulties increased by 3. However, the shield cannot be moved to cover the right side, and so attacks from the character's right are resolved as usual.

Note that shields do not protect a character from attacks from the rear.

SPECIAL MANEUVERS

As is the case with all rolls, the default difficulty for any maneuver is 6. If the maneuver is designed to fool an opponent, the difficulty is usually the opponent's Wits (or Perception) with a + 4 constant modifier. Sometimes the difficulty is an opponent's Ability + 4, or, rarely, an opponent's Attribute plus an Ability (such as Wits + Brawl), in which case the constant modifier is not used.

RESISTED ROLLS

Sometimes a character can resist an attack against him, whether by dodging, performing an evasive action or using another maneuver. The Storyteller should decide whether a combatant should receive a resistance roll. The resistance roll will often require the combatant to split his Dice Pool if he also wants to attack that turn.

SUCCESSES

Generally, an attack needs only one success to hit; damage is then rolled. In some instances, however, a set number of successes is required, such as when a character tries to grapple an opponent; he must gain more successes than the opponent's Strength score.

DAMAGE (EFFECT)

Use the Brawling Chart to determine damage and adjust from there for special conditions.

If the effect is to fool or confuse an opponent, the general rule is that each success on the attack roll subtracts one die from the opponent's Dice Pool. In this case, only the attack roll is made; there is no separate damage roll.

Multiple Actions: As always, a character will have to split his Dice Pool to perform multiple actions in one turn.

Movement: Normally a character may not move and attack in the same action. The Storyteller can allow movement-based maneuvers to be performed with the following guidelines:

Armor	Protection	Dexterity Adjustment	Perception Adjustment	Minimum Strength
Light Armor	1	-	-	1
Composite Armor	2	-1	-	1
Heavy Armor	3	-1	-1	2
Knight's Armor	4	-2	-2	3

If a character is performing some acrobatic feat, such as leaping, swinging from a chandelier, etc., then a Dexterity + Athletics roll may also be required. The difficulty depends on the complexity of the maneuver. A simple roll to determine leaping distance has a difficulty of only 3 (see "Jumping," pp. 207), while a leap from a hurtling train onto a running horse may have a difficulty as high as 9. The character must split his Dice Pool between the acrobatic roll and the attack roll. However, the Storyteller should use the Automatic Success rule whenever possible.

There are some exceptions to this rule, in the interest of dramatic license. If a player has seen many swashbuckler movies and wants to use similar flamboyant moves, the Storyteller might allow her to swing from a chandelier and attack without having to split her Dice Pool.

GENERAL COMPLICATIONS

• **Changing Actions:** The difficulty increases by one.

• **Immobilization:** The difficulty to hit an immobilized target is decreased by two.

• **Stunning:** When Health Level damage exceeds Stamina rating, the target is stunned and cannot act next turn.

MELEE AND BRAWL COMPLICATIONS

• **Multiple Opponents:** If a character is battling multiple opponents in close combat, that character's attack and dodge difficulties are increased by one per opponent (to a maximum of 10).

• **Flank and Rear Attacks:** The difficulty of a flank attack is lowered by one, while that of a rear attack is lowered by two.

MELEE COMPLICATIONS

• **Disarm:** This maneuver is an attempt to knock the weapon from an opponent's hand. The character rolls Dexterity + Melee; add one to the weapon's normal difficulty. If at least three successes are scored, then she rolls the weapon's damage; if she scores more successes than the opponent's Strength rating, the opponent is disarmed. A botch usually means the character drops her own weapon.

Roll: Dex + Melee	**Difficulty:** +1
Damage: Special	**Actions:** 1

• **Double Strike**

Knife fighting is based on speed and reflexes. A character using this specialty can split her Dice Pool between two attacks against the same target (without the use of Celerity). Each attack Dice Pool receives one additional die. The difficulty for each attack is 5. Damage is determined normally for each attack. The character's Dexterity + 1 is the maximum number of dice that may be used for each attack.

The maximum number of additional attacks is determined by dividing the character's skill by two. If a character has six dots in Melee, she can attack three times in one turn by dividing her Dice Pool three ways. Dexterity + 1 is still the maximum number of dice that may be employed in any attack. Also, the difficulties for all attacks increase to 7.

Roll: Dex + Melee	**Difficulty:** +1
Damage: Special	**Actions:** 1

• **Parry:** A character using a melee weapon may elect to parry an attack, using her weapon to block the blow. Like a dodge, a parry can be performed at any time, so long as the character still has dice in her Dice Pool. A character cannot parry with a weapon as small as a knife, but she can use a sword or axe. She rolls Dexterity + Melee (difficulty 6). Each success subtracts one from an opponent's number of attack successes.

A botch on a parry roll usually means that the parrying weapon is knocked from the character's hand.

Roll: Dex + Melee	**Difficulty:** 6
Damage: none	**Actions:** Special

• **Stake:** If you are going for the heart, your difficulty is automatically raised by two, and you must achieve at least five levels of damage for it to penetrate the heart sufficiently to immobilize your opponent.

Roll: Dex + Brawl	**Difficulty:** 8
Damage: Strength	**Actions:** 1

• **Sidearm Throws**

This powerful but difficult technique is best used with smaller throwing weapons, such as hatchets and daggers. Rather than using an overarm throw as normally seen in knife throwing competitions, this technique involves swinging the arm around to the side of the body when throwing, releasing the weapon in an underarm style. This uses many more of the large muscle groups of the body (even the legs and hips, when done correctly), resulting in a longer, harder throw. The disadvantages to this style are that the character must have room to swing the arm widely, and that accuracy is much harder to achieve. When a character is using a sidearm throw, her effective Strength is increased by two, but her effective Dexterity is decreased by one.

Roll: (Dex -1) + Athletics	**Difficulty:** 8
Damage: Strength + 2	**Actions:** 1

• **Sweeps**

Staves can be used to "sweep" an opponent's legs out from underneath him in a fight. Treat this maneuver like a throw, ending with the opponent falling in place — but with the additional advantage that the character does not need to close in with the opponent.

Roll: Dex + Melee	**Difficulty:** +1
Damage: Special	**Actions:** 1

BRAWL COMPLICATIONS

• **Block:** A character can elect to block instead of dodge. Like a dodge, a block can be performed at any time, so long as the character still has dice in his Dice Pool. Blocks may be made only against fists, kicks or blunt weapons. A blocking action cannot block a sword or arrow. Roll Dexterity + Brawl (difficulty 6); each success subtracts one from an opponent's number of attack successes.

Roll: Dex + Brawl	**Difficulty:** 6
Damage: none	**Actions:** Special

• **Body Slam:** A character charges forward, hurling his weight into his opponent. It is possible to take damage with this attack; bodies were not meant to be used as battering rams. A character needs three successes to unbalance an opponent. He inflicts one Health Level of damage on himself for each success fewer than three.

If the attack succeeds, the opponent is thrown off-balance; difficulties for the rest of her actions this turn are increased by two. Also, if the opponent does not succeed in a Dexterity + Athletics roll (difficulty of the attacker's successes + 3), she falls to the ground. The base damage done equals the attacker's Strength; each success scored on the attack roll above the minimum adds one to this base. If the attacker does not score at least three successes, this maneuver fails. He falls to the ground and is treated as though he has no dice left in his Pool.

The character can move his full running distance, but he must run in a straight line; weaving around in circles does not build sufficient momentum.

Roll: Dex + Brawl   **Difficulty:** 7
Damage: Special   **Actions:** 1

• **Grapple:** An attacker can try to grab a foe, hoping to immobilize him or get a better chance at biting. If the attacker scores more successes than the opponent's Strength, the attacker can immobilize him. In the next round, she can begin to inflict harm. Any character struck by this attack loses his attacks for the current turn.

If the attacker misses altogether (by failing the Dexterity + Brawl roll), she is knocked down and must spend an action getting to her feet.

Continuing to grapple during each turn after the first requires the combatants to make opposed Strength + Brawl rolls. Whoever accumulates more successes may immobilize the other. If both score the same number of successes, neither gains the upper hand this turn.

Roll: Dex + Brawl   **Difficulty:** 6
Damage: Strength   **Actions:** 1

• **Kick:** A kick can range from a very simple front kick to aerial spins. Depending on the circumstances, the difficulty and damage modifier may be adjusted (Storyteller's discretion). The damage from a kick is never aggravated.

Roll: Dex + Brawl   **Difficulty:** 7
Damage: Strength + 1   **Actions:** 1

• **Punch:** The attacker balls her hand into a tight fist and swings it with all her might. The Storyteller may adjust the difficulty and/or allow extra dice if the attacker decides the type of punch she wishes to deliver: hook, jab, haymaker, etc. The damage from a punch is never aggravated.

Roll: Dex + Brawl   **Difficulty:** 6
Damage: Strength **Actions:** 1

• **Bite:** After a successful bite, a character may subsequently drain his victim's blood. Causes aggravated wounds.

Roll: Dex + Brawl   **Difficulty:** 6
Damage: Strength + 1   **Actions:** 1

• **Claw:** Only those with Protean, and claws extended, can attempt this maneuver. Causes aggravated wounds.

Roll: Dex + Brawl   **Difficulty:** 6
Damage: Strength + 2   **Actions:** 1

Horses

In the Dark Medieval world, horses are used much as motor vehicles are in the modern world — to allow mortals to travel more swiftly and with less effort. However, they are not mere vehicles, like cars or motorcycles, nor are they unthinking automatons. They are living creatures, often with recognizable personalities. Keep this in mind.

Horses are easily startled. They shy away from loud noises, and may panic and bolt if startled or if confronted with a frightening situation (like an angry Lupine or a battle in progress). They hate dogs. Some also have annoying habits, like a tendency to bite or kick, a dislike of one particular type of person (e.g., men, women, children), a refusal to jump fences or ditches, a tendency to stop for a snack of grass despite the rider's efforts to spur them on, etc. Cainites should also note that horses aren't suicidal, and won't want to gallop through the night, especially through woods or over uneven medieval roads. They also need a lot of care (generally at least two hours per day per horse).

Storytellers should try to make characters' horses individuals, with their own foibles and traits. Characters may be able to train horses to some extent (such as training a horse to kick on command, or to remain calm in frightening situations) but the characters should never be able to make their horses behave like machines.

Mounted Combat

Fighting from horseback is not easy. Some weapons are simply unusable by mounted combatants. Storytellers should be suspicious of players who claim that their characters are swinging huge great swords or polearms from horseback. Long bows cannot be drawn back fully by a mounted archer.

In any case, a character's ability to fight from horseback is limited by her Ride Ability. When a mounted character's Attacks are resolved, use either the Melee or Ride Ability, whichever gives the smaller Dice Pool.

So, if a character has a Dexterity rated at 3, Melee 4, but Ride of only 1, she rolls four dice to resolve the attack, not seven. Only if her Ride rating equaled or exceeded her Melee rating would she roll her full Dexterity + Melee Dice Pool to attack.

Maneuvers Table

Maneuver	Initiative	Roll	Accuracy	Damage
Grapple	-1	Strength + Brawl	0	Strength
Body Slam	0	Strength + Brawl	+1	Special
Block	—	Dexterity + Brawl	—	0
Kick	0	Dexterity + Brawl	-1	Strength + 1
Punch	0	Dexterity + Brawl	0	Strength
Bite	-2	Dexterity + Brawl	+2	Strength + 1
Claw	0	Dexterity + Brawl	0	Strength + 2

Character Development

This section discusses the ways a character can increase (or decrease) in power and abilities.

Experience

During a story, characters learn many things. Much of what they learn is not the type of thing that can be recorded on character sheets, but something the players keep in mind thereafter. They may learn never to leave a window ajar during the day, or never to walk into a dark alley with a light behind them. Sometimes, however, what characters learn can be recorded.

At the end of each story, the Storyteller awards experience points to each character, normally giving the same amount to each one. The players then record the points on their character sheets. Experience points can be used to increase Traits.

The cost for raising Traits varies widely; see the chart below for specifics. The cost is almost always based on the product of the present rating and a certain number. Thus, if the character has an Alertness rating of 2, and the player wants to raise it to 3, it costs four experience points to do so. If the character does not have the Trait at all, the cost is listed as a "new" Trait. A Trait can only be increased by one dot per story.

Roleplay It

As the Storyteller, you should not let a player spend her experience points to raise any Trait she wishes — it's a little more involved than that. The increased Trait must be something the character had a chance to learn or use during the story; either the character achieved great success through use of the Trait, or she made a big mistake from which she can learn. In the case of Willpower, something must have actually occurred to bolster the character's self-confidence.

You should only allow Trait increases if they have been or can be woven into the story. At the very least, changes need to make sense in terms of the story and not simply be changes the player makes because she wants her character to gain certain powers or skills. The more you force the players to make sense of their experiences, the more character development as a whole is furthered.

Awarding Experience Points

Assigning experience points requires a careful balance between rewarding the players and maintaining game balance. If you follow the guidelines below, you probably won't get into too much trouble, but feel free to experiment as you see fit.

End of Each Chapter

Give each character one to five experience points at the end of each chapter (game session). One point is given, whatever the outcome, as a function of simply participating (remember, sometimes we learn despite ourselves).

- **One point — Automatic:** Each player gets one point after every game session.

- **One point — Learning Curve:** The character learned something from his experiences during the chapter. Ask the player to describe what his character learned before you award the point.

- **One point — Acting:** The player roleplayed well — not just entertainingly, but appropriately. Award for exceptional roleplaying only; your standards should get increasingly higher. In most cases, award this only to the person who did the best roleplaying in the troupe.

- **One point — Concept:** The player acted out her character's concept very well.

- **One point — Heroism:** When a character risks herself for others, such as when she fends off several enemies with torches in order to allow the rest of the group to escape, give her an experience point. Don't let characters take advantage of this; there is a fine line between heroism and stupidity.

End of Each Story

At the end of each story, you can assign each player one to three *additional* experience points over and above the one to five points earned for completing the chapter.

- **One point — Success:** The characters succeeded in their immediate mission or goal. Perhaps it was not a complete success, but at least a marginal victory was achieved.

- **One point — Danger:** The character experienced great danger during the story and survived.

- **One point — Wisdom:** The player (and thus the character) exhibited great wits or resourcefulness, or came up with an idea that enabled the group to succeed.

If you want to award even more points, thus allowing the characters to develop even more quickly, simply invent new categories in which to award experience. These can even vary from story to story and can be based on the specific circumstances of that story.

Increasing and Decreasing Traits

The costs for permanently raising the Traits listed below are listed on the Experience Chart.

Experience Chart

Trait	Cost
Attribute	current rating x 4
New Ability	3
Ability	current rating x 2
Virtue	current rating x 3
Road	current rating x 2
New Discipline	10
Clan Discipline	current rating x 5
Other Discipline	current rating x 7
Willpower	current rating x 2
New Thaumaturgy Path	7
Thaumaturgy Path (primary)	current rating x 4
Thaumaturgy Path (secondary)	current rating x 5

RAISING DISCIPLINES

Disciplines are probably the most difficult aspect of a character for a player to develop, though it is certainly a high priority if the character indeed wishes to live forever — only vampiric power provides real and continuous safety.

Though characters gain Disciplines simply by spending experience points, the Storyteller may want to restrict the process somewhat more. For instance, if a character wishes to learn a new Discipline in which she had no current rating, she may have to search out a tutor or discover a magical amulet which awakens her latent Discipline. How this works is up to the Storyteller; unless the Storyteller says otherwise, players can simply use experience points to purchase Disciplines.

GAINING VIA

Players can raise the ratings of their Roads as well, but only after prolonged and consistent artistic or aesthetically based behavior. A player may spend experience points to increase her standing on a Road only after her character has done a "good deed," as defined by his particular ethos. The Storyteller, as always, is the final adjudicator of when this occurs.

As the Storyteller, be very strict about how characters can regain Via. Remember that over the course of the chronicle, the characters may slowly lose more and more Via. Preserving the status quo should be difficult enough for a character, and actually gaining Via should be next to impossible.

You may wish to make Via gain a specific reward for a particularly vigorous story in which there was no real or practical reward offered or given. Only the rescue of some unfortunate or the persistent search for some kernel of truth or goodness will be enough to gain new Via. Even then the gain doesn't have to be certain; you could require a Virtue roll to gain the point.

GAINING WILLPOWER

Characters can buy permanent Willpower with experience points, but sometimes you may give a player a specific chance to raise his Willpower. The opportunity to gain Willpower makes a great motivation for a story, especially your more bizarre ones.

Characters can lose permanent Willpower as well. This occurs whenever a player botches a Willpower roll. Luckily, this is a rare thing, for Willpower is usually only rolled during frenzies, when employing the dangerous forces of Thaumaturgy or in order to resist Dominate.

BACKGROUNDS

Background Traits never change through the use of experience points. Instead, the change happens as a normal course of events during the chronicle. Eventually, the Storyteller will note the changes, and the character's Traits will increase. A player may wish to ask the Storyteller if one of her Background Traits should be changed, but this should not be done too often. The Storyteller may design a list of things characters must accomplish in order to gain in a Background — the players may or may not be shown the list. To gain a new retainer, for example, a vampire has to find the right subject, befriend or Dominate him, and train him in the duties she wishes performed.

PERSONALITY DEVELOPMENT

A character's personality can change over the course of the chronicle, but for the most part the changes come through roleplaying, not by simply changing the character sheet. For instance, as time passes, character motivations change as well. Deciding when and how a character's motivations change can add a great depth to your roleplaying. However, when a character's Demeanor or true Nature changes, it should be recorded on the character sheet as well. No aspect of personality can ever be changed through the use of experience points.

DEMEANOR

Though the Demeanor listed on the character sheet is simply the way the character most commonly presents herself, it is not an absolute standard of behavior. Changing the Demeanor of a character may help the player focus on the change in personality. A player may change his character's Demeanor at any point in the game, but should either tell the Storyteller he has done so or make it evident through his roleplaying.

Sometimes the Storyteller might suggest the change after watching the way the character is played, simply as a way of alerting the player that she has noticed the change in personality. Keep in mind that it really isn't all that important. Demeanor is only a tool the player uses to focus and direct roleplaying. If a change in Demeanor is called for or seems appropriate, the player should feel free to go right ahead and change it.

NATURE

A player may also change her character's Nature, but rules for this are somewhat more restrictive than those for changing Demeanor. A character's Nature is central to who and what he is — it is the locus of his being. A change in Nature is akin to a change in personality; everything is different after it occurs. It should not be decided on the spur of the moment, but must be thoroughly considered. The Storyteller should force a player to roleplay the change over a number of game sessions; a story might even be created around this tumultuous transformation. Conversely, sometimes it may simply make sense that the change in personality comes about suddenly as a reaction to what has occurred to or around the character. Though it is certainly up to the Storyteller's discretion, a change in Nature sometimes results in a reshuffling of Virtues, though never a change in the ratings of a character's Via and Willpower.

PHYSICAL STATES

These systems discuss the parameters of health and the lack of it. Injuries and healing are discussed, as is the difference between the vampiric and mortal frames.

INJURY

There are many different ways a character can sustain injuries, but **Vampire: The Dark Ages** measures injuries in only one way: the Health Level. A player records injuries in terms of Health Levels; each wound causes the loss of one or more Health Levels. Simply check off Health Levels as the character loses them, so that the last check made indicates the character's current Health Level. As the character regains Health Levels, erase the marks.

Think of Health as a spectrum with Bruised at one end and Incapacitated at the other. As a character takes more wounds, he travels down the spectrum until he finally reaches Incapacitated. When he heals, he simply removes the marks, one by one, until he is again in perfect health.

Each success on an opponent's damage roll causes the loss of one Health Level. If an enemy scores (for example) two successes, the player checks off two Health Levels, starting with Bruised and going down to Hurt.

When a vampire reaches Incapacitated, she is one Health Level away from death. If she is injured one more time, or if it is impossible to stem the flow of blood from her body, she will die.

HEALING

Vampires are dead and never recover naturally from wounds. They must always use Blood Points to heal themselves. One Blood Point will heal one Health Level; this always takes one turn to accomplish.

Normally, a vampire remains still when healing, taking no other action, but he can attempt to heal while performing other actions. A character must make a Stamina + Survival (difficulty 6) roll to see if such healing is successful. Success indicates the character heals successfully while engaged in other activities. A failure indicates that the Health Level is not regained and the Blood Point is still lost. A botch causes the character to lose an additional Health Level.

AGGRAVATED WOUNDS

Vampires occasionally suffer wounds so severe they cannot simply use Blood Points to heal them. These are known as aggravated wounds, and are commonly created by sunlight, fire or the claws and teeth of other undead. Aggravated wounds require both blood and time to heal. Aggravated wounds can only be soaked by vampires who possess the Discipline of Fortitude.

Aggravated wounds can only be healed at the rate of one per day of rest and cost of five Blood Points per Health Level healed. Additional levels can be healed in a night if the character spends five additional Blood Points and one Willpower point per level cured. Aggravated wounds should be indicated on the character sheet with an **X** rather than a check. The Storyteller can also deem any injury to be an aggravated injury.

FINAL DEATH

Though vampires are no longer mortal, they still face the possibility of Final Death. It may be tempting to imagine vampires as virtual gods, capable of doing nearly anything and of withstanding nearly anything, but there are ways to kill even vampires. A vampire who dies again may not be brought back to unlife and is said to have suffered the Final Death.

Inflicting aggravated wounds on a severely injured vampire is the most common way in which he can be extinguished. If a vampire has no Blood Pool or Health Levels left, and sustains an aggravated wound, he is utterly destroyed. Sometimes the Final Death will result in the complete and rapid disintegration of the body, and within minutes all that will be left is a pile of ashes.

Vampires can also be killed if all the blood is sucked from them by another of their kind. Deep water pressure, certain vampiric diseases and decapitation are other ways in which a vampire can be

extinguished. You will need to decide how death can result from these dangers in your chronicle, based on the rules given in this section.

MORTAL DEATH

When a mortal reaches Incapacitated, she is one Health Level away from death. If she is injured one more time or it is not possible to stem the flow of blood from her body, she will die. Death is final for mortals unless they are Embraced just before they are snatched away to the everlasting. It is possible for a vampire to take a newly dead corpse and turn it into a vampire if no more than five minutes have passed since death.

Of course, mortals heal differently than do vampires. With proper medical attention, mortals recover based on the following chart. Note that the time given is how long it takes to recover that level — other levels must be healed as well. Thus, if the mortal

takes three months to recover from being Mauled, he must still take the time to heal Wounded, Injured and so one.

SOURCES OF INJURY

There are many ways to inflict harm upon a character. These sources of injury are described below.

COMBAT

Combat wounds are dealt with more fully above. Each success on an opponent's damage roll causes the loss of one Health Level.

FALLING

Occasionally, characters will fall. Use the chart below to calculate damage. Characters can make Stamina rolls to try to "soak" damage. The difficulty is 8; each success means one fewer Health Level is lost. A botch means an additional Health Level is lost.

Health Level	Time
Bruised	One Day
Hurt	Three Days
Injured	One Week
Wounded	One Month
Mauled	Three Months
Crippled	Three Months *

*Not only do mortals have to heal this Health Level, but they lose one point from one of their Physical Attributes as well. Mortals who reach Incapacitated heal at the Storyteller's discretion; some will go into a coma for the rest of their lives.

Distance (in feet)	Injury
5	One Health Level
10	Two Health Levels
20	Three Health Levels
30	Four Health Levels
40	Five Health Levels
50	Six Health Levels
60	Seven Health Levels
70	Eight Health Levels
80	Nine Health Levels
90+	Ten Health Levels

FIRE

Fire is quite hazardous to vampires, and they fear it more than nearly anything else. Fire always causes aggravated damage, and therefore it can kill vampires. Any size flame can potentially harm a vampire, but they can resist the effects if (and *only* if) they possess Fortitude. Have players roll Stamina + Fortitude (difficulty varies, see the chart below for ideas). The characters must roll every turn they are in the flames to see if they can resist the damage. If they fail, they take from one to three Health Levels of damage (see the second chart below), while if they succeed, they take one fewer level of damage per success than they normally would. If they botch, then they are harmed in some special way — perhaps they lose their eyesight or an arm is maimed.

Difficulty	Heat of Fire
Three	Heat of a candle (first degree burns)
Five	Heat of a torch (second degree burns)
Seven	Heat of an intense bonfire (third degree burns)
Nine	White-hot metal
Ten	Molten metal
Wounds	**Size of Fire**
One	Torch (part of body burned)
Two	Bonfire (half of body burned)
Three	Raging inferno (all of body burned)

SUNLIGHT

Sunlight is one of the few ways to kill a vampire. Sunlight causes aggravated wounds, and each turn a vampire is exposed to sunlight, he is burned. If the character has Fortitude, let the player roll Stamina + Fortitude each turn the character is exposed to the sun. The difficulty is dependent on the directness of the rays, the time of day and the cloud or fog cover. See the chart below for a rough guide to assigning difficulties. If no successes are rolled, then the character takes from one to three levels of damage, depending on how much he was exposed (see the second chart below). If he succeeds, he takes one fewer level of damage per success. Botches indicate the character has actually caught fire, and the character must now resist both the sunlight and the fire.

Difficulty	Rays
Three	Indirect rays, heavy cloud cover or twilight.
Five	Fully covered with heavy clothing.
Seven	Through a window.
Nine	Struck by one small direct ray of sunlight, or being outside on a cloudy day.
Ten	Direct rays from an unobscured sun.
Wounds	**Size of Fire**
One	Only part of body exposed (only a hand).
Two	Part of body is exposed (wearing a hood).
Three	Much of body is exposed (wearing normal clothing).

DISEASE

Though vampires can catch and even transmit human diseases, they cannot die from them. They may become ill and may lose Health Levels, but they cannot die from a human disease. While lost Health Levels may be aggravated, once they are healed the Cainite is cured. In some circumstances, the disease will not even affect the vampire, in which case he becomes a carrier and transmits the disease to all those from whom he feeds. However, rumors exist of a number of vampiric plagues capable of killing Cainites within days.

STAKES

A stake through a vampire's heart does not cause death, but does completely immobilize her. If a vampire has been staked through the heart and cannot move, she will still lose one Blood Point a day. Once all Blood Points have been lost, the vampire will begin to lose Health Levels at the rate of one per day. Once the vampire has reached Incapacitated, then she is assumed to have entered torpor. Note that vampires cannot "die" from deterioration.

It is extremely difficult to aim a stake precisely through the heart during melee. At least five successes are required for it to impact such a precisely delineated area.

EXTREME COLD

Though vampires cannot die because of the cold, they can suffer the effects of frostbite and even become entirely frozen in severe temperatures. The cold is especially dangerous because vampires do not have any body warmth except in the minutes immediately following a feeding, so clothing of any sort is of no use. Characters need to make rolls after they have been outside in the cold for a certain period of time. This varies depending on how cold it is, but usually it's about half an hour. Then they make Stamina + Fortitude rolls with a difficulty starting at 3 but increasing by one per roll. The time between the rolls is determined by the Storyteller, but keep in mind that vampires are much more resistant to cold than humans. Vampires can burn Blood Points to give themselves warmth, but such activity will not provide lasting heat.

TORPOR

As demonstrated above, death does not come easily to vampires. However, when their injuries grow too great, they can go into a very deep sleep known as torpor.

When a vampire becomes injured beyond Incapacitated and loses all Blood Points as well, then the vampire goes into torpor (though if the injury is aggravated, the result is Final Death instead). The character is completely immobilized and unconscious, though more powerful Cainites (such as the Antediluvians) can still use some of their Disciplines in this state.

Additionally, the character loses a rating point from a Physical Attribute once torpor has been entered. The player must choose which Physical Attribute suffers.

Vampires with a Via rating of 10 come out of the deep sleep within a day or so, while those not as advanced on their Road sleep for a few weeks to a few months. The blood of an Ancient can sometimes prematurely revive a vampire in torpor.

While in torpor, a vampire uses blood normally at the rate of one per day, but once the blood is gone, no Health Levels are lost.

Via rating	Length of Time
10	One day
9	Three days
8	One week
7	Two weeks
6	One month
5	One year
4	One decade
3	Five decades
2	One century
1	Five centuries
0	Millennium +

A character may go into torpor voluntarily. When the character goes to sleep, the player simply informs the Storyteller that the character is entering torpor. Many ancient Cainites voluntarily enter this state in a protected place so they will not have to put themselves at risk of frenzies or other dangers.

MENTAL STATES

These systems discuss the changes that can overcome a character's psyche. It includes such conditions as frenzy, whereupon the characters allow the Beast within to become the Beast without; Rötschreck, where the fear induced by sunlight and fire becomes an overwhelming passion; and Degeneration, whereupon the loss of Via is considered. Also described are the various Derangements vampires are prone to assume (and which all Malkavians must possess), as well as the mystical Blood Oath.

FRENZY

Vampires, like mortals, are creatures of instinct. However, the instincts of the vampire are those of a hunter, not a gatherer. Vampires are the ultimate predators and stand at the apex of the food chain. They are highly developed killing machines — the harbingers of death.

For vampires to survive in society, however, they must learn to keep the Beast in check. The impulses of violence so essential in the wild serve only to endanger the vampire in the Dark Medieval world. The power the Beast's rage provides has its uses, but the blindness it creates far outweighs its benefits.

Vampires struggle to suppress the Beast but, no matter how hard they try, they do not always prevail. Every vampire must constantly struggle to restrain this Beast within him. The following rules describe when and how it comes to be released upon the world.

In situations where the Storyteller believes a vampire's instincts might kick into action, the player has to make a Self-Control/Instinct roll. If she makes that roll, her character has overcome the impulse of rage. If it fails, the character descends into a temporary frenzy as the madness of the Beast takes hold. The character is only partially in the player's control.

PROVOCATIONS

It is always up to you, the Storyteller, to decide what circumstances might provoke a frenzy. You may ignore some very blatant factors, but force the players to roll for what they consider very minor things. Your interpretation of the nature of the Dark Medieval world is reflected in what frenzy rolls you ask the players to make.

These frenzy rules are intentionally loose so that they work in whatever way best suits your chronicle. If you want a more action-oriented chronicle with characters who can be fairly confident of themselves, then you will not want to have many frenzy rolls. On the other hand, if you want the players to be very conscious of their characters' essential weaknesses, and you want them to roleplay out and face these weaknesses, then be more strict.

Hunger often provokes the frenzy and can result in the death of the vessel as the character drinks it dry. This occurs only if the character is hungry (three or fewer Blood Points), and is brought on by the sight, taste or smell of blood.

Frenzy can also be provoked through anger, and can turn into a great vampiric rage. Rage can be created by many things and can vary widely from character to character. It is most often provoked by humiliation or taunting.

SYSTEM

You do not need to resist the frenzy, but if you wish to do so, make a Self-Control/Instinct roll (difficulty varies). It is an extended action, and five successes must be collected before the frenzy is entirely overcome. However, even one success temporarily prevents the frenzy from taking effect (one turn only). The difficulty for the roll is the number indicated on the chart below. You may not roll more dice on the roll than you currently have points in your Blood Pool — the Hunger invariably overwhelms even the best of intentions. A success indicates the character does not frenzy, while a failure indicates she does. A botch indicates a Derangement of one type or another at the Storyteller's choice.

Provocation	Difficulty
Smell of blood (when hungry)	3
Sight of blood (when hungry)	4
Life threatened	4
Taunting	4
Being bullied	4
Provoked into anger	5
Taste of blood (when hungry)	5
Regent in danger	6
Outright humiliation	7

ROLEPLAYING

During frenzy, a character is capable of nearly any sort of immoral, risky and psychotic behavior. While in a frenzy, she must behave with animalistic abandon, concerned only with immediate gratification. Whether that means a berserker attack or stark raving madness depends on the stimuli. No logical thought occurs, and all reactions are instinctive and emotional.

If blood is available, the character will drink until she can drink no more. It is likely the character will kill a vessel, for she is consumed by the desire for blood. If no blood is nearby, she will rush off in search of it. The character becomes enraged and attempts to destroy everything and anything in sight. While she will head for her enemies first, if her friends get in the way (or she has no enemies near), she will attack them as well.

However, while in a frenzy, the character gains some benefits as well as the obvious detriments. First of all, she may ignore Health Level penalties equal to her Stamina — she simply does not have to apply that number of dice as a penalty. Secondly, she does not have to make many Willpower rolls, since she is capable of doing nearly anything.

The player can decide to use a Willpower point in order to control the character's actions on a single action for a single turn. This provides just enough time to formulate a single thought or purpose, and unless other events get in the way, the character's behavior can be guided over the following few turns. Just keep in mind that using Willpower cannot stop the frenzy — it only offers a little control over what form it takes.

As the Storyteller, use this to provoke players into roleplaying frenzy more accurately. If players describe actions for their characters that go against what you believe to be appropriate during a frenzy, allow them to do so, but then announce that they have lost a Willpower point. Frenzy is not something trivial.

DURATION

Frenzy can last a variable length of time. It is up to the Storyteller to decide when it comes to an end. In some ways, frenzy moves along a simple adrenaline-type cycle. When adrenaline in a mortal would stop flowing, things calm down, the tension level falls, and slowly the frenzy comes to a stop. Frenzy lasts for the duration of the scene. When the scene comes to an end, let the player begin to roleplay his character normally again.

A player can use Willpower points to regain control temporarily, or to restrain his character from one particular action, but this will not last long. If the Storyteller does not believe the player is roleplaying the frenzy properly, she can declare that the character has used a Willpower point.

A character's friends can help him overcome a frenzy by confronting him and speaking with him. They must make appropriate Social rolls, with success allowing the character a chance to make a Willpower roll (which, if successful, can end the frenzy). However, only those who have successfully resisted frenzy in the presence of the character or are emotionally close to him may attempt this. A botch on the player's Willpower roll may well mean he attacks those who tried so hard to help him.

RÖTSCHRECK

Vampires do not fear much, but, despite being immortal, do fear that which can put an end to them. The two greatest threats to their existence are sunlight and fire, and these dangers provoke in Cainites a terror which goes beyond all normal fear — the Rötschreck.

SYSTEM

Whenever a vampire encounters the sun or fire, the Storyteller can call for a Courage roll. This roll can be provoked by anything the character truly fears — most commonly the rays of

the sun or open flames. At the Storyteller's whim, this roll may sometimes be required when a new vampire is first confronted with a holy symbol or even a stake.

The difficulty for the Courage roll is usually 6, but can vary according to circumstances as detailed in the chart below. Each success on the roll indicates the number of turns the character can stay in the presence of the thing or circumstances creating the fear. When those turns have passed, another Courage roll must be made. A failure indicates the character enters the Rötschreck, a frenzied state, and loses all control. A botch indicates the character not only enters the Rötschreck, but gains a Derangement of some sort. The type of Derangements created by a botched Courage roll are generally twisted versions of the basic urge to flee in terror.

The players can spend a Willpower point in order to take a single action otherwise impossible to the character because of the Rötschreck.

Effect	Difficulty
Torch in close proximity	6
Obscured sunlight	7
Bonfire	7
Open sunlight	8
Being burned	8
Trapped in burning building	9

ROLEPLAYING

When a character fails a Courage roll, he is incapable of taking any action other than fleeing. Even if he is trapped with no place to run, he is incapable of taking any sort of sensible action. This reaction will last at least a few minutes (longer in some cases) after the character reaches cover and is no longer in sight of the sun or the fire.

When the character reaches a safe place, the player may make a Willpower roll to regain control (difficulty 8). Each success reduces the amount of time needed to recover (from a base of 10 minutes).

DERANGEMENTS

Some Cainites possess or pick up various quirks, neurotic tendencies or even psychoses which will take them a great deal of time and effort to overcome.

The effects of the Derangement may present themselves in a variety of ways. How and why a Derangement begins, in terms of the story, is a joint decision of the player and the Storyteller. Normally, it begins soon after a botched frenzy roll, but it can be caused by many other factors. Malkavians, for instance, begin the chronicle with a Derangement of some sort.

When a character gains a Derangement, the Storyteller must determine the type. You can roll a die to decide what Derangement the character gains, but we don't recommend this method. In many circumstances, you could even allow your more experienced players to create their own unique Derangements.

ROLEPLAYING DERANGEMENTS

These Derangements are not meant to be all-consuming, forcing the player into roleplaying in a tightly constricted way. Rather, they are meant to add some fun and a little bit of reality into the game. A character does not have to exhibit the Derangement all the time, since people can slip in and out of it, and it may only surface in particularly tense moments. The Derangement does not have to *rule* the mind of the character — it need only influence it.

As Storyteller, it is incumbent upon you to keep a careful eye on making sure that things do not get out of hand. Players have two bad habits when it comes to Derangements: they either forget they have them, or they let them get so out of control that the Derangement takes over the story and the game session.

To stop players from conveniently forgetting they have Derangements, simply tell them every once in a while they have successfully controlled their Derangement, but had to use up a Willpower point to do so.

To prevent the players from getting out of control with their Derangement, you'll sometimes have to use more forceful tactics. Take them aside and tell them that you like their sense of drama, but that they're overplaying it just a bit. If they continue to use their Derangement to hog all the attention, give them a new Derangement that forces a certain degree of retreat from the world — like catatonia.

Below are listed 10 sample Derangements.

• **Multiple Personalities:** You possess a number of new personalities. For the duration of the Derangement, you have more than one Nature, and during the story you will switch back and forth between the personalities. Thus you behave in radically different ways at different times, and regain Willpower points in different ways at different times. During this suspicious age, nearly anyone aware of your persona-shifts will assume that you are being possessed. And can you be so sure that you are not?

• **Fantasy:** You enter a self-created world of delusions in which you are the unappreciated hero. Your desire to be good and pure is fulfilled by accomplishing imaginary achievements which sometimes overlap with reality.

• **Regression:** You become childlike, retreating to an earlier time in your life when less was required of you; probably very early in your childhood, as children in the Dark Medieval world assume adult duties as soon as they are able to carry them out. It is very difficult for you to do anything for yourself, and you may need others to do things for you.

• **Perfection:** Everything must be perfect in your life. You use all your energy to prevent anything from going wrong. When it does, as inevitably it must, your control cracks, and you must make a Willpower roll to resist frenzy.

• **Overcompensation:** You cover up your moral weaknesses by playing up one of your moral strengths to an extreme. You believe you are exceptionally moral and virtuous in one way or another — that you are honorable, loyal, brave, compassionate or self-controlled. Your behavior is thus straitjacketed by your desire. You constantly lecture others on their moral weaknesses and demonstrate extreme arrogance about what you believe to be your strengths. Of course, when the forces of reality reveal the emptiness of your delusion, the embarrassment will be great. You do not believe yourself capable of falling into frenzy and will thus do nothing to prevent or avoid situations that might cause it.

• **Obsession:** You become obsessed with some interest as a reaction to what you have experienced. It is a sort of perverse ambition toward which you direct all of your energy, like an obsession for power, a certain person, amulets or even blood. You need something to focus on to give your life meaning.

• **Paranoia:** You are convinced that you are being hunted and that there is no escape. You are obsessed with those you believe to be chasing you and make all kinds of preparations to protect yourself. Under no circumstances will you trust anyone, for you hold even your closest friends under suspicion.

• **Amnesia:** In order not to think about what you have done, you forget a segment of your past — perhaps even the experience of becoming a vampire. This can make things very interesting for a time. This repression prevents those dangerous memories from entering the consciousness, and you simply forget the event ever happened. More than the event can be forgotten, however, and total amnesia is even possible. Additionally, in some cases a character may "forget" some Abilities and be unable to use them for the duration of the Derangement.

• **Melancholia:** You sink into deep and fitful depressions, showing no interest in anything that used to capture your imagination. You view the world as flat and gray, with nothing in it for you. You cannot rouse yourself to do anything, though you will go along with others rather than expend the energy to resist. Conversely, occasional fits of great energy grab hold of you, and you will work for hours or even days on your projects. During this time you will resist even the need for sleep as you burn up blood and Willpower on your schemes.

• **Delusion of Grandeur:** You imagine that you are far better and greater than you really are — you adopt a glorious self-ideal. Perhaps you think of yourself as prince, or you may believe yourself to be the mayor or a religious leader. By imagining yourself safe from that which you fear, you avoid the terror that looms so near. However, whenever the delusion is broken, a Courage roll (difficulty 5) must be immediately made to see if the character frenzies or not.

Blood Oaths

It is possible to create a Blood Oath with another vampire, thereby making him your servant and, in some ways, your lover. Blood Oath is spoken of as holding Regnant over another. The one who holds it over the bound vampire is known as the Regents, whereas the one who is held in Regnant is commonly known as the Thrall. Usually it is the elders who are Regent and neonates who are Thralls, but not always. An essential strategy in the Jyhad is to hold many in Regnant, for it gives you powerful retainers whom you can trust. Many Cainites are suspicious of one another, for they are never sure who are the Thralls of ancients and who are not.

Creation of the Oath

The Blood Oath is created by the exchange of Blood between two vampires. The Thrall must drink the Regent's blood three different times on three different occasions (on different nights). It can be any amount of blood; but a sip or even a taste

if the Regent is of ancient blood. Unlike the limitations of the Dominate Discipline, it is possible for weaker blood to hold Regnant over more potent blood. Thus, a 10th-generation Cainite could hold Regnant over one of the ninth generation.

The more times the Thrall takes blood, the more the Oath is reinforced. Most Regents have their Thralls drink of their blood several times a year, just to make sure the bond remains potent. Many of them are fearful that if the Oath is broken, the Thrall will plot against them. This is perhaps why so many Thralls are fairly well treated by their Regent — after all, any bond can fail. Hate can build up beneath the power of the Oath and weaken it.

Once a vampire has made a Blood Oath, she cannot again be sworn by another. Characters can only be sworn to one vampire at a time and are thus safe from it if already bound by an Oath. Every character is already on her way to making a Blood Oath, for her sire has already given her at least one taste of blood. Thus, if the character partakes of her sire's blood two more times, she will be held in Regnant.

Power of the Oath

A Blood Oath is primarily an emotional bond. Thralls view the vampire to whom they are sworn as a central figure in their life and are invariably obsessed with him. Though they may despise their Regent, they will do nearly anything to aid him. They will do nothing to harm their Regent and will even attempt to protect him against others who might attack him. It is very likely that the character will understand what is happening to her, intellectually at least, but she will be unable to do anything about it.

The Blood Oath is like falling in love — once it happens, you are caught in its grip until somehow you break free. You may know you are in love and hate what it makes you do, but that does not stop you from being in love, and it doesn't prevent you from doing some of the stupid things people in love sometimes do. Blood Oath is possibly the closest to that vaunted emotion many vampires ever reach. When roleplaying Blood Oath, use this "love" metaphor to understand just how deeply and completely the character is obsessed with the Regent. A Regent with a strong conscience may feel this "love" to some measure in return.

One of the primary powers a Regent has over the Thrall is that she is able to Dominate the Thrall without requiring eye contact. As long as the Thrall is able to hear the words of the Regent, he can be Dominated. All difficulties are two higher whenever the Thrall makes a roll to resist the Dominate of the Regent.

The Blood Oath sometimes (but not always) gives the Regent insight into the mood and feelings of the Thrall, and she may even know where the Thrall is from moment to moment if the Blood Oath has been held long enough.

If a character's Regent asks him to do her a favor, he will do so if it is at all possible. If it requires him to risk his life, he does not need to do it. Even love is not that blind. If there is an emergency and the Regent is being attacked, the Thrall's first instinct will be to go to aid her. Self-sacrifice is not unknown, especially if the Oath has been reinforced over the years. If the Thrall is treated well, the Oath is reinforced, and it grows stronger. If he is humiliated and degraded, the hate that develops will diminish its influence on the Thrall.

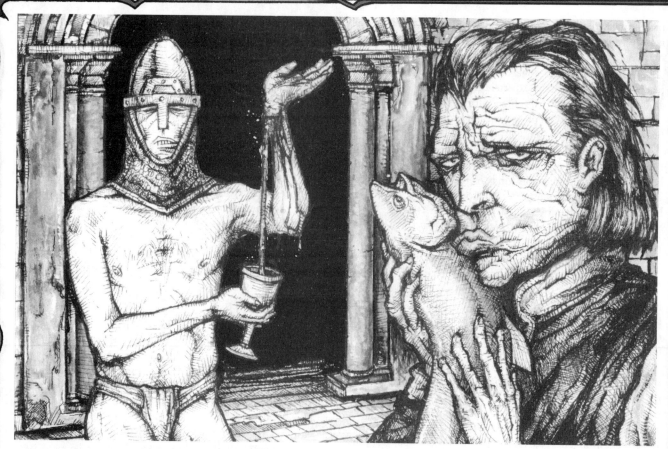

At the Storyteller's discretion, Willpower may be expended to resist the power of the Blood Oath temporarily. First the character must accumulate a number of successes on a Willpower roll (difficulty 8) equal to the number of times he has drunk from his Regnant. Then, depending on the circumstances, a single Willpower point will eliminate the effects of the Oath for a single turn to an entire scene. If the character simply wishes to plot against his Regent, one Willpower would enable him to do so for an entire scene. However, if he wanted to attack his Regent, it would take at least one Willpower per turn, and the player would probably have to make an additional Willpower roll each turn just to get the nerve to spend that Willpower point.

It is possible to break a Blood Oath, but it can be difficult. It requires not only the massive expenditure of Willpower over a long period of time, but also necessitates that the character completely avoid his Regent. If a Thrall does not see the Regent for some time and does not interact with the object of his attachment, the Oath will eventually die away. Some types of Natures, such as Child and Fanatic, may never escape the Blood Oath, while others may do so very easily. The breaking of a character's Blood Oath of a character cannot be achieved through experience points or successful rolls, for it must be roleplayed.

Dramatic Systems

Described below are a variety of different systems to resolve actions, or, to put it simply, a bunch of ways to make rolls. If you prefer to roleplay through dramatic scenes, just use these systems as suggestions of what sorts of things can happen during the scene. Physical dramatic systems are the most numerous, because these actions are the most difficult to resolve through roleplaying alone.

Physical

These systems describe physical actions and confrontations, dramatic situations in which Physical Attributes predominate.

Awakenings

Sometimes a character will need to wake up in the middle of the day. This is extremely difficult for vampires to do, as they are highly nocturnal creatures. When something occurs that may require the character to rouse, such as a noise or a motion near the "coffin," a Perception + Auspex roll (difficulty of 8) must be made. Any success indicates that she arouses enough to notice what is going on. Failure indicates she doesn't wake up, while a botch indicates she won't wake up at all.

Once the character is slightly roused, the player makes a roll versus the character's Road rating to see how long he can remain awake. The difficulty is normally an 8, and each success indicates that the character can stay awake for one turn. Five successes mean he awakens completely. No actions can be taken until the character is completely awake. A failure means he goes back to sleep, but if something else happens which might rouse him, he can roll again. A botch means that he goes back to sleep and nothing will rouse him short of Gehenna.

Throughout the rest of the time that the character is awake, you may require her to make further rolls to see if she can remain awake. The difficulties of these rolls are also 8, but only one success is needed for her to remain awake. Failures and botches have the same results as they do above.

Remember, during the day, no roll made by a vampire can use more dice than the vampire's Road rating.

CLIMBING

When a character attempts to climb any sort of surface (a tree, cliff or building), ask the player to roll the character's Dexterity + Athletics. The difficulty depends on the sheerness of the climbing surface, the type of surface being climbed and, to a lesser extent, the weather conditions. Each success indicates that the character has climbed five feet. Once he accumulates enough successes to get to where he wants to go, he can stop rolling. For example, Samuel is trying to climb a 25-foot wall, so he needs five successes to get to the top. A failure indicates the character is unable to make any progress during the turn. A botch indicates the character falls and cannot attempt to climb again without expending a Willpower point.

2	Easy climb: a tree with many stout branches
4	Simple climb: a cliff with many handholds
6	Straightforward: a tree with thin branches
8	Treacherous: very few handholds
10	Extremely difficult: a nearly sheer surface

FEATS OF STRENGTH

A character's Strength is often used without an Ability for actions where brute force is all that matters. This system works on the same basis as automatic successes. If the character's Strength equals or exceeds the difficulty of the task she is attempting, she succeeds automatically. Only if the difficulty is higher than her Dice Pool must she make a roll.

Dice Pool	Feats	Lift
1	Rip a silk shirt	40 lbs.
2	Winch a crossbow	100 lbs.
3	Bend a longsword	250 lbs.
4	Throw a barrel of wine	400 lbs.
5	Break down a stout oak door	650 lbs.
6	Rip chainmail	800 lbs.
7	Bend a 1" thick metal bar	900 lbs.
8	Throw a riding horse	1000 lbs.
9	Punch through a metal breast plate	1200 lbs.
10	Lift a portcullis	1500 lbs.
11	Throw a draft horse	2000 lbs.
12	Break a small tree	3000 lbs.
13	Throw a stone sarcophagus lid	4000 lbs.
14	Punch through a 1' stone wall	5000 lbs.
15	Throw a catapult	6000 lbs.

When the character makes the roll, however, it is based on Willpower, not Strength. It is a simple roll, so the character gets only one chance to make it. The difficulty is almost always 9, though it can vary according to the surface conditions, the structure of the object being lifted and Storyteller whim. Each success increases the character's effective Strength by one step on the chart below (to a maximum of five steps). Thus, if the character has a Strength of 4 but wants to flip over a wagon, she needs three successes on the Willpower roll to do it.

JUMPING

Jumping requires a Strength roll, or a Strength + Athletics roll if it is a horizontal jump and the character gets a decent running start. The difficulty for a jump is almost always 3 (unless there are difficult weather conditions or there is a narrow landing space). The Storyteller calculates how many successes are required to make the jump. There are no partial successes in jumping; the character either succeeds in one roll or she falls.

Type of Jump	Feet per Success
Vertical (up)	2
Horizontal (across)	4

PURSUIT

This simple system is used when one character attempts to catch another. One opponent starts with a certain number of successes. This number is either determined by the Storyteller (this is the preferred method), or by having the pursued character roll Dexterity + Athletics (difficulty 6) for each turn of headstart he has. Add up the number of successes achieved. This number of successes must be achieved by the other character before he can catch up. Once he does, he can try to grapple the fleeing person (see the combat rules). The pursuer might only want to catch up halfway in order to get a better shot at the fleeing character.

SHADOWING

Sometimes a character will want to follow someone. In order to be led somewhere interesting, this needs to be done as discreetly as possible. This is what shadowing is all about — following someone without the pursued knowing the character is there.

There are two components to shadowing — keeping track of where the subject is, and making sure he doesn't see his tail. Shadowing can be conducted on foot or on horseback.

The character attempting to shadow must make a Perception + Investigation roll. The difficulty is normally 6 (though it can vary from 5 to 9 depending on the thickness of crowds, relative speeds of travel and weather conditions). Each success indicates that the target has been followed for a turn. A certain number of successes is required to follow the subject all the way to his destination. A failure indicates that the character has temporarily lost the subject, but can try again next turn. If she fails a second time, she has lost the subject completely, and the chase is off (unless she can think of a new approach). A botch indicates that the character has not only completely lost the subject, but she is so involved in shadowing that she gets into trouble of her own — she is attacked by brigands, accused of pickpocketing a noble, or her horse throws a shoe.

Though the Perception roll is the most important aspect of shadowing, a Stealth roll must also be made to see if the subject notices he is being followed. Each turn the Perception roll is made, the Stealth roll must also be made. The player must roll Dexterity + Stealth (or Dexterity + Ride if the character is in on horseback). The base difficulty is the subject's Perception + Alertness, but this can be modified by up to three points in either direction depending on the circumstances (empty streets or thick crowds, for instance). A single success indicates the shadower is not detected, and each additional success also makes it more difficult for the subject to spot the shadower, even if he is actively looking. A failure indicates the subject becomes suspicious, and starts to glance surreptitiously over his shoulder (and may make Perception rolls of his own; see below). A botch indicates the character completely reveals herself, and the subject now *knows* he is being followed.

If the subject is alerted somehow (by the shadower's failure on the Dexterity + Stealth roll), or simply looks to see if he is being followed (out of habit, perhaps), roll Perception + Investigation. The difficulty is the Stealth + 5 of the shadower. Each success on this roll indicates a higher degree of suspicion. Successes can be accumulated from turn to turn; see the chart below to see how alert the subject is to the fact that he is being followed. Failure means that nothing out of the ordinary is seen, and the "suspicion value" of the subject decreases to zero. A botch means the subject is convinced he isn't being followed and no longer looks behind him.

Successes	Suspicion
1	Hunch
2	Suspicion
3	Near-certainty
4	Positive knowledge
5	The shadower has been spotted

Buddy System: Two or more characters can share shadowing responsibilities by trading off. However, they must have previously worked or trained together in this technique; otherwise, the difficulties of all rolls for the pair are increased by one. One player shadows for a turn or more, trading off whenever her partner gives the signal. If the pair switches off, the subject can't accumulate successes for very long, which makes it much harder for the subject to spot shadowers.

SNEAKING

When a character attempts to hide in shadows or sneak up on a guard, she must roll Dexterity + Stealth (difficulty of the guard's Perception + Alertness). Anyone who is on watch or actively looking for intruders can be considered a guard.

The sneaking character needs to collect a certain number of successes in order to make it to where she wants to go. A Perception + Stealth roll can be made if the player wants to estimate how many successes will be needed; the difficulty of this feat is usually 7.

Failure of any sort on a Stealth roll indicates detection.

SWIMMING

Although total immersion in water is not fatal to vampires, it is not very pleasant. Because vampires do not breathe, they cannot drown; however, they can sink.

Any vampire immersed in water without any means of support must roll Dexterity + Athletics with the difficulty determined by the severity of the water conditions. The number of successes obtained determines how far they swim (or alternatively, how long they have stayed above water). Normally it is five feet or five minutes, but that can vary according to the needs of the story. A botch means the character has lost ground (the current drags you along, or the tide pulls you back).

If vampires are caught underwater during the day, they can be harmed by the sun's rays — water is no barrier (treat as the same as a cloudy day). If you get deep enough, the sunlight will not penetrate, but at that depth the character might be crushed or suffer the effects of the cold temperature.

SOCIAL

These systems involve social interaction between people. They nearly always require a Charisma, Manipulation or Appearance roll. Often these systems are best left unused, with the success or failure of a particular social ploy instead resolved through roleplaying.

CREDIBILITY

This system is used when a character attempts to convince someone she is telling the truth: for example, when she attempts to persuade a noble she is not lying, or tries to convince a guardsman of her identity. The player must make a Manipulation + Leadership roll. The difficulty is the other subject's Intelligence + Subterfuge. Lower the difficulty by one to three if the character is telling the truth (it does make a difference). Each success indicates a higher degree of credibility. Five successes indicate the subject is completely convinced. A failure indicates disbelief, and a botch indicates the character is caught in a lie (or the subject thinks he has caught her in a lie).

FAST-TALK

Fast-talk is a means of verbally browbeating and confusing someone into submission. Manipulation + Subterfuge is the most common roll for such a feat; Charisma or Appearance can sometimes be substituted. The difficulty is the target's Wits + Larceny.

Success indicates that the target becomes confused, and is likely to agree with the subject, at least momentarily. Failure indicates that the attempt has faltered, and the target can try to interject something — an attempt to explain himself, or even an attempt to fast-talk back. A botch indicates that the target doesn't get confused, only angry. Fast-talk attempts by the character will never again work on him.

Repeated rolls might be necessary to confuse the target. As Storyteller, you need to run attempts at fast-talk in a manner consistent with the mood of your game. It can be as slaphappy or as deadly serious as you like.

Willpower points can be expended to resist fast-talk.

INTERROGATION

Interrogation can be used in a number of different situations. It is a form of questioning, not torture, though intimidation is certainly employed. Torture can be used, but you will have to develop your own rules for that if you wish to include it in your chronicle.

The player makes a Manipulation + Intimidation roll (difficulty of the victim's Willpower). The number of successes indicates the amount of information obtained (see the chart below). A failure indicates the character learns nothing of value. A botch indicates the subject tells the character nothing, and will never tell him anything — or worse, the subject lies. For this reason, the Storyteller should often make the roll for the player.

Successes	Interrogation
1	Only a few mumbled facts
2	Some relevant facts
3	Much interesting information
4	The subject talks on and on
5	Everything of import is discovered

ORATION

If a player wants her character to give a speech, but doesn't actually want to recite it, you can use this system. The player should at least describe what her character says and maybe recite a memorable phrase — that might even get her started into roleplaying the speech *verbatim*. Oration is often very difficult to roleplay, so never force your players to do so.

The player makes a Charisma + Leadership roll. The difficulty depends on the mood of the crowd, its willingness to hear what the orator says and its penchant for throwing rotten vegetables (difficulty is usually 7). If the orator has any sort of reputation, you may wish to adjust the difficulty accordingly. The number of successes indicates how impressed the crowd is (see the following chart). It is a simple roll, so the player has only one crack at it. A failure indicates the crowd ignores the character. A botch indicates the character may be attacked by the outraged onlookers.

Successes	Crowd Reaction
1	They listened, but aren't excited
2	The character has convinced them somewhat
3	The crowd is won over
4	The crowd is completely enthralled
5	The crowd is in the palm of the character's hand

If the speech is vital to the story, the player may make several rolls. If you want to spend some time on it, you can make it an extended action, interspersing each roll with roleplaying. The character can spend as many turns as she would like on the speech; after the third turn, however, the difficulty increases by one each turn. More successes than five might be required to win over the crowd completely.

PERFORMANCES

This system is used whenever a character gives any type of performance, whether it be comedy, music, acting or storytelling. It can be at the high court or on a street corner, and can be formal or informal.

The player must roll the appropriate Attribute + Acting (or Music, or whatever Ability is most appropriate). The difficulty is based on how receptive the audience is. A failure indicates a lackluster, eminently forgettable performance. A botch indicates a miserable performance that cannot even be finished — the instrument breaks, or the character is booed off the stage.

The number of successes indicates how moved the audience is (see the chart below). These successes determine the artistic merit or technical verisimilitude of the piece.

Successes	Your Performance	Reaction
1	Mediocre	Polite applause
2	Average	Approval
3	Good	Genuine appreciation
4	Superior	Vigorous applause
5	Exceptional	Ecstatic reaction
6	Superb	Immediate sensation
7	Brilliant	Miracle, *magnum opus*

SEDUCTION

Seduction is distinguished from courtship in that the latter is always a slower process, stretching out over weeks or even years, while Seduction is designed to culminate more quickly, usually in only a few hours at most. Courtship should always be roleplayed out rather than trusted to dice. Seduction takes place in stages, and unless a person succeeds during each consecutive stage, he will not succeed at all. This system is designed to replicate the activities of a dominant person over a more submissive one. If the emotions and motives are true, then you should ignore this system and roleplay it out.

VAMPIRE: THE DARK AGES

Opening Exchange: The player rolls Appearance + Subterfuge. The difficulty is the Wits + 3 of the subject (the player gains a bonus of one to three dice if it's a good line, minus one to three if it's a stupid one). Each success after the first adds an extra die to the roll on the next stage.

Witty Remarks: The player rolls Wits + Subterfuge. The difficulty is the Intelligence + 3 of the subject. Again, give bonuses and penalties for roleplaying. Each success over and above the base adds an extra die to the roll on the next stage.

Conversation: The player rolls Charisma + Empathy. The difficulty is the Perception + 3 of the subject. Again, roleplaying bonuses come into play here.

Intimacies: At this point, the couple may move to a private area and become physically intimate. No roll is required.

MENTAL

These dramatic systems deal with the use of the mind and Mental Attributes. They are employed in situations where drama is caused not so much by the action as by psychological tension.

SEARCH

This system enables a character to search for something in a confined area, like a room. Have the player roll Perception + Investigation; the difficulty depends on how well the object is concealed (it is usually between 7 and 10). Each success indicates that more is found. Sometimes a certain number of successes is required to find a cleverly hidden object. If you want, a lower number of successes could warrant a hint or clue from you, thus encouraging roleplaying and a degree of puzzle-solving. As much as possible, lead the player through the search step by step. Have her describe to you where she looks. Don't let her succeed if she doesn't specifically search in the right area, and let her succeed automatically if her description is detailed enough.

TRACK

This system is used to track people and things by following the physical trails they leave. The player rolls Perception + Survival. The difficulty is based on weather conditions, terrain and the age of the tracks, but averages around 8. Each success lowers the difficulty of the next roll by one.

The character needs to succeed for a certain number of turns; the exact number depends on the length of the trail. Each turn is usually about five minutes long. If the character misses a roll, she can try again; this time, however, the difficulty is one higher. Once it goes above 10, the character loses the trail.

Two leagues from the city, in
the witch-darkest hour,
Come two of Caine's blood to
a lone, o'erlooked tower
"There – one can see that the
tower is mann'd,"
Says Anatole, of the mad
Malkav's clan.

Speaks fair Lucita, "Your
lord spoke aright;
Mayhap we'll root out the
source of his blight
His childer have stray'd
much too distant, I fear
But silently, now, for we
grow ever near"

Draw they both near to the
tower full batter'd,
Lucita lays hands on the door
partly shatter'd,
Calls, "None wait beyond," to
her Malkavian friend,
"Well," says the mad one, "let's
steal us within."

No creature nor vermin can
either detect
In the tow'r defeated by
ruin and neglect
From the stairwell above
does nothing descend
But the sweet smell of
taint borne by a soft wind

PANEL 1:

Ethan has gathered two of his players, Kathy and Justin, together for a game of **Vampire: The Dark Ages**. Kathy is running Lucita, a Lasombra runaway from a noble house; and Justin is running the mad zealot Anatole.

Without any real dice-rolling, they go through the beginning of the evening: a quick hunt, meeting each other and so on. During the course of the night, Anatole introduces Lucita to his sire, who tells them of grave troubles brewing. He explains that two of his childer have gone missing, and that a local Nosferatu told him that they were last seen on the road to an abandoned tower.

Hoping to gain the favor of Anatole's powerful sire, Lucita and Anatole agree to search for the missing Malkavian neonates. They soon arrive at the edge of the tower's grounds and note that a light burns in the uppermost window.

PANEL 2:

Ethan tells his players that a wide stream crosses the ground between the characters and the tower. The two decide just to go ahead and jump it. It's fairly wide, so Ethan decrees that they need two successes on a Strength + Athletics roll. He doesn't mention a particular difficulty, so the default 6 becomes the target. Anatole has Strength 2 and no Athletics. Since Athletics is a Talent, he can still try with no penalties. Justin rolls a 6 and an 8…just barely! Lucita also has a 2 Strength and no Athletics; however, she also has Potence 3, which adds three automatic successes to any Strength roll. Ethan lets Lucita jump the ditch without any dice-rolling. Even though she could roll two botches and miss the jump, he decides that her success is pretty much assured.

PANEL 3:

The tower door is obviously unguarded. Kathy tells Ethan that she wants Lucita to see if there's anything beyond. Ethan knows that no one is on the lower floor; still, he has Kathy roll Lucita's Perception (3) + Alertness (2), to keep the players in suspense. She rolls a 3, 5, 7, 8 and 2 — two successes. Ethan tells her that the other side seems still as the grave. She pushes the door open; it's heavy, but not heavy enough to resist her unnatural strength.

PANEL 4:

The lower floor is obviously uncared for; still, both characters say they want to try to perceive anything unusual. Both make Perception + Alertness rolls at difficulty 6. Anatole rolls (3 + 3) six dice, earning four successes; Lucita rolls five dice, gaining three. Ethan tells the players that nothing seems to be alive downstairs, but that there's a peculiarly acidic reek coming from above.…

Both mount the stairs with
cold fears unsaid,
And creep ever careful with
caution and dread.
Malkav's secrets hide his scion
from sight;
Lucit garbs herself in cloth
spun of night

The reek gains a name as
they climb the gray stair:
Atrocity's stink tills the
strange hermit's lair
And Anatole and Lucita
silent swear by their kin
To enter this Hell and
slay the devl therein.

But resolve turns to horror, as
Anatole's eyes
Pull forth a monster from
shadows disguise
"Milady, beware! shouts the
mad childe of Caine.
"The fiend works a summing
—he calls forth our bane!

The fiend hisses oaths of
blasphemous bile
Calls Anatole, "Tis an
incubus vile!
Lucita sees clearer their
foes profane mark
Of loyalty sworn to the
Baalchilder dark.

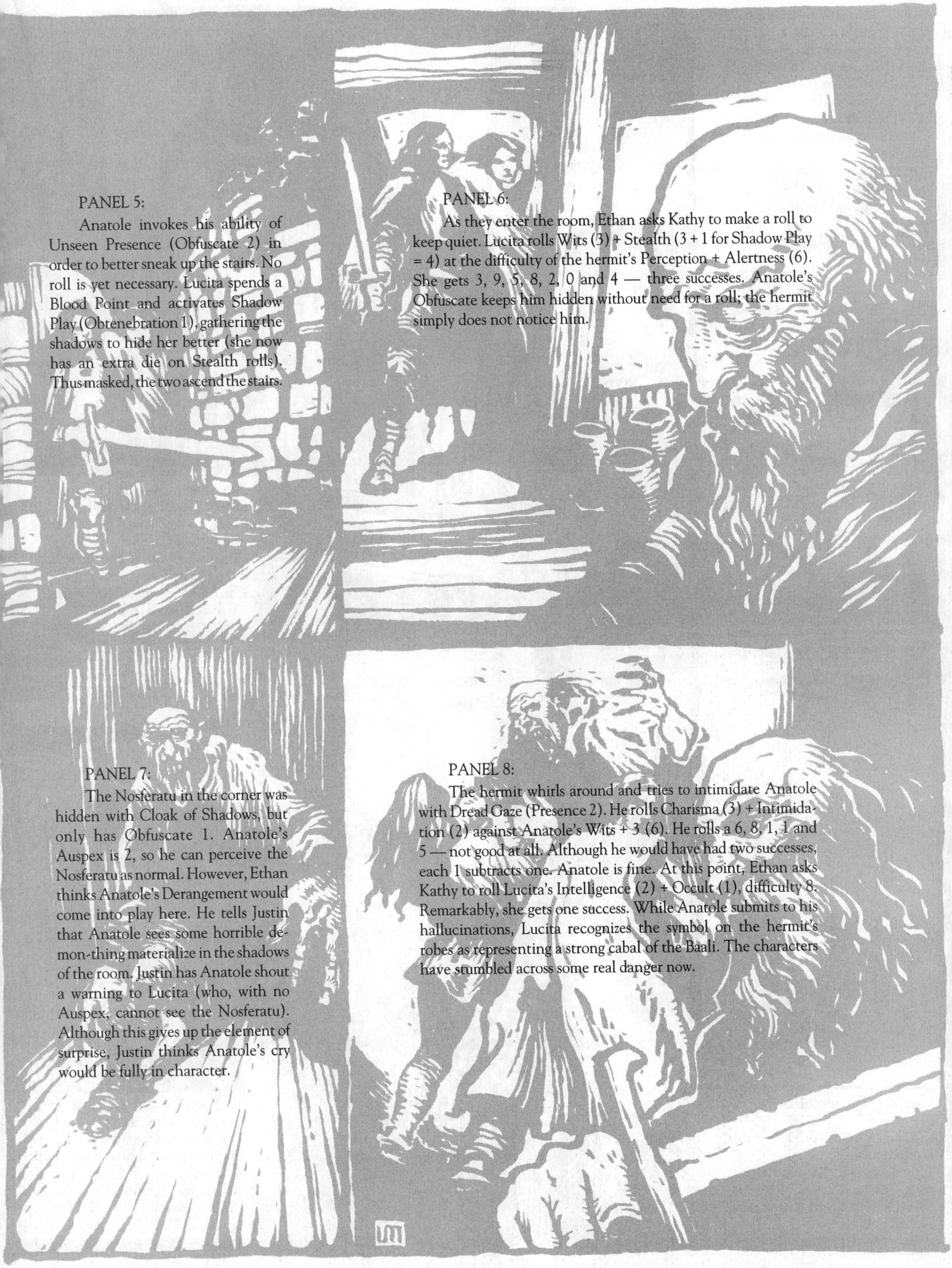

PANEL 5:

Anatole invokes his ability of Unseen Presence (Obfuscate 2) in order to better sneak up the stairs. No roll is yet necessary. Lucita spends a Blood Point and activates Shadow Play (Obtenebration 1), gathering the shadows to hide her better (she now has an extra die on Stealth rolls). Thus masked, the two ascend the stairs.

PANEL 6:

As they enter the room, Ethan asks Kathy to make a roll to keep quiet. Lucita rolls Wits (3) + Stealth (3 + 1 for Shadow Play = 4) at the difficulty of the hermit's Perception + Alertness (6). She gets 3, 9, 5, 8, 2, 0 and 4 — three successes. Anatole's Obfuscate keeps him hidden without need for a roll; the hermit simply does not notice him.

PANEL 7:

The Nosferatu in the corner was hidden with Cloak of Shadows, but only has Obfuscate 1. Anatole's Auspex is 2, so he can perceive the Nosferatu as normal. However, Ethan thinks Anatole's Derangement would come into play here. He tells Justin that Anatole sees some horrible demon-thing materialize in the shadows of the room. Justin has Anatole shout a warning to Lucita (who, with no Auspex, cannot see the Nosferatu). Although this gives up the element of surprise, Justin thinks Anatole's cry would be fully in character.

PANEL 8:

The hermit whirls around and tries to intimidate Anatole with Dread Gaze (Presence 2). He rolls Charisma (3) + Intimidation (2) against Anatole's Wits + 3 (6). He rolls a 6, 8, 1, 1 and 5 — not good at all. Although he would have had two successes, each 1 subtracts one. Anatole is fine. At this point, Ethan asks Kathy to roll Lucita's Intelligence (2) + Occult (1), difficulty 8. Remarkably, she gets one success. While Anatole submits to his hallucinations, Lucita recognizes the symbol on the hermit's robes as representing a strong cabal of the Baali. The characters have stumbled across some real danger now.

Out from the dark springs
the henchman most foul,
And the serpent fast falls on
Lucit with a howl,
The Beast fills her Blood as
her dead heart burns hot;
Lucit locks grasp with foul
Nosferat.

The mad would-be angel
strikes fearsome wild,
And is met by the Devil's
own bastardy child.
Anatole pierces the tainted
one's chest;
His foe's jaggd steel rips
through to his breast.

Lucit calls her Blood to harden
her weal;
Caine's gift hardens arms into
iron and steel
Lucit hoists the henchman,
and gives a great throw
Hurls him from the tower to
break far below

"It's well, Anatole, that you
wear a steel shirt,
"Ah," sighs the madman,
"There's worse than my hurt.
The worker of foulness, he
has taken flight.
"Worry not, friend,There's
much left to the night."

PANEL 9:

Now Ethan calls for initiative — Wits + Alertness rolls. The Nosferatu has six successes, Anatole and the Baali tie at five, and Lucita scores only four. The Nosferatu springs on Lucita, rolling Dexterity + Brawl. He only makes one success, which Ethan rules is enough to get a loose grip on her. Ethan asks Lucita, known for her short temper, to make a frenzy roll. She rolls her Self-Control (Lucita is on the Road of Humanity) and achieves one success. Lucita's under control for now.

PANEL 10:

Anatole and the Baali act simultaneously, and both opt to take a slash at the other. Justin doesn't want to split his Dice Pool to dodge, and the Baali doesn't bother. Each rolls Dexterity + Melee, difficulty 6. Anatole scores three successes and the Baali four; they're both hit. Anatole gets four successes on his damage roll (Strength + 4 for a broadsword), and the Baali gets seven (ow!). Anatole rolls his Stamina to soak, plus three for his chainmail shirt. He does badly, only making three successes; Anatole takes four Health Levels, bringing him to Wounded. He now subtracts two from his Dice Pools. The Baali earns only two successes, and drops to Hurt.

PANEL 11:

Kathy announces that Lucita is furious, and will spend a Blood Point to increase her Strength. Her Strength rises to 3. Lucita then tries to hurl the Nosferatu out the window. Ethan thinks for a bit, then has her roll Strength + Brawl, at a difficulty of 8 (the Nosferatu's loose grip is impeding her). She rolls 8, 0 and 5. With the three free successes from her Potence, that's five in all. Ethan decides that's plenty, and the thug sails out the window.

PANEL 12:

Lucita moves to check on Anatole. He's injured, but it's nothing that can't be healed with Blood Points. The Baali, however, has escaped, using his Obfuscate to flee. What next? Do the two try to track the Baali somehow? Has he even left the tower at all? And what about the Nosferatu? And where exactly do the missing Malkavian childer fit in? Lucita and Anatole were very lucky to do so well against these two for the nonce, but now they must quickly determine their next move....

Chapter Eight: Storytelling

This is the point, to speak short and plain,
That each of you, to shorte with oure waye
In this pilgrimage, shall tell two tales –
– Geoffrey Chaucer, The Canterbury Tales

This chapter is about the art of telling stories. If you've never done this before, it might seem a little strange at first. If you've done it countless times before, we should begin by saying that Vampire: The Dark Ages has its own inherent virtues and pitfalls. This game, like many roleplaying games, has a broad expanse of themes, settings and ideas. Therefore, it helps to have a structure we can use to develop stories. This chapter sketches a map of the territories ahead. Exploring that territory is up to you and your troupe. You're the navigator, the helmsman and the captain. You are the Storyteller.

Remember the last time you saw a really great movie? Remember how it felt? When we watch a film we really enjoy, time seems to stand still. The rest of the world is set aside, and the experience consumes our senses. From the opening scene to the end credits, that film becomes our world. Afterward, we can say that it's "just a movie," but then again, part of us knows that isn't exactly true.

A movie is a way of telling a story. If it's a really good film, we find a reason to get caught up in it. Maybe it's a character with whom we can identify or a scene that makes us feel something. We watch hoping to find something we like. The motion-picture medium has one big drawback, however — it's a passive experience. A person in the audience can choose whether he'll have butter on his popcorn or where he wants to sit in the theater, but that's about it. He will have his own reasons for liking the film, but someone else has put the meaning into it.

A lot of stories are like that. With books or plays, television programs or comics, the end result is the same. Someone else tells the story, we watch it or read it, and take what we're given. The best we can hope for is to read something into it that wasn't originally there.

Storytelling games are another medium for telling stories, a medium just as valid as movies or television. Each entertainment has its own strengths and weaknesses, but storytelling has an overriding strength — it's a personal experience. The people involved tailor it to what they want it to be and rework it for themselves.

With the assistance of a group of players and the advice in this book, each of you will bring your own story to life. You're not going to perform for an audience of millions, nor will you be dependent upon a budget of millions. With a few dice, some friends and maybe a little pizza, you'll lead your troupe of players on a journey that no movie or television program can ever fully reproduce. A game is just a game, but a well-told story is a work of art.

The Storyteller

But when it was midnight Sharazad awoke and signalled to her sister Dunyazad who sat up and said, "Allah upon thee, O my sister, recite to us some new story, delightsome and delectable, wherewith to while away the waking hours of our latter night."

— *The Arabian Nights Entertainments*

For the uninitiated, let's begin with the basics.

The players have a rather straightforward job — each focuses on developing a single character. The Storyteller is responsible for everything else. As one would expect, running the world is no minor task.

The first responsibility of the Storyteller is to act out the role of anyone the characters encounter. Going back to the analogy of films, it's as if the players are the stars and the Storyteller is responsible for the supporting cast.

Second, and very important to the flavor of **Dark Ages**, is the task of defining the setting these characters live in. The Storyteller describes the streets they walk on, the homes they live in and even the culture they've developed. For regular 20th century **Vampire**, this is easy — take our world, throw on a coat of black paint, add monsters and stir. For **Dark Ages**, it's a little harder.

The next responsibility is to interpret the rules. As the characters explore the world you've created, you'll have a set of rules to help you interpret events as they happen. Whether a character is

Life by Candlelight

The Dark Medieval world is one in which things of a fantastical nature are made possible. In your everyday life, there is one very easy way to dispel nearly any fear of a supernatural nature — turn on the light. A flick of the switch, and the closet monster, the creaking thing in the hall and the imp scratching at the window are all banished. But what if the only way to find out what was making that noise was to walk right over to it with a candle? No candle can match an electric flashlight for range or brightness, which means you'll have to get up awfully close. And if there *is* something there, do you really want to get that close? It becomes easier to understand the superstitions of people in years past once you take away the safety of electric light.

Think about the way people look by candlelight — more romantic, or more menacing? Do they look less, or more, like themselves? The characters in **Vampire: The Dark Ages** rise at sunset and slink back to their havens at dawn, so their entire world is lit by torch and candlelight. The play of light and shadow provided by flickering firelight seems to make all things possible. So it is with Storytelling — the world is your canvas.

climbing a tree or Dominating the Duke of Milan, it helps to have a set of rules to back you up. These rules should allow you to focus on the most important part of your game — your story. Beyond the math and mechanics, rules serve as a guide to describing the events of the game. The Storyteller interprets the raw numbers and dice rolls, and weaves their revelations into the story. If the rules get in her way, she simplifies them or sets them aside. The story's the thing.

The story itself is the last consideration, but by no means the least important one. Begin each chapter of your story with a rough idea of where you want that story to go and what you want it to say to your players, then guide their characters into the world you've created. Things won't always go the way you've planned — players will always come up with variations and twists you never considered — but that's part of the fun of collaborative storytelling. With a little practice and a helpful group, the lot of you can turn your concepts into full-fledged tales.

This book gives you the elements you need to begin to put a story together. There's a set of guidelines for creating characters, an elaborate background to integrate into your setting and a framework of rules to guide you through the story. Once you've prepared what you need, you can then chart the course of your chronicle. Take what you want, and leave the rest behind. It's your world. It's your story.

The Troupe

Fortunately, you're not going into this task alone; storytelling is an interactive activity. Each player, by designing a character, has given you a set of cues for what type of story she wants to hear. Is the story romantic? Is it filled with action and violence? Is it ultimately tragic? The players in your troupe aren't your audience — they're your collaborators. Through a process of give and take, you shape the story with them.

The players will give you a lot of freedom to create, but never forget that they're also part of the creative process. Each of you makes an investment of time and effort when you game together; any of you could be reading a book or going out on a date instead. Your players have put a degree of trust in you to make their investment worthwhile. Naturally, you will.

This doesn't mean that you should give players whatever they want. If there's no danger or conflict in your story, there's no drama. If a story seems completely arbitrary, the illusion is shattered. There's a balance between setting up obstacles the characters must overcome and realizing when the game becomes unwieldy. A great Storyteller plays off what her players say, and keeps the balance between organization and improvisation. This requires a degree of empathy and a sense of what works in a story and what doesn't.

It's tough, but rewarding; when a room full of people is captivated by a story, the Storyteller feels the reaction. The players become enthusiastic, and the session is better because of that energy. There are moments in a story when it becomes so compelling that everyone is drawn into it. Storytellers live for these moments. Time stands still, and the mechanism of the game is set aside as the story becomes "real." If you remember to make sure that the characters are having fun, and collaborate with your troupe to create a good story, that bliss is your reward.

TELLING STORIES

Keep to moderation, keep the end in view, follow nature.
— Lucan

Before we get down to the nuts and bolts, we should take a look at what we're really trying to attain by telling stories. The Storyteller has a vision of an elusive ideal. Life rarely measures up to our ideals, but by pursuing them, especially in our stories, we come closer to our goal of what Storytelling should be. Storytelling is not a technique or a process, but an art — a journey.

Over the last century, a certain four-letter word has been corrupted and abused. That word is *myth*. Myth is commonly defined as a set of lies about things that cannot be. Throughout the evolution of storytelling, artful wordsmiths have proven that wrong. A myth doesn't need to be academic or elitist. A "real" myth is a story we can believe in because it tells us something about the world. The events may not be true, but the theme behind the events is based on true things.

A myth is a metaphor. By examining myths and constructing our own, we come to understand what's important to us. When we create stories — and aspire to create myths — we take what we value from the real world and weave it into our story. The greatest inspiration often comes from what we know, or at least what we want to learn. If you can take the feelings and ideals you experience in the real world and bring them to life in a story, you've created a metaphor. Your story world is still an illusion, but you and your troupe can still care about the characters and events.

CHAPTER EIGHT: STORYTELLING

Unfortunately, the world at large often tells us that caring about a story, or even setting aside time for a game about telling stories, is wrong. But if it's acceptable for us to get caught up in books, films or television programs, then it's certainly okay for us to care about the games we play. Crafting stories and weaving them into existence with a troupe is an experience no passive medium can duplicate.

The journey you undertake as a Storyteller extends as far as you want to go. If, for instance, all you're interested in is playing a quick, fun game for a few hours, that's fine. If you game to have a dumping ground for your angst, that's certainly your choice. Should you choose to go beyond that, though, the opportunity for artistry is there.

It would be the height of pretense to say that a roleplaying game will show you the truths of existence. However, the creative energy you generate with your troupe should be something that stays with you even after the story is finished. If you choose to undertake the journey of Storytelling, pursue it to the fullest and seek out that element of truth in the myths you create, you'll have done more than find diversion. If you and your players care about the characters and ideals you bring to the world of **Dark Ages**, then you are at the center of the experience the entire time.

CHRONICLE

Look with favor upon a bold beginning.

— Virgil, *Eclogues*

Now that you've seen the theory behind Storytelling, it's time to put it to work. The practical side of preparing for a game involves planning your chronicle, a series of connected stories that builds into something bigger. If a story is a chapter in a book, a chronicle is the entire novel or the entire series.

A chronicle can be as lengthy as you like, from a few sessions to a campaign that takes years to fully develop. Because there are characters at the heart of the story, there's always the chance to develop a chronicle further. If you've created a thorough background and supporting cast for your chronicle, there's always room for a "sequel" to the initial story. Your players will hopefully find your chronicle intriguing enough that they'll want to develop it further. Always leave them wanting a little more.

Long before the players begin to create their characters, take the opportunity to map out where you want the chronicle to go. An exciting setting and cool subplots are good places to start. Along the way, there should be issues to examine, problems to solve and places to discover, but the basics of your chronicle come first.

GETTING STARTED

Dark Ages is a fairly easy game to run once you know your territory, but the set-up can seem intimidating at first. After all, this is a game about bloodsucking monsters living and dying in a time you may not be familiar with, in a land and place that you may never have seen or heard of (what modern country *is* Transylvania a part of?). Fortunately, if you tackle your problems one by one, everything is very simple. Here are a few tips:

- **Conceptualize**

First, decide on the kind of story you want to tell. Will the characters be swept up in court intrigue, noble betrayals and the power-plays so loved by the elders? Or is their fief already embattled (in disputes human or otherwise), and are the characters faithful war lieutenants of their sires? Do they have a permanent home, or do they wander, either as rag-tag, suspicious creatures or the trusted emissaries of a powerful prince? Define the direction as you like. The rest will flow from there.

• Brainstorm

Now for the fun part — daydreaming. As you reflect on your chronicle, things from the real world will inspire you. Anything can act as inspiration — a story on the news, an encounter at the bus stop, an insight into another person or a song that's stuck in your head are a few examples. Take notes. Draw. Outline. Visualize. Your creativity will lead you from there.

Good things to plan at this stage include: strong antagonists, allies and local subcultures, the common goal, the overall setting (is it urbane, brilliant Constantinople? the squalid backstreets of primitive London? the wild and lonely Pyrenees mountains? or even nervous and besieged Jerusalem?), major themes you wish to explore and so on. Running a game will become much easier once you know where you want to go with it.

• Get Input

Your players will, of course, want some say in the game they'll be playing. After all, if your troupe wants to kick ass, and you want them to run or die, your game will have problems from the start. The players are your collaborators, after all. Get their input before you begin.

You need not tell them what it is you have in mind; a little misdirection is not a bad thing — some of your actual plans mixed in with a bit of daydreaming should keep the players from knowing what to expect. Keep an open mind at this point; the suggestions you get may lead to something better than you originally planned.

• Set Boundaries

Obviously, your game cannot be all things to all people. Once you have a good idea of your chronicle's direction, lay out what you need in solid form (See "Packing," below), and let the players know what they can and cannot play.

A group needs some kind of coherence. If you have a pack of vampires who would never stay together without a player group behind them, your campaign will fall apart. Before you begin, let your players know what kind of characters they should design. If the game will be combat-heavy, tell them to load up on fighting skills; if it's to be an intrigue-laden mystery, Social Attributes and Abilities (or the lack of them) will be important. Most of all, try to establish some sort of a reason for the characters to work together — a quest, a common haven, mutual revenge, family ties, romantic interest, etc. Make them have some motivation to stay together.

Above all, make sure this common bond is strong but not binding. Nobody wants to play a game in which they remain slaves to the Storyteller's demands.

• Plan First Scene

The first scene will set the mood for the entire chronicle. If it begins with the usual, "Um, all you guys are in this tavern, see, and all of a sudden, a fight breaks out…," the game will have a random feel to it. When the first scene is strong, however: "The streets of Effelheim are blanketed by an unseasonable, blinding fog, and the Great Square is filled with tired, stumbling mortals heading home from market day. You reach the marble steps of the house where Baron von Sprenger, a Ventrue, is holding court tonight. As you climb them a figure runs past you in the gloom, throwing a cloth-wrapped bundle up to you. It lands with a cracking thud at your feet. The sacking comes loose with the impact, and in the deathly pale, bloodied face it reveals, you recognize the adopted mortal daughter of the Baron…" — the tale begins with a kick, a tone and an overall goal. Writers call this the "hook"; give your game a powerful hook, and you'll be off to a good start.

SETTING

Had I been present at the creation, I would have given some useful hints for the better ordering of the universe.

— Alfonso the Wise

Any story needs a strong setting. With **Dark Ages**, it can be the most important element of the chronicle. It's important to think out how you will cope with historical and geographical details before the game begins. There are basically three ways to approach the problem.

You can wing it completely in a fictional European country of your own devising (e.g., Ruritania in the High Middle Ages). This gives you complete control over customs, currency, political structure, social order, etc., and still lets your players' characters come from whatever country and background they choose. The major disadvantage is that your players will only know about the setting what you tell them of it. The minor disadvantage is that you have to invent an entire country and work out its relation to the rest of the World of Darkness.

You can set it in a real place that you know through a few books, Hollywood and TV, and just fudge the details. Most people could do a decent job starting a campaign in Robin Hood's England, for instance. The important thing in this case is to warn the players ahead of time that the story and the atmosphere will override any conflicts in historical details. If you are drawing from a specific work of fiction, let the players see it or read it so that everyone will have the same expectations.

And finally, you can set it in the historic version of Europe, and keep track of major events that affect the region or city as they happened. This may involve quite a lot of research if the area was an important one, and has the obvious disadvantage that well-read players could run the city's most accurate fortune-tellers. Still, what happened in Rome in 1214 in the World of Darkness isn't necessarily what happened in Rome here.…

A happy medium between the three is probably best. With an historic timeline, fictional city, common-knowledge customs and a relaxed attitude toward accuracy on the part of the troupe, a campaign could go a long way before becoming bogged down in textbooks. Use historical references for inspiration and flavor, but don't allow yourself to be shackled by them. The Bibliography has a few suggestions to get you started, but you should make any city your own, with details to fit your particular chronicle.

With all this in mind, the area the characters know best, or the one where they'll be spending the most time, is the place to focus on first. Choose a city, or imagine one. If the characters are inclined to venture into the werewolf-infested countryside, research or invent the surrounding territory.

As you think through your setting, you'll develop the details. Minor details can be just as useful as major ones. What places will the characters visit often? Where can they go for gossip? Where do they hunt? Where can they sleep safely? Plan out the basics. If you have a variety of elements prepared beforehand, you'll glide into them effortlessly when you need them. If you haven't prepared a particular detail, you'll find inspiration on the spur of the moment, but having something to fall back on will make you more comfortable.

Supporting Characters

Add to this background a group of supporting characters. Who shares the world with the characters? Who rules the area for the kine? What about the prince of the Cainites? What are the supernatural threats that remain hidden? What other vampires live in the city, and whom do they serve? One temptation here is to fall back on stereotypes or choose the obvious, but character comes from personality, not templates. If you stick to the obvious, your chronicle will become predictable and shallow.

Even small details can go a long way toward defining a character's personality. How does a character speak? What inspires his trust? What color cloak does he wear? A toothless old fisherwoman with the eyes of a hawk and a nose for "witches" might be a better story hook than the information-selling Nosferatu in the cellar. Fleshing out a character involves giving her little quirks and petty flaws, and any character, even a supernatural one, must be able to relate to the world around her.

To keep your story realistic, don't forget to include the "normal" world. Not everyone the characters meet will be a Lasombra with a plan to wrest control of the city from his Ventrue rivals. Before you escalate the danger level of your campaign, remember that putting personality into "mundanes" can make the setting richer and more robust. If your supporting cast is a series of combat statistics or neat critters, you *don't* have a supporting cast. You have got a bunch of stereotypes. Any character needs a degree of motivation and depth, even a supporting one.

Motivation puts a character in motion. Consider: Every character has a goal. That character will work toward that goal until he meets outside opposition. In physics, "an object in motion stays in motion… until acted upon by an opposing force." The same applies to your supporting cast. Outside opposition usually comes from the characters, the most potent motivators in the story. If the opposition doesn't come directly from them, it might still come from the consequences of their actions. Things happen for a reason, and often, the rationale "she does it because she's *e-vil*…" just doesn't cut it. To give your stories verisimilitude, focus on making the supporting characters realistic.

This applies to antagonists as well. If there's no conflict, there's no drama; antagonists provide opposition. Don't set up a series of cut-out figures — giving a "villain" a motivation is a challenge. A game gains depth when the adversaries aren't so much villains as characters with different points of view. Don't think of them as guys in black hats; the phrase "alternative morality" is useful here.

It's hard to play an antagonist convincingly if you can't understand him. This doesn't mean that you have to agree with him, but you do need to have an idea of how he thinks. This makes the game more challenging for your players. A black hat is easy to overcome, but a detailed antagonist, with his own particular idiom and point of view, makes for a worthy adversary. Even the darkest adversary has an element of humanity.

The Center of Your Story

Forget clans and Cainite politics for a moment. Set aside chronology, historical detail, settings, conflicts and antagonists. The core of your story involves people. And for **Dark Ages** Storytellers, the good news is that the basic model hasn't changed much in the last thousand years. Whether they get their news from the smelly old peasant who sells them dried cod in the marketplace, or over the radio as they drive to the doughnut shop in the morning, people are still people.

The most important of these are the players' characters. As you paint the elaborate backdrop for the stage of your drama, don't forget that the players' characters are at the center of it. It's very easy to fall into the trap of developing such an extensive background that there's no room for the characters. The chronicle must center around the characters and the conflicts they endure.

Establish how the heroes tie into the background. Why are they there? Why are they risking their lives to explore your dark and dangerous theater of the mind when they could just flee for their lives or hole up in a cave somewhere? If the characters don't have a motivation to interact with your background, you have no story. As the characters grow, tailoring an adventure to them gets easier. Each character is incomplete in some way; the world brings the opportunity for fulfillment. The players will also give you clues, either directly or indirectly, for the kinds of stories they want to play.

It's also a good idea to have a way for the characters to work together. They all belong to the same coterie, so do they share a common haven? What motives bind the characters together? Family? Revenge? Redemption? The destruction of their kind? Power, money and territory? Once you and your players have found a reason for the characters to be together, it's easier to chart out a route for them to take.

The meaning behind the Dark Medieval world is not that the world is dark. That's atmosphere. The real meaning in a chronicle comes from the characters.

Nuts and Bolts

Where the lion's skin will not reach, you must patch it out with the fox's.

— Plutarch, *Lives*

Don't feel an obligation to create a modern myth before lunchtime tomorrow. Take your time. Once you have a sense of direction, it's simply a matter of starting out on the path. Regardless of whether you're setting out to inspire art or just provide an evening's entertainment, the first few steps on the journey are the same.

First, make sure a good story is told. That doesn't mean you just *tell* a story. The troupe creates it with you. In each chapter, the Storyteller leads the story in the direction he wants it to go. If you're working with your players (and not just performing for

them), you'll eventually find yourself struggling to keep up with what they want to do, commenting and elaborating on what happens rather than simply laying out a narrative. The result is a collaborative effort, a "consensual reality."

The story will often deviate from your plans. If you feel that the story is naturally drifting in another direction, don't force the players to follow your plans; work with them. So long as the tale stays within reason, go with it. You're usually the guide, but elements of the story often come together naturally. An experienced Storyteller often feels as though the story is flowing almost without effort. Just as your players try to anticipate what you're going to do, try to anticipate the characters' actions. They'll surprise you from time to time, and that makes the story come alive.

Packing

Before you begin, be prepared. When you're just starting out, it will be easier to create the story if you spend plenty of time preparing. These preparations include creating a setting, envisioning a rough idea of the plot you want, and establishing a few good plot hooks. A "cheat sheet" of important details can be a critical aid to running a smooth game. Cheat sheets might include brief reference descriptions of significant characters (name, story role, physical description, motivations, powers or important skills, and relationships with other characters), a combat summary (who can do what, the average damage they do, weapons they use, amount of damage they can take) and short listings of important places and things (the layout of a brothel, the distance between points A and B). A relationship chart, if you can create one, makes character reference easy.

You may want to use a premade story, or one adapted from another genre or system. If you do, read through the text carefully a few times beforehand. Make sure you know when and where everything happens, who is where at what time and so on. Pay close attention to the major antagonists, their personalities and motivations, and some ways to portray them convincingly. You can start with a very linear or straightforward plot; there's nothing wrong with that. You must learn the basics first; defying reality and creating dreams comes later.

Such aids are useful, but not mandatory. As you become more experienced, it will be easier to deviate from what you've planned. The structure you adopt and the rules you use are the game itself; the events you and your troupe create are the actual story. Storytelling is ultimately a balance between the story and the rules.

Rules

This book is filled with rules. In reading them, you might feel as though you're studying for a test. Players will question you about them, other Storytellers will argue about them, and, remarkably enough, some people will really get worked up over them. Despite the fact that **Vampire: The Dark Ages** is just a game, some people enjoy giving themselves (or others) grief over those rules.

First off, you have to be consistent and fair. Some people interpret that as meaning that you must be strict. That is not the case. We've done our best to make sure these rules are consistent, clear and useful, but you and your troupe are the final judges of how well they serve your story. The framework of rules in the game is the set of guidelines we recommend, and serves as a common ground for everyone who plays the game. You, as the Storyteller, must get a sense of how well this system works for your troupe. Eventually, you'll customize it to a size and shape you feel is right. You're the final judge of what will work.

Having said that, here's a word of advice — don't worry excessively about rules. In Storytelling, like many things in life, there are no rules, only guidelines. The game is not a test of your ability to memorize. Learn the basics first. Later, you'll take the bits and pieces that work for you. You'll simplify, expand, alter and amend. If you eventually make things up on your own, no one is going to kick down your door and take this book away. Your game belongs to you and yours.

There is no "official" way to play this game, only the way that works best for you and your troupe. Most people who use rules fall between two extremes. Their preference is largely a matter of style.

STYLE

If you've watched other people run games, you've no doubt seen a variety of styles. Most Storytellers run somewhere between the "rules lawyer" and the "freeform gamer." You won't get a sense of which style works best for you until you start to play. Style comes from experience.

A "rules lawyer" relies on an extremely strict interpretation and application of the rules of the game. If the chart on page 952 says that a player describing a certain action should roll Stamina + Dominate and cross-reference the number of successes against a resisted Willpower roll at a difficulty of 8, then that's the way it's gotta be. Rules lawyers often pursue "realism"; for some reason, they feel that adding more rules will make a game more realistic.

This extreme has definite disadvantages. If a rules lawyer gets so caught up in rolling dice and looking up rules that he forgets to concentrate on his story, the story suffers. To us, rules should serve the story; the story is not just a cheap excuse to use rules.

Some players tend to be rules lawyers, too. Rather than holding on to the concepts that make a good story, they'll try to solve problems by bending the rules their way. The character's personality is set aside, and the structure behind the game becomes more important than the game itself. Storytelling should be seen as a collaborative activity, not a contest of wills between the Storyteller and his players. The troupe as a whole ideally works together to create the events. Rules lawyer players have to learn to play the characters, not the rules.

An extremely "freeform" Storyteller doesn't need any rules at all. If the game only consists of guidelines, why bother with structure and mechanics? A situation may call for tossing a coin or generating a random number, but that's about it. If you have to roll dice, then something has gone wrong. The character sheets provide a rough idea of what characters can do, so dice become superfluous. If the troupe really wants something to happen, it happens. This type of game resembles improvisational theater more than anything else.

While this approach is valid, it also has obvious drawbacks. If anything can happen at the whim of the Storyteller, then everything that happens is, by definition, completely arbitrary. Players who like to have a framework of rules feel lost when they enter the realm of freeform gaming. They'll have certain expectations of what should work, and find themselves in situations in which the only measure of success is their ability to amuse and humor the Storyteller.

All sarcasm aside, the style that's right for you will probably fall somewhere between these two camps. Both extremes can destroy a game. Consistency is one way to build that particular mindset. Once the players feel comfortable with your style, telling stories comes naturally. Never radically alter your style without letting the players know you're experimenting. If you're going to do something freakish with the rules, the players tend to appreciate it if you let them know beforehand.

ADJUSTING YOUR STYLE

It's possible to shift your style a little during a session to suit your game. Think of taking your journey through the story as if you're driving a race car. When you go into a turn, you downshift. When you're on a straight road, you shift back into high gear again. During your story, for instance, if there's a critical combat coming up, you may slow down and throw a little more detail into the fight. Once it's over, if you want the characters to focus on their discussion of what happens as they search the building, you can shift back up to high speed so that the characters aren't distracted by the dice rolls. As long as you don't radically shift in the middle of a session, you won't ruin the transmission and bring things grinding to a halt. Most players will sense what you're doing and react.

Unfortunately, some people are a pain on long car rides. Certain players delight in trying to circumvent the rules of your game. The goal here is allegedly "success." An individual character's success becomes more important than the game's. The structure that's been built into the game gives you some measure of protection against rules lawyers, but rules alone are not enough to protect you from an overly aggressive player. One option is to build further layers of rules to shield you from assaults, but then the game becomes so structured that the flow of the story is sacrificed. The best recourse is to find players who work well with you. Over time, you'll find ways to adjust to different types of players, and good players will make an effort to adjust to you. When that happens, you've assembled a worthwhile troupe. Then you can let go of the wheel… and the rest is the magic of storytelling.

There can't be rules for everything, but you can find an amount of detail that suits you. Give the players a chance to offer feedback, especially at the conclusion of each chapter. Through this process you'll develop a set of "house rules" that will make everyone comfortable. Just as you tailor the story to what your troupe enjoys, you'll discover your own particular style of using rules. As long as you're consistent, the players won't feel as though you're being arbitrary. Consistent rules and sound judgment reveal the path; drama and passion make the journey worthwhile.

TIPS

Style ideals are all well and good, but they're nothing without practical skill to back them up. Here are a few basic ideas to help you along.…

• The Dice Should Guide You, Not Control You

Dice are a random element, a helpful device to use when stories get stuck or an outcome should be left to chance. In the end, however, they're a tool, nothing more. How you use that tool will affect the feel of your story. Ultimately, the game is played by human beings, not dice. Use die rolls for inspiration, or for adjudication if you really need it, but remember to balance the game and story.

- **Describe Dramatically**

Vampires should never be boring. Your players will no doubt put as much melodrama, angst, tragedy, pathos and power into their characters as they can muster. You need to return the favor by making the world around them equally so.

Try not to fall into game terms or die rolls until you really need to. While you're telling the characters what the visiting Transylvanian noble looks like, be as visual as possible. If his clothes are outlandish, don't just say that — describe his sweeping blue velvet cloak with the cloth-of-gold and ermine trim, the perfectly cut black silk tunic and hose, and blue suede pearl-buttoned boots. When he enters the tavern, don't tell the players that he's using his Presence to attract attention — tell them that every eye in the room is on him, and (since they are obviously looking at him too, if description is necessary) don't ask them to roll to notice it until few moments have passed and the reason for asking is less obvious.

- **Improvisation**

A vampire's world, like a Storyteller's, is full of surprises. Intent may shape reality, but reality often has its own ideas. Dice rolling is one way to inject this element of uncertainty into the game, but what can you do when a player (or circumstances) comes up with something no rules can cover?

- **Be Creative**

Many questions can be resolved with a little imagination. If all else fails, however, adjust difficulty levels or die pools. Gena wants her Gangrel to sneak up on the Toreador Justicar? Fine. Just up her difficulty by +2 or +3. Adding or subtracting modifiers for imaginative descriptions can also encourage players to be inventive, although this can get out of hand. The rules suggest a maximum adjustment of + or - 3. You may want to stick to that, if only for your own sanity.

TECHNIQUES

Once you've got the basics down, there's still room to grow. After you've structured your plot, established the background and set the characters off and running, certain techniques can enhance the experience. To begin with, a well-done game will have a certain atmosphere that will evoke a particular mood.

CREATING MOOD AND ATMOSPHERE

What characters do is one part of an adventure; what they *feel* is almost as important. Evoking those feelings is achieved with atmosphere. If the cast is at the center of the stage you set, then the atmosphere is the lighting. If it's turned too low, everyone will stumble in the dark; if it's turned too high, the actors will sweat and squirm. When designed properly, the atmosphere will convey the proper mood. If you're fresh out of tallow candles, there are other tools you can use to create the mood and atmosphere of a scene:

- **Remember All Five Senses**

"Virtual" reality is usually a misnomer. An environment isn't virtual unless it draws upon all five senses. Storytellers have known this for millennia. A setting can be something as simple as a mapped-out room, but an atmosphere assaults all the senses at once. A run-of-the-mill dungeon cell can be described as a room with a set of shackles and a bucket, but a terrifying dungeon cell might be filled with the smell of gangrene and nightsoil; the sounds of the torturer's workshop next door; the hard stones,

rotted straw and sections of previous occupants that make up the floor; the blood of the carrion-eating rat that becomes your meager meal, and the pale starlight drifting in from the small, barred, south-facing window. The first example is a map; the second example is an environment.

• Use Analogies

If you want to convey a feeling for a scene, incidental events can convey subtle clues to the mood you want to instill. A minor occurrence can be used as an analogy to the mood of a scene. For instance, suppose the atmosphere you wish to create in a scene is one of fragile hope. The setting might be a desolate stretch of road by the city walls, three hours before dawn. Autumn leaves drift lazily in a gentle breeze, and moonlight fights to hold back the night. The characters walk past two beggars rubbing their hands over a small fire. Then one of the characters notices the silhouette of two young lovers holding hands in the distance. In the middle of the street, the lovers pause, embrace and then walk their separate ways. None of these elements has to be tied to the plot in any way, shape or form, but they contribute to the scene by lending cues. If your players pick up on them, they'll respond by adjusting their roleplaying to fit the mood.

• Vary Tone

The way you use your voice is another cue. This may seem like an obvious remark, but many Storytellers forget about the versatility of the human voice. Softly whispering to draw your player's attention, frantic dialogue to hurry them along, matter-of-fact description to render a scene sterile, or boisterous blustering to describe a rambunctious crowd are but a few examples.

Another effective technique is to use a tone that's the exact opposite of what your players expect. Describing an intimate scene in third person with no embellishment can convey that a supposedly romantic encounter might just be an attempt to manipulate someone. If you're describing a house where a family has been slain, relating the condition of the children's toys can make the scene far more sinister than the standard clichés associated with gore. Less is indeed more, and an unexpected approach can lend a routine description an intriguing atmosphere.

• Detail Supporting Characters

The details of supporting characters can also add to the atmosphere of a scene. Any human being has little quirks and foibles that reveal minor bits of his personality. If a minor character is usually identified with a specific location, his little quirks can contain cues about that location. Suppose you want the characters to feel remorse over the destruction of a human servant of their enemy. If they bump into the weeping widow, Beatrice, returning to her cottage after the wake with toddlers and teenagers in tow, they may think twice about killing anyone and everyone associated with their foe.

Those little cues might also shape a character's view of a group of people. Suppose a Brujah, hating for philosophy's sake the nobility and everything associated with it, should be skulking near the king's palace garden as the ladies of the household fetch flowers for their royal mistress. He sees that the girls are very young, very pretty, and overhears their nervous, excited chatter about the visiting Transylvanian ambassador. The youngest seems to have caught the

VAMPIRE: THE DARK AGES

man's eye, and the other two help her practice her dancing in preparation for that evening's entertainment. Our idealistic Brujah can put two and two together — but will he act in time to save the rich and titled girl's life, or will he let the nobility feed upon itself and wait until his plans are fully matured? There's an emotional component to the scene... and that's what mood is all about.

STORIES

Then Merlin said, "Let everyone sit quietly and do not move, for now begins an age of marvels, and you will see strange happenings."

—Sir Thomas Malory, *The Acts of King Arthur and His Noble Knights*

Once you've evaluated what you're doing in the long run with your chronicle, it's easier to put your short-term goals into perspective. Keep in mind that you can play a game without committing to a lengthy chronicle. The "one-shot" is an art form all its own. Whether you're planning for a skirmish or a siege, it helps to remember the overarching goals of chronicles and storytelling.

Structure, atmosphere, mood, theme and technique are just as useful in a short chapter as they are in an extended chronicle. Rudimentary as these elements seem, never underestimate the power of the well-timed gust of wind or the melancholy flashback. Storytellers throughout time have known the value of such flourishes.

To begin with, any story has structure. The basic structure of a *chronicle* consists of two steps: a series of chapters (or *sessions*) tell a story, and a series of stories compose a chronicle. We tend to favor a literary analogy for this, but any analogy can work. You might choose to see the story as a series of acts, like a play or a television show. Or perhaps the scenes are like sections of a comic book mini-series, or a series of movements in a symphony. Use the metaphor that works for you. If you can draw upon your knowledge of another art form, you can develop your understanding of the process of creating stories.

THEMES

Theme is one of the hardest things to develop in a story. You don't have to preach when running a story or chronicle, but there are definite themes that will come up in a **Dark Ages** chronicle. Angels may not descend from the heavens to weep tears of blood at the beauty of your story, but a strong theme, or series of themes, will elevate your game beyond simple critter-hunts.

Subtlety works. If we can't sympathize with the motivations of the characters or the antagonists, the story, as one person would say, is "just a bunch of stuff that happened." You can work your chosen themes into the game with characters (whose personalities, motivations or circumstances force the players to think), situations (which put them into dilemmas), relationships (which incorporate both) and symbols, omens or mindscapes which emphasize the theme. Just remember — go easy.

Some common themes for **Dark Ages** chronicles include:

- **Survival**

A chronicle describing a fight for survival centers on more than Health Levels and Ability rolls. Existence itself should be a trial. The characters live in a dangerous era, one where survival is a day-to-day crisis. This might be anything from a rough stretch of wilderness to a zealous priest out to rid the world of evildoers. The world doesn't care whether they live or die, and unless the characters struggle and learn, neat tricks with vampiric Disciplines won't be enough to save them. This takes more than raw force. In fact, a story centered on survival doesn't have to involve force at all. If you want to make a character's life more difficult, it's more effective to do it through ingenuity than to have someone hit him on the head. There are also other definitions of "survival": What compromises do we make in life to get by? Staying alive exacts a price; idealists defy that temptation and succeed in spite of it.

- **Espionage**

Politics among Cainites are always fraught with deceit, and it takes cunning as well as luck to survive. The characters may be caught between two rival factions, or they may be attempting to sabotage the rule of a powerful prince. Either way, it will be difficult to determine who can be trusted, and one mistake could prove fatal. What happens when you can't trust anyone? What happens when paranoia overwhelms reason? If the Jyhad was entirely blood and thunder, fighting it would be comparatively straightforward. But in a duplicitous world such as this, sometimes it's hard to determine who the "bad guys" are....

- **Power**

After the Becoming, characters are possessed with more power than they probably ever dreamed was possible. To transform into beasts or disappear into the shadows are commonplace feats now; how does that effect a character's view of the world? Kine are but pawns, and even the mighty tremble in view of most vampires. We all know the cliché that "power corrupts," but how does it happen? If we know this is true, why does it still happen so frequently? There's one more complication: In the world of the game and the real world, you do have the power to rebel against the established order. So what are you going to do if you succeed?

- **Identity**

In the modern age, we like to think that we determine who we are. We have the freedom to carve out our own identity, and we are told that race, gender, sexuality and social class need not stand in our way. But things are far different in the Dark Medieval world, where these things are the defining factors in who you are in the mortal world. You are born to a given role in society, and to challenge that is to speak heresy. Now consider this: Once Embraced, all vampires begin on the same footing, without regard to their mortal identity. It becomes impossible to judge someone's strength or importance on the basis of such superficial things; you never know when the chambermaid might turn out to be a 700-year-old fifth generation vampire. How does that affect (or corrupt) something as fragile and malleable as a vampire's concept of self? In game terms, how much does clan or generation define a vampire? This type of story takes roleplaying beyond the simple limits of class, gender and other stereotypes. The result is a mirror to the world around us.

STORY CONCEPTS

Now we enter the realm of the story. There are an endless number of stories you can run, but some ideas are more obvious than others. If you need to prime the pump, the supplements to this rulebook and the suggestions below are good places to start. If you want to begin with the time-honored formulas, that's another option. Hopefully, though, you'll move from the obvious to the innovative. To set you on your way, here are a few simple adventure ideas. Build on them long enough, and you'll make them your own.

Outcasts

Before their Becoming, each of the characters was a member of a victimized or disadvantaged social group. This may be a racial or religious group, or an economic underclass. Now, as vampires, the characters continue to watch over and protect the other members of this class.

You may wish to make this a very specific social group (prostitutes), or a broad group (women). Playing female characters in a sexist society can be an illuminating experience, especially for male players, and particularly intriguing chronicles might revolve around the characters all being lepers or Jews.

As an example, the characters might be attached to a community of Moslems in Spain, merchants and artisans who remain in their home city after the Christians capture it. The Moslem community is vilified, and individual members are pressured into becoming Christian. The characters must help the community through these troubles and deal with the changing Cainite politics of the region. The Lasombra back the Christian conquerors, the Gangrel and Toreador back the defeated Moors, and following the Christian *Reconquista*, an anti-Moslem Lasombra prince seizes control of the city.

The Paladins

The characters believe that they are Heaven's servants, imbued with dark powers all the better to seek out and destroy evildoers. (At least, most of the characters believe this; others might have their own agendas, and merely pretend to hold this belief.)

The characters hunt down and destroy bestial vampires, demons, homicidal Lupines, witches' covens, corrupt bishops, sadistic barons — whatever you want to tell stories about, or whatever your troupe wants to go for. They believe that they fight for God or for justice, but few others would agree with them, and theirs should be a very lonely crusade.

This works particularly well with troupes who enjoy detective work and planning, with a little combat, and allows you to play around with questions of ends versus means, of who has the right to judge and so forth.

Hell's Pawns

The characters are in the service of a demon or group of demons. Perhaps they believe that they owe their undead existences to these creatures, perhaps they actually want to work for them, or more interestingly, they need some favor from the demons and serve them for now to pay for that favor. What favor might the characters want? That's up to your troupe; perhaps protection, their mortality returned or assistance in slaying some powerful enemy?

The demons might call on the characters occasionally (allowing you to run other stories, or combine this with another chronicle archetype), or might have one specific, permanent duty for the characters. The demons might want characters to rescue their other servants from danger, kill their enemies, guard an important site, spy on local churchmen or recruit and lead a coven of diabolists.

As an example, the characters might be "debt collectors" for the demons, collecting the souls of those who have signed them away in demonic contracts. The characters may simply have to track down and kill such mortals, or they might have to be at their deathbeds to somehow magically ensnare their souls — you decide. If the characters seem capable of it, the demons may also ask them to persuade mortals to sign their souls away (the mortal must agree freely!), and then return later to collect, so that the characters come to act as the demons' proxies.

As demons' servants, however, the characters will also gain a good many enemies — rival demons, the Church and other Cainites, Lupines and mages who dislike what they are doing. The relatives of those whose souls they have taken might come looking for them in revenge, and the demons for whom the characters work should pose a considerable threat to them, too. The demons, ultimately, may not want to owe the characters a favor, and may conspire to have them killed as soon as they become a liability, or may try to trick them into signing their own souls away.

Dust to Dust

Another vampire seeks out the characters, and explains that she was recently discovered and driven from a nearby village by the local peasants. Before she left the settlement, she Embraced her favorite ghoul, only to see him beaten into torpor by her pursuers as she fled.

She briefly returned to seek out her friend and childe, and discovered that the peasants believed they had killed him. They had buried him in the churchyard, but worried that he might "rise from the dead," so they laid a huge stone slab over the grave, and intend to stand guard around it for 40 days and 40 nights with burning torches and constant prayers.

Not only is the neonate degenerating in the grave, but he lies in consecrated ground, attended by the prayers of holy men. There is a possibility that he will never come out of this torpor.

So, the vampire asks the characters to release her torpid progeny as swiftly as possible. They must get to the grave, move the stone slab, dig up the vampire and escape with him. However, the grave is constantly guarded by the local villagers, and attended by praying monks (the leader of whom perhaps has Faith and/or carries a holy relic). The guards are armed with spears, clubs and flaming torches, and are already nervous that vampires or some other demons might attack them.

Moreover, there is a faction among the local peasants that wants to exhume the neonate's "corpse" and burn it, just to be on the safe side. If the characters bungle the rescue, these might persuade their fellows to cremate the vampire. On the other hand, if the characters blatantly rescue the neonate (charging in and massacring the guards, for example), they might spark off a wave of witch-hunts and other persecutions in the area, making them unpopular with their prince, other local Cainites and various groups of mages, witches and diabolists. They will need to hatch a fairly cunning plan.

A Profitable Slander

A character who maintains a haven in a rural or wooded area discovers that a young boy is being held captive in a shack in the woods nearby. Investigations reveal that the boy recently vanished from a neighboring city, and the Jewish population is being blamed for the crime.

The rumor around the city claims that Jews kidnapped the child for sacrifice in a Satanic ritual, and anti-Semitism is so rife that people believe this nonsense. A merchant in very deep debt with the local Jewish moneylenders started the rumor, and not surprisingly, it is his relatives or hirelings who kidnapped and now guard the boy. He hopes to start a riot against the local Jews, during which his henchmen will target the moneylenders, killing and robbing them. So he expects to clear his debts, and — as medieval Christians considered Jews to be sub-human — he feels no guilt at all.

However, the merchant underestimates the tenacity of the city's authorities. They are not taken in by the rumors of a Jewish plot, and eventually work out how the child was kidnapped and how he was spirited from the city. Then their soldiers start searching the area around the character's haven.

The soldiers comb the woods, search through caves and scour houses. The character may not want to free the child (though both his family and the city's Jews will be grateful if he is returned and the conspiracy revealed), but might find it necessary to do so. If the character does not free the child, the soldiers will continue their search and likely find her haven.

Caught Between the Devil...

Two factions of hedge wizards drag the characters into their ongoing feud. The fighting began when a group of sorcerers in the city stole an ancient tome detailing dozens of spells and rituals. These sorcerers are merchants and artisans, led by a wayward exorcist, who want to use magic to gain wealth. The book originally belonged to a group of diabolists who meet in the forests nearby, typically nasty sorts who want the book to gain power, compel women to bed them, slay those who annoy them, etc.

It is important that the characters can't make heads or tails of the book; they are supposed to be in a quandary as to whom they support — not just gunning to steal the book for themselves. (If any of the characters have Thaumaturgy, then claim the book has protections they cannot pierce.)

Seeking allies to help them recover the book, the diabolists conjure a demon who tells them of the characters. The diabolists then approach the characters, and offer them magical favors in return for the book. If they refuse, the diabolists summon another demon, who repeatedly attacks them, steals their possessions and makes trouble for them, informing them that it will only stop tormenting them if they agree to help the diabolists.

The area's spirit-conjurers have protected themselves from the diabolists' dark spirits (erected wards, bound guardian spirits, etc.), but are vulnerable to the characters' physical attacks. However, they are no less powerful than the diabolists, and can offer the characters equal magical favors — including protection from the troublesome demon. Of course, they want something from the characters in return — they want the characters to break up or drive away the diabolists' group. They can protect themselves well, but need the characters to strike back at the diabolists.

Who do the characters support? That's up to them. The demon's attacks should be disruptive enough that they cannot simply ignore the feud, and eventually must take sides. In the end they could make a group of useful allies, and a group of deadly enemies. Or they might just betray the diabolists to the Church (except, of course, that the diabolists could do the same to the characters and the city's sorcerers if they were arrested and interrogated). And how do the city's other Cainites respond to the feud and the characters' involvement in it?

Rescued, Dead or Alive

The ghoul of one of the characters was caught committing some crime against a mortal nobleman, and now languishes in his dungeons. However, while interrogating the ghoul, the nobleman has noted her obsessive, tormented behavior, and has come to believe that the unfortunate has been "bewitched" or is possessed by demonic spirits.

So, the nobleman has neither sentenced nor released the ghoul, but has kept her imprisoned beneath his castle, occasionally interrogating her. For weeks or even months, the ghoul has been locked up. In two more weeks, her Blood Oath will cease, and she might then betray her master to the nobleman.

It is imperative that she be released or killed before the Blood Oath expires. Either way, the characters must somehow get into the castle and to the dungeon beneath it.

As an added complication, the suspicious nobleman might have contacted the local bishop, describing his "bewitched" captive. As the characters plot to release or kill the ghoul, envoys from the bishop — perhaps even an inquisitor — might arrive to examine her. The Church might even plan to take her away from the castle, to imprison her in one of their own strongholds.

The Blood of Life

A mage or alchemist is working on a method to animate clay figures or statues, but has had little success. However, it occurs to her that a vampire's blood might be just the ingredient needed to make her magic charm work.

The mage seeks out a place where a vampire hunts — either one of the characters or an acquaintance of theirs — and there lays a trap for the creature. If the trap is set for one of the characters' friends, the characters hear of the mage's plan, and must rush to warn him before he is captured. If one or more of the characters are the mystic's prey, then they may be set upon by her or her minions as they hunt.

The characters should escape this first ambush, but the mage and her minions continue to hunt them, so that they (for a change) are the prey.

Of course, the characters might negotiate a satisfactory conclusion to this. For example, they might supply their hunter with a little blood, for a price. (Incidentally, if the statue were animated using the vampire's blood, then maybe, unknown to the wizard who animated it, it would function as that vampire's ghoul....)

For the Love of Christ

A young friar comes to the characters' city, preaching and tending to the poor. Rumors begin to circulate that he has healing powers, and has aided several beggars and vagrants.

If characters investigate, they discover that the friar has an old, battered cup which he believes to be the Holy Grail. He conducts Masses for the poor in houses, fields, woods — wherever they want — and some who drink from the ancient chalice seem cured of minor ailments.

The friar's teachings are mildly heretical, claiming that the Church should give its wealth to the poor, denouncing clerical corruption and conducting Mass outside of churches. The local clergy become irritated, and he is forced to go into hiding.

Then an inquisitor arrives in the city, ostensibly present to investigate charges of heresy against the friar. However, the inquisitor is really concerned with confiscating the "grail."

Soon after that, a large group of Templars arrive, equally set upon seizing the grail. There are about 20 of them, many with the Faith Background. Further, their leader may have a relic of his own, and one of his retainers may be a mage. In any case, the characters should not be able to defeat the Templars.

The presence of these churchmen poses a threat to the local Cainites. The crass Templars follow rumors of the friar with violence and little tact (breaking into the houses of his supporters, ransacking suspected hiding places), and they may come to endanger the Cainites by prying around their havens, or by troubling their herds, retainers or allies. The inquisitor's prying might also threaten the Cainites. A character's herd or allies might be supporters of the friar, held as hostages or threatened with trial for heresy by the inquisitor. The whole situation puts the characters and the area's other Cainites in considerable danger.

If the characters do not take any action on their own initiative, the local prince or another respected vampire could ask them to deal with this situation. How the characters do this is up to them. Different characters will have different goals and priorities. They might murder the inquisitor (bad move — the local bishop will only send more people to investigate), discredit, intimidate or attempt to control him. Shrewd characters might be able to have the brutal Templars driven from the city, either by an incensed mob or by the local authorities. Or the characters might just search out the friar, and hand him and his chalice over to the inquisitor or Templars; even this shouldn't be too easy, though, as the friar has many supporters in the city, and has the Faith Background augmented by the relic that he holds.

In any case, the characters are free to choose any approach that they wish, and thereby perhaps make long-lasting friends or enemies among the mortals.

And what of the "Holy Grail"? Well, it's unlikely to be the real Grail (unless you want to give it some awesome supernatural powers and make it the center of your chronicle). It may, however, be a minor relic, perhaps with some healing powers. Or the friar's healing powers may be little miracles deriving from his own Faith, or he might be a mage. (If he is a mage, then what does he really want in the characters' area?) Or perhaps the tales of his healings were just hopeful rumors.

The Madness of Prince Roland

The prince of the characters' city has apparently gone insane. He becomes a martinet in his court and a tyrant to his subjects, demanding ruinous taxes and hounding those who displease him. He even demands the heads of his vassals for goblets one evening, and flies into a murderous rage when it is not carried out. One of the nobles approaches the characters and asks for aid. After all, an outsider might see something that those within the palace cannot. One of the character's sires or a clan elder may be similarly approached, and the characters area charged by that person to investigate.

As the characters make their investigation, they must tread carefully around the erratic prince, whose personality changes at the drop of a hat, at times apparently rational and cool, suddenly shifting to terrifying rages. Many of the prince's retainers and other vampires are fearful of his wrath if they are seen aiding the characters. Some whisper of demonic possession, and others fear the kiss of Malkav. As they talk with those closest to the prince, the characters realize that he is not entirely in control of himself; perhaps outside influences have something to do with this.

A number of sects fall under heavy suspicion for their relations with the prince. The local Tremere, backed by their clan, are on the brink of all-out war with the prince. A chapter of Knights Templar has been circling the prince in stand-offs for some time, unaware of his vampire nature. In the shadows, the sinister *Manus Nigrum* extends a taloned hand to "encourage" him in decisions that aid their dark agendas. However, the most telling clues lead the characters to believe that one of the prince's own knights is set against him. But who, and more importantly, why? All have a keen interest in who will sit on the throne when the prince is removed, and each would obviously prefer it be him. At least one of them has ties outside the fief that suggest more sinister purposes.

As the prince's actions become more and more bizarre, they begin to attract the notice of the Church. If they send in their own investigation, things will take a disastrous turn. The characters' time is running down, and they must hunt down the traitorous knight to find the root of the prince's madness — a sword of Tremere design.

The Tremere decided to circumvent their long-standing feud with the prince by whatever means available. With the aid of their Hermetic brethren, they have created a sword to use against him. The blade itself is not the problem; the scabbard, however, is the true power in this charm. Whoever possess the sword can be manipulated by the will of who holds the scabbard.

The knight, when found, tells the characters that the Tremere and he had struck a deal, whereby he was to present the prince with the sword as a gift from himself (with apologies for the missing scabbard). However, a falling-out occurred between him and the Tremere, and he now seeks to recover the sword before more damage can be done. The blade is constantly at the prince's side, and he is never seen without it. Removing the sword from the prince will calm his madness, but whoever still holds it will next fall victim to the inflicted insanity. Destroying the sword will render the scabbard useless.

Another possiblity is that the scabbard-holding Tremere is bold enough to appear at court, his talisman disguised by another, unmagical sword in the sheath. The characters may trace the prince's abrupt shifts of personality to this person's appearances in his presence. If the characters have found the knight by now, he may be able to point out the offending scabbard. However, before barging in and accusing the Tremere, they must have proof of his actions, and the knight's word will be useless when he admits that he made any deal with the Tremere. Whatever choice is made, only by destroying either sword or scabbard (or both) will end the prince's madness for good.

RESOLUTION

No story is complete without a resolution. The events of the story may have loose plot threads, and the antagonist may not be utterly defeated, but the story can still end with a sense of completion. A chronicle must reach some resolution as well. In the ideal chronicle, that resolution comes when the meaning behind the series of stories is crystal clear. Not every chronicle reaches that apex, or has to, for that matter, but completion brings a sense of accomplishment and satisfaction.

Some Storytellers get lost along the way. Branching out further and further from the original chronicle concept is a common distraction. This is a valid approach, but maintaining a clear focus can ensure the chronicle's longevity. The alternative can be a growing sense of obligation to resolve *every* plot thread, no matter how minor. One lesson bears repeating, then: Depth is richer than detail.

Remember one key concept: The main characters are the core of the stories you tell. In this game, and the others in the series, there's a heavy emphasis on defining and developing a character.

If a player can sympathize with that character and make her "real," then the character resembles a real person. And a real person never stops learning and never stops growing.

Of course, while stories resolve, even a completed chronicle can still go further. If your characters stayed at the center of the chronicle, any resolution you give is, in essence, a temporary one. If you care about the characters, there are always new directions in which you can take them. If a character has ideals, she can always find a way to refine those ideals further. So long as your characters have authenticity, a chronicle may continue, even long after you've set it aside….

…And if you take the strength of idealism and the energy of telling a story back with you into the real world, there will always be a way in which to draw upon that, even long after the game has been set aside.

To summarize, then. When telling a story, follow a few basic principles:

Create myth. Inspire ideals. Entertain. Summon darkness. Intensify light. Evoke passion. Use empathy. Guide the story.

The rest is just details.

Chapter Nine: Antagonists

*Consider your origins: you were not
made that you might live as brutes, but
so as to follow virtue and knowledge.
— Dante Alighieri, The Divine Comedy*

As with any Storytelling game, a Vampire:
The Dark Ages chronicle requires opponents to
threaten and challenge the characters. Note
that in this case, an antagonist is not simply
someone for the characters to whack until dead:
an antagonist is a character whose goals are
not necessarily the same as those of the player
characters. This conflict of interest will usually
not result in combat, and characters who think
they can kill everyone who opposes them will
probably be in for a shock the first time they face
something more powerful than themselves.

The sections below cover many of the foes whom Cainites might face in the Dark Medieval world, as well as information about the other supernatural creatures in the medieval World of Darkness. We have included alternate ways of running encounters with creatures from other Storyteller games for Storytellers who don't have the other rulebooks, though they are purely optional. Feel free to set up conflicts between the characters and other social groups and institutions, or to create your own foes.

The Church

True Faith

Faith is a Numina (like an Ability, described in the **Vampire Players Guide**, pages 29-30, and elsewhere) which some people in the Dark Medieval world possess. It can also be a Merit (see Appendix). Of course, most people have faith with a small "f," in that almost everybody accepts the Church's teachings quite uncritically. But only a small number have the burning zeal, the profound conviction which can protect them against creatures like vampires.

This Faith is not necessarily a skill to be increased through experience. Certainly, it may rise as a result of a person's experience, but it is more vital than that, more a measure of conviction and strength of mind. At the Storyteller's discretion Faith should rise or fall to reflect a person's religious certainty and zeal. Nor is it something which comes from outside the individual, from some God or angel. Whether or not their beliefs are correct, these people believe so fervently that their own conviction protects them.

Note, therefore, that heretics may have as much Faith as devout Christians. Jews, Moslems and pagans can also have Faith, whether honoring Jehovah, Allah or the Goddess. Even an Infernalist might have Faith in the dark spirits which she venerates.

The Faith Numina, like any other, has a rating of 1 to 5. However, the medieval person's Faith Numina may offer her more protection than a modern person's Faith. Religious ideologies and assumptions underpin medieval life, creating a sort of collective unconscious which actually shapes reality.

Exactly what protection is afforded to the individual by the Background depends on this rating, as described below. Of course, these are just guidelines. Storytellers should amend them as required to fit the tone or to add drama to their stories.

- Any character with Faith may attempt to ward off vampires by brandishing a holy symbol or uttering prayers. (This is the Hollywood cliché of the vampire being held back by a crucifix.) The person rolls Faith against a difficulty equal to the vampire's Willpower. The number of successes indicate the number of steps backward which the vampire is forced to take. If no successes are scored the vampire need not step back, but may not advance. A botch indicates that the vampire may advance unhindered. Further, if the cross, Bible or other symbol is placed against the vampire's body, each success causes an aggravated Health Level of damage, burning into the flesh.

•• A medieval person with a Faith rating of 2 or more is a "neutral," immune to Dominate.

••• A person with a Faith of 3 or more may sense the presence of a vampire. She need not consciously try to sense a vampire's presence, but must be in peaceful, quiet surroundings — perhaps alone in thought, praying, reading pious books, meditating on the Bible, etc. The person will not sense the vampire's presence if she is preoccupied (e.g., arguing) or in a crowded, noisy place (jostled by a mob, in the midst of a raucous banquet, etc.). This ability need not be infallible; the Storyteller should let the person sense the vampire only when it is dramatically convenient. Note that the person cannot know exactly what she senses through her Faith; all that she will know is that something unclean or evil is nearby.

•••• The person may not be turned into a ghoul, and is unaffected by any mind-affecting Disciplines like Presence and Obfuscate.

••••• The person is so pure, so holy, that she can fill a vampire with self-loathing, disgust, terror, even physical pain. Any vampire hearing the person pray, preach or recite psalms, or being touched by the person, may be forced to flee immediately by any available means. A vampire who is unable to flee is reduced to a gibbering wreck, flailing on the floor and screaming, sobbing or begging forgiveness. To avoid fleeing, the vampire must either expend one Willpower point per scene, or must make a Stamina roll each round (difficulty of 5 + her own Intelligence). That's right — the higher the vampire's Intelligence the higher the difficulty, because the more tortured and guilty she will feel.

In theory, a mortal might have a Faith rating of greater than 5, but these people are one in one-billion — the sort of people who are venerated as saints. They are unlikely to enter your chronicle (and certainly no more than once), but their powers would be enormous.

There is actually one easy way for a vampire to detect a person with a Faith rating, other than bitter experience — Aura Perception always reveals it. A mortal with Faith has her aura permanently altered so that she has a silver/gold halo around her. The strength of the Faith determines the brightness of the halo. Note that the halo is not normally visible; only Auspex reveals it.

Finally, remember that Faith represents a person's total commitment to her religion. She will act accordingly. Those with high Faith ratings may seem fanatical, even insane to those not of their religion.

Note that Cainites will not normally have Faith ratings. They consider themselves the Damned, after all. Think very, very carefully before letting any vampire have this power.

RELICS

Relics are items intimately associated with a saint or other holy person from Christian legend, and which are believed to have some holy power derived from their connection with a saint.

In fact, these items do have power. They have absorbed the Faith of their original owners, and of the pious Christians who have venerated them through the years. The most powerful relics are the most famous, those associated with the greatest saints, before which thousands of pilgrims have prayed. Any saint's relic has some power, however, and even a fake relic might gain power. If enough people believe strongly that a relic has power, then it gains a little Faith.

The greatest relics of all are the Holy Grail (Christ's cup), the True Cross (on which He died) and the Holy Shroud (in which He was buried). Thousands of shards of wood circulate in Europe purported to be part of Christ's Cross.

Most relics, however, are bones — parts of the corpses of the saints. Finger bones are the most common, skulls are considered potent relics, and unscrupulous traders make healthy profits selling animal bones and unremarkable mortals' remains to the credulous.

There are also more unusual relics. The Serpents of St. Kyne, for example, are snakes turned to stone by the sixth century St. Kyne, although modern people would dismiss these as fossils.

Other, petty "relics" may also have power. For example, a badge from a major pilgrimage site may have some power, such as a scallop shell brought back from Santiago, in Spain.

Each relic has a Faith rating of its own. If a person carries or stands near such a relic, temporarily add its Faith rating to his. Even a person without the Faith Numina may thereby gain a Faith rating. If a person has more than one relic, then only add the rating of the most powerful to her own Faith rating — don't add all of the ratings together!

Finally, in addition to their simple Faith ratings, potent relics may have special powers.

Some, for example, are thought to promise an army victory in battle. The spear which supposedly wounded Christ on the Cross was one such relic; its effect might be to add one die to all dice pools of every soldier in the army that possesses.

Feel free to create relics with unique powers to serve your stories.

EXAMPLE FAITH RATINGS:	
The Holy Grail or Shroud	5
Skull or blood of a major saint	4
Bone of a major saint	3
Shard of the true cross	3
Skull or blood of a minor saint	3
Bone of a minor saint	2
Fake bone of a major saint	2
Fake shard of the cross	2
Fake bone of a minor saint	1
Major pilgrimage badge	1

Holy Water

It is the Church's custom to bless a variety of items and instruments, either for its own use or for the good of the people. Almost anything from an army to a sack of grain might be blessed.

Most obviously, churches create "holy water," usually by blessing normal spring or well water. Such water is kept in the church font for the people to take and use as they wish, although in some areas the fonts are kept locked, as diabolists and mages sometimes steal the water for their unholy rituals.

Medieval people use holy water as a medicine, sprinkle it on fields and animals or scatter it around their homes to drive away evil spirits and keep them safe from witchcraft.

Exactly what effects holy water might have is left up to the Storyteller. In general, assume that any water properly blessed by a priest has a Faith rating equal to his Faith Background. If the priest does not have a Faith rating, the water still has a Faith of 1. Water blessed by a bishop has a Faith rating of at least 2. A vial of holy water may not be carried as a charm like a relic. It does not augment a mortal's innate Faith rating. However, it has certain other uses, given below. Note that holy water retains its powers only for about a month.

- • An area sprinkled with holy water causes discomfort to Cainites. Mortals notice this discomfort on a Perception + Empathy roll (difficulty equal to the vampire's Willpower).

- •• Water with a Faith rating of 2 or more may be used to attack a vampire, inflicting damage equal to the water's Faith rating. This damage is Aggravated.

- ••• An unbroken line of holy water with a Faith rating of 3 or more forms a barrier against all manner of dark creatures. Cainites must make a Stamina roll against a difficulty of 10 to step across such a line, and it cannot be crossed by any but the most powerful demons. This may be anything from a short line across a doorway to a broad circle warding an entire village.

- •••• An area sprinkled with holy water with a Faith rating of 4 or more causes discomfort to both Cainites and ghouls. Mortals notice this discomfort on a Perception + Empathy roll (difficulty equal to the creature's Willpower).

- ••••• Holy water with a Faith rating of 5 (very, very rare!) may be sprinkled across an area to create a "safe zone" from vampires' powers. Any mortal within the area is considered a "neutral" (immune to Dominate), is unaffected by Presence, is not fooled by Obfuscate, etc. Ghouls are not freed, however, and Blood Oaths remain firm. Cainites in the area may still use powers that affect only themselves (Fortitude, Potence, innate healing powers, etc.). This area only lasts for one day and one night.

Other Blessed Items

The Church also blesses a host of other objects, from farmers' seed corn (to make the crops grow strong) to warring armies.

Here are a few examples of items which might be blessed, and what effect the blessing might have on them. In general, assume that a blessing requires a formal ritual to be conducted by a priest with the Faith Background. Of course, for dramatic effect you may occasionally allow non-priests with Faith ratings or priests without Faith to bless, or you might want a blessing to have no effect on a particular occasion. That's your prerogative. You are the Storyteller. Also, remember that these are only suggestions. Modify and disregard these as you want, or add more of your own.

- **Church Bells** are usually blessed. The blessing is permanent, and as a result all malign or ill-intentioned spirits hearing the tolling bells are forced to flee.

- **Houses** are blessed if some supernatural is believed to threaten the occupants. A blessed house, like a building sprinkled with holy water, causes discomfort to Cainites. Mortals notice this discomfort on a Perception + Empathy roll against a difficulty of the creature's Willpower. This effect lasts for about one week.

- **Pilgrims' Staves** are usually blessed before pilgrims start their journeys. A blessed stave (used as a walking stick) counts as a relic with a Faith rating of 1, but only in the hands of that one pilgrim, and only until she has completed her pilgrimage.

- **Weapons** may be blessed for a particular endeavor, or to fight a particular foe. If blessed to slay a specific vampire (or Lupine, etc.) and used within a month of the blessing, the weapon causes aggravated damage. This effect lasts for one combat or scene.

- **Armies** are routinely blessed, but this shouldn't usually have any effect on game play. Soldiers in a blessed army are more likely to make it to Heaven if they are killed, but that is about all. In exceptional circumstances, however (e.g., when the blessing is made by a priest with a high Faith rating, or if the army fights a particularly evil foe), each member of the army might gain a Faith rating of 1 for the duration of the battle.

- **Bread and Wine.** Perhaps the most extreme "blessing" is the dedication of the bread and wine during the Mass. This is the most sacred of the Church's ceremonies, and it is believed that the bread and wine essentially become the body and blood of Jesus Christ. (Of course, they still look and taste the same.) This "transubstantiation" takes place whether the presiding priest has the Faith Background or not. This bread and wine, called "the Host," has no particular powers, but is sometimes stolen by witches and mages for dark, blasphemous rituals, and is deadly poison to Cainites. Any vampire drinking or eating the wine or bread takes aggravated damage. Roll one die + 1 damage for even the tiniest taste. Damage from a full mouthful should be extreme (say one die + 5).

Holy Ground

There are sites across Europe that are considered holy ground. Such places include the areas around the altars of churches or cathedrals, places where saints were martyred (slain), where saints are commonly believed to have been martyred, or the tombs of saints.

The effects of holy ground are:

• Holy ground causes discomfort to Cainites. Mortals notice this discomfort on a Perception + Empathy roll (difficulty equal to the vampire's Willpower).

• The difficulty of any roll involving the Exorcist Background is reduced by two.

• Any character with the Faith Numina has her Faith rating increased by one while on holy ground. (Those without Faith do not gain a rating.)

MIRACLES

In medieval legend, holy men and women have an array of powers which cannot be reduced to simple rule mechanics. Very rarely a person with a high Faith Numina, particularly if operating on holy ground, may be capable of some special feat.

For example, such a remarkable person may be able to heal the sick, restore a person's sanity, foretell the future, instinctively identify a sinner or a place of evil, survive for weeks without food or water, calm storms through prayer, etc..

To do any of these things a person requires a Faith Numina of at least 4. Each individual should be able to do only one or two of these things, and then very rarely. Remember that such supernatural abilities are just that — supernatural; make them unreliable and unexpected, not mechanical and predictable.

Many medieval miracles are harder to pin down. Some saints were said to have driven out serpents from areas, to have been brought food by birds or animals, or to have survived burning and other tortures unscathed. Again, you might allow especially pious people to perform these functions occasionally (a Faith rating above 5 would really be necessary), or you might rule that such "miracles" are the magicks of mages.

INQUISITORS

An inquisitor is someone (almost always a priest) appointed by a bishop to investigate a particular "blasphemy." This blasphemy may be an outbreak of sorcery, witchcraft, heresy or vampire activity.

The inquisitor commands the respect of the clergy and most other mortals. Other priests are obliged to assist him however they can, and when his investigation is complete, the secular authorities (kings, barons, etc.) are expected to punish those whom he deems guilty. Note that these rulers may refuse to punish those found guilty, but to do so is dangerous; at best the uncooperative noble is excommunicated, at worst denounced by the inquisitor.

Inquisitors have no special supernatural powers, as such. However, many have the Faith or Exorcist Numina and a high Occult rating. As long as the secular (noble) powers cooperate with them, they are dangerous enemies to the Cainites.

EXORCISTS

An exorcist is a priest or minor cleric trained and formally empowered to cast out evil spirits, drive away vampires and generally protect the righteous from the forces of darkness. Each exorcist is trained at a cathedral or monastery and installed by a local bishop, and owns a book of prayers and rituals with which he may battle the creatures of darkness.

As a rules mechanic, Exorcism is a Numina available to mortal clerics. The rating of the Numina reflects the rigor of the cleric's training, the quality of his book, his confidence and the Faith of the bishop who conferred the rank upon him.

Whenever the exorcist wishes to exorcise a spirit, harangue a vampire, bind a demon, etc., he must roll dice equal to his Charisma + Exorcism. The difficulty of each challenge is given below. Note that these difficulty ratings assume that the exorcist has his book of rituals and a supply of "holy" ingredients and props (salt, candles, a Bible, holy water, a crucifix, etc.). If any props are lacking, the difficulty should be increased. If he does not have his book of exorcisms he must only roll Charisma, without adding Exorcism. Note also that the exorcist's rating is largely determined by the quality of the book that he owns, and so the rating may rise or fall if an exorcist gains or loses important texts.

These guidelines might also be adapted by the Storyteller to cover non-Christian exorcists. A pagan priest, for example, might have the powers of an exorcist. A witch or diabolist might be granted equivalent powers by the spirits that she serves.

Task	Difficulty
Prayer to cause a vampire to flee in terror.	Vampire's Willpower + 4
Prayer to cause a ghost to flee in terror.	Wraith's Willpower
Prayer to cause a minor demon to flee in terror.	6
Prayer to cause a major demon to flee in terror.	9
Ritual to permanently expel a demon from a place.	10
Ritual to permanently expel a ghost from a place.	8
Chant to inflict aggravated damage (vs. a demon, wraith or vampire).	Target's Stamina + 4
Ritual to detect the presence of vampire, ghost or demon.	10 - Exorcist's Perception

RELIGIOUS ORDERS

Europe has a score of religious orders, loose organizations that run monasteries, hermitages and convents for men and women who want to dedicate their lives to God. These groups range from the huge Benedictine order, with its thousands of religious communities, to petty local orders like England's Gilbertines.

Many (like the Benedictines) have only two real concerns: praising God and watching their backs — but not in that order. They are vastly wealthy landowners who pray, study, administer their estates and try to ignore the outside world. Members need not be particularly pious (many are quite lax, attracted to monasteries and convents because they had no other employment or no chance to inherit family fortunes), although a few have the Faith Background, some with ratings of 4 or 5.

Others are more practically minded, like the Augustinian (or Austin) Canons, who often rebuild derelict churches, maintain hostels and hospitals for the poor, and run schools for the children of wealthy, often based around large cathedrals. Members may have the Faith Background, and have many practical skills (like Medicine).

The Order of Camaldori and the Carthusians train men and women who would live as hermits. These deeply motivated solitaries inevitably have the Faith Background, and typically spend their days praying, crying for the sins of the world, praying again, flagellating themselves, fasting and praying some more.

Further, two new orders will shortly come into existence. The Franciscans give all that they have to the needy and consecrate themselves to helping the poor and wretched. The Dominicans dedicate themselves to preaching against heresy and instructing the people; in the years to come they will form the basis of the Inquisition.

And lastly there are the military orders. They consist of highly trained soldiers dedicated to fighting paganism and defending the Holy Land (Palestine), the most notorious of which are....

THE KNIGHTS TEMPLAR

Officially recognized by the Pope in 1128, the Poor Knights of the Temple of Solomon (called the Templars) are one of the most feared and respected forces in Europe. Immediately recognized by their white surcoats with red Crusader's cross insignias, and by their beards (most medieval men are clean-shaven), these highly trained warriors are answerable only to the Pope himself, and are committed to recapturing the Holy Land from the Moslems. But some outsiders have come to suspect that they have other aims, and perhaps unorthodox methods.

The Templars are indeed primarily committed to recapturing Palestine, and particularly Jerusalem, from the Moors (Moslem Arabs). Jerusalem is their target because it is the holiest city in Christendom, but also because the Templars know that it contains the buried cellars of the Temple of Solomon; they believe that by harnessing the spirits bound in these cellars, they will come to dominate the Holy Land and forever keep it from the hands of the Moors.

Many of the Templars, and particularly its leaders, will go to any lengths to win and safeguard the Holy Land. They will risk everything for this — even their souls. Many have begun to dabble in sorcery and alchemy, and rumors of their esoteric studies have attracted several mages to join their ranks.

The leaders tolerate all manner of experimentation and heresy — anything short of Satanism — in the hopes of regaining the Holy Land. They have become masters of herbalism, often specializing in poisons. They have conspired to find, win and steal a collection of relics to aid them in their fight, and always listen for rumors of other holy treasures; the Holy Grail in particular. They have also established links to exchange books and favors with the Assassins (Assamites) of Syria, and have used questionable magicks to conjure spirits to aid them (see Hedge Wizards, below).

Of course the Templars' leaders are careful to keep these experiments secret from the outside world, and from the lesser ranks of their own order. Their rituals and studies take place in great secrecy, and woe betide anyone who stumbles upon them. This duplicity is necessary, perhaps, but can also be counterproductive; behind this veil of secrecy more twisted and depraved men can experiment with still darker sorceries and studies, and can manipulate the order for their own less pious ends.

With its often fanatical warriors (many of whom have the Faith Background), its collection of relics and its secret skills, its alliances with magi and even Assamites, the order can be a match for even the oldest vampire. But at present the Templars are unconcerned with Cainites. All they care about is the recapture of the Holy Land, and they do not wish to distract themselves with a war on vampires.

As a postscript, the order is denounced for heresy in 1314, and its last Grand Master, Jacques de Molay, is burned at the stake by the King of France. The trumped up or exaggerated charges include infernalism, black magic, practice of Islam and pedophilia. (The king needs money badly, and finds looting the Templars a quick and profitable way to fill his coffers). As the Grand Master dies, he curses those who conspired against him; within a year the Pope and the King of France, among others, inexplicably die.

Merchants

The merchants of the Middle Ages have no particular reason to hate vampires. Of course, as any other Christians they are immediately hostile to Cainites, and to any other creatures that exhibit dark supernatural powers. However, they are more likely to report their discoveries to the Church or nobility, and then leave these groups to deal with the characters.

However, the characters may earn the enmity of specific merchants, and then find them tenacious opponents. Merchants are often wealthy (and so able to hire spies, mercenaries and other scoundrels), and have contacts in all of the towns and cities in which they trade.

Characters may earn a merchant's enmity in a number of ways. A merchant may want revenge if a vampire Embraces or kills his son or daughter. If a merchant's friend or relation was turned into a ghoul, the merchant might try to free her from the vampire's control.

Characters might provoke a merchant by preying upon his wagoneers (who may be mere hirelings, or his family), or by hunting in an area upon which he is dependent for trade. For example, a character might discover that charcoal burners are easy pickings (these are men who camp out in woods to turn timber to charcoal for use as a fuel). However if she kills many charcoal burners or frightens them away, the supply of charcoal dries up, and the merchant who used to ship and sell the fuel finds his profits falling.

The Nobility

Throughout the countryside and in many towns, noblemen are responsible for enforcing laws, keeping the peace and punishing offenders; it is they who will investigate and seek to punish most crimes committed by the characters.

They also own the vast bulk of the land in medieval Europe. Young vampires — unless permitted to hunt inside a city — usually hunt on their land, often preying upon their people. Nobles also administer bridges and ferry crossings, act as servants, messengers and guards for greater dignitaries, collect taxes and control vast amounts of wealth. Most havens, too, will be on nobles' estates.

It is very likely that characters in your chronicles will come up against the nobility at some point. If the characters break the law, or are spotted skulking on a noble's estate, a conflict could develop. Characters may seek to control or befriend nobles because of their wealth and influence. Petty nobles may routinely obstruct or irritate the characters. Powerful or determined noblemen may become long-standing enemies, mobilizing their military, financial and political might against the characters.

Don't forget that the vast bulk of Europe's nobles are sincere Christians, who would most likely consider Cainites to be the Devil's pawns. Nobles may need no further reason to attack a vampire than piety and fear, and most are highly trained warriors.

CAINITE ANTAGONISTS

Other Cainites can make excellent foes for the characters. Scheming princes and power struggles within princedoms, feuds between elders or clans, the rebellions of younger Cainites, the need to keep the mortals' ignorant of the Cainites' numbers and powers, the Jyhad and Amaranth — all of these work. But remember that in the Middle Ages' smaller princedoms, such conflicts are likely to be more personal, and so the protagonists will often use mortal pawns rather than vampire pawns in their struggles.

There are also some unique options available to you in running medieval chronicles. The Lasombra and Tzimisce — before their corruption and creation of the Sabbat — should make intriguing enemies — or allies. No other clan has such links with the mortal world or such a sense of family and community as the Tzimisce, and no modern vampire could match a thousand-year-old Lasombra for sheer cunning.

The emergence of the "new" clans, such as the Tremere, is also intriguing. Established Cainites, fearing that these upstarts will take their hard-earned power and influence, may try to turn the characters against these clans. Or the characters, themselves young and powerless, might form alliances with these rising stars.

The Baali are also active in the Dark Ages. There are more of them before the Inquisition is founded, and they are well organized.

Other clans also have vested interests binding them to mortal nations or institutions. The Brujah and Toreador in Spain and the Assamites in Syria are the clearest examples, but in many instances squabbles between Cainites will spill over into the mortal world, complicating feuds that would (in the modern world) remain simple inter-Cainite conflicts.

BAALI

The Baali bloodline originated in Mesopotamia long ago, though few if any quite know how. In a rare show of solidarity, an alliance of clans broke the web of Infernalism the Baali had created, finally forcing them to go underground.

In darkness and secrecy, the remnants of the shattered Baali slowly rebuilt themselves. They founded "mystery religions" to recruit mortal lackeys and prospective neonates in the ancient world, often disguising their covens as pagan shrines.

The Baali use trickery and deception, Presence and Blood Oaths to control their mortal dupes. Those mortals who would work with dark spirits do so for their own gain, little dreaming what the Baali actually plan.

The Baali are more committed to complete depravity and evil than even the Followers of Set. They firmly believe in the eventual ascension of utter darkness, and hold that vampires are the minions of the Adversary, whatever form it may take. They care nothing for fitting in with human society or even dominating it — their ultimate goal is to literally bring about Hell on Earth.

The Baali Embrace intelligent, driven and utterly callous people. Every member of this polluted lineage has at least some knowledge of the occult, and it would be easier to find a unicorn's horn than a Baali not on the Road of the Devil.

Baali neonates are kept in the company of a clan elder for several years after their Embrace. The elders' havens, called "nests" (as in "nest of vipers"), often become the centers of the clan's organization, and from these centers individual Baali set out to search for unholy relics, manuscripts and treasures with which they can hasten the coming of demons to the Earth. Some Baali may not return to a nest for years or even centuries, but may wander or set up covens to gather information, artifacts and followers. Most, however, return to a nest every year or two to report to the elder and pick up information of other Baali plots.

These Cainites do not, however, always cooperate with one another. The entire clan is devoted to establishing the rule of demons on Earth, but each member wants to be the one who is responsible for actually calling up the creatures. They often work in secret, keeping their plans and discoveries from one another; the older members are particularly competitive. Each nest plots in isolation from the others, sometimes even plotting against the others, as each elder strives to be the harbinger of doom. Whoever establishes the demons' reign will rule eternally as their regent over the mortals, or so the Baali say.

It is rare for outsiders to have dealings with the Baali on any terms but the Baali's. The damned among the Damned rarely contact other Cainites, and when they do so they usually claim to be Caitiff.

The Baali clan Disciplines are Obfuscate, Presence and Daimoinon. Their clan weakness is their vulnerability to religious symbols. They are repelled by crosses, Stars of David and the like, and suffer double damage from True Faith.

Gargoyles

The Gargoyles were created during the precarious early days of Clan Tremere, and were perhaps the only reason that the Tremere survived their first years as vampires. With the transformation of these mortal wizards into vampires, the Tzimisce feared the Tremere would grow powerful enough to push them from the lands of Eastern Europe. The fights begun during the Tremere's breathing days escalated as the Tzimisce allied with the Nosferatu and Gangrel to launch wave after wave of assaults on little-protected chantries.

In his besieged mountain chantry, Goratrix worked endlessly to find some means of turning the tide. He ran a number of experiments on captured Tzimisce and Nosferatu vampires, finally discovering a bizarre hybrid he called "Gargoyles." Vicious and instilled with a hatred for the vampires they had been created from, the Gargoyles proved to be excellent watchdogs and guards. Since then, the Gargoyles continue to serve the Tremere faithfully, and any who approach a chantry will be met by these grotesqueries.

The Nosferatu blood they inherited has made them into repulsive, "demonic"-looking creatures with enormous bat-wings. As gargoyles age, their skin grows harder and more rocklike, sometimes sprouting strange protrusions. They prefer interior or underground areas that are surrounded by a great deal of stone, such as caves and catacombs, to use as havens. No Gargoyle should have more than 29 or so years of unlife; all Gargoyles have been created in approximately the last 30 years.

Gargoyle Disciplines are Fortitude and Potence. Because Gargoyles are a composite race, a victim Embraced by one loses nearly all memory of his present life in the wash of magic and memory from the sire's vitæ. They can come from any Background, but Physical Attributes and Talents become primary with the change. Also, as a race created to be slaves, their Willpower is reduced by two when resisting Dominate or mind-control spells.

Werewolves

Pray thee, what's his disease?
A very pestilential disease, my lord;
They call it lycanthropia.
— Webster, *The Duchess of Malfi*

What the legends say about werewolves is true. They do indeed exist, and they hate humankind and its works. Cursed by the Devil to live in mindless rage, these beings are the worst marauders to haunt the villages and cities of the medieval world. They come at night, most often under the full moon, and rampage through the muddy or cobbled streets, hunting for human prey and sometimes stealing babes away into the deep woods, never to be seen again. The people pray for the Lord to deliver them from such horrors, but in the Dark Ages, the Devil is ascendant and walks abroad across the heaths and glens, corrupting the unfaithful and the sinners. A werewolf can be recognized by the following signs: his eyebrows grow together, and his hands are excessively hairy, perhaps with hair on the palms themselves. But above all, the mark which betrays the beast is the pentagram branded onto his left palm by the Devil, the sign of his fall into bestiality.

This is what most medieval people believe.

They are wrong.

Werewolves are actually a race of beings breeding among human- and wolfkind, heirs to a paleolithic culture and tradition unchanged since before the First City was built. They are magical beings whose bodies are part spirit, and who can, at times, leave the material world to travel the Invisible World, the realm of spirits which they call the Umbra. They interact with all manner of primitive and forgotten Nature, creating magical fetishes and enchanting earthly glens with otherwordly power (called "caerns").

There are many tribes of werewolves, each distinct and distrusting of the other tribes (although they will band together against common foes). Each tribe claims a human populace — "Kinfolk" — as its exclusive breeding flock, and the culture of these humans heavily influences the ways of the tribes bred from them. Wolf packs are also breeding partners, for a werewolf can be born from either human or wolf.

In much the manner a medieval churchman gives his life over to God, the werewolves worship and faithfully serve the Earth Mother, known to them by many names, the most common being Gaia. And in much the same manner a medieval churchman reviles and fears the Devil, the werewolves recognize a cosmic being of great evil which they call the Wyrm. The Wyrm births monsters and sends them out across the earth to plague Nature, humankind and werewolves.

Werewolves know themselves by many names. In modern times, they call themselves Garou, a term spread by French and Norman Silver Fangs. But in the Dark Ages, the tribes are scattered and distinct, and each tribe views its own name and customs as the true and best way. Hence, the Fenrir (Get of Fenris) call most Lupines Fenrir, believing them all to be sons and daughters of Fenris, regardless of whether others recognize this or not.

Werewolves in Legendry

The history of the werewolf in human legend has evolved with cultural outlook. In early, primitive times, shapechangers were seen as holy, for they communed with predators and brought animal secrets to the people, vital lore necessary for the hunt. As civilization rose, and communion with nature became less important and even feared, the werewolf became a symbol of untamed savagery. By the Dark Ages, werewolves are seen as minions of the Devil, men cursed to wreak havoc on their fellows.

Some doctors of this period are aware of lycanthropy as a disease, although it is considered an imbalance of the melancholic humour. Paulus Aegineta, a seventh-century physician studying in Alexandria, described the characteristics of a patient suffering from "melancholic lycanthropia" (an excess of black bile): They are pallid, lacking tears and saliva (and thus excessively thirsty), and their legs are in poor condition from running on four legs at night. Perhaps this was a description of a metis, Black Spiral Dancer or deluded human, but not a normal Lupine by any means.

Humans cannot really be blamed for failing to understand werewolves. They are genetically and mystically incapable of doing so. Ages ago, the Lupines waged a war against humans, a period when they enforced a culling of the human population. The primal terror engendered by this time still lives in every human; whenever one witnesses a Lupine in its half-man/half-wolf form, a "Delirium" descends upon her, and her mind desperately tries to convince her that what she is seeing is not real (see **Werewolf: The Apocalypse**).

Medieval people do not have the bulwark of disbelief and rational science to protect them from the full horror of a werewolf revealed. They will most often remember the sight well, and will tell their children (if they survive) of the time they saw such a terror, the Devil's servant unveiled. (Medieval humans receive no bonus on the Delirium chart — fear is their most common reaction. However, substitute Berserk for Disbelief.)

The Tribes

Of the 13 tribes of werewolves, only a few are represented in medieval Europe. Humankind has not yet pushed Lupines into shared territories, and inter-tribal conflicts are thus rare. In the Dark Ages, werewolves respect each other's territories (for the most part), and know full well the price of crossing them.

• **Fianna** — This tribe claims the Celtic races as its Kinfolk. At this time, their lands have dwindled to include Wales, parts of Scotland and the whole of Ireland. Their continental cousins either migrated to Britain long ago, or have interbred too much with continental tribes to be considered Fianna any longer.

The Fianna are, like the Celts they spring from, boisterous and imaginative. They are well-known among the Garou as excellent bards and lorekeepers. While quick to anger, they are also quick to forget a slight — unless it is a grave one, in which case they will pursue a vengeance into many generations.

Many villages and farms in the territories described above are under the protection of the Fianna, or have Kinfolk living in them who can summon aid from the Lupines when in dire need.

• **Get of Fenris** — Fierce Vikings, the Get have invaded Fianna lands and settled them with their Kinfolk. This has created an enmity between the tribes which will last well into the 20th century. While the Get are mainly a Germanic and Nordic tribe, they can be found in the south of Britain and along the east coast of that isle, wherever Saxon heritage is strong.

They are much like the Norsemen they spring from, brutal and violent to outsiders but loyal to their own. Family is sacred to them, and kinslayers are especially reviled. Woe to any who cross them or their Kin.

The mainland Get still call themselves Fenrir, the original name for this tribe. The new term has come into use mainly by the English Saxon Get to distinguish themselves from the Fianna, who are by no means progeny of great Fenris Wolf, their spirit totem.

• **Silver Fangs** — This tribe was born to rule. The Silver Fangs are the legendary leaders and heroes of their kind, being the purest bred. Their migrations follow powerful human cultures, and they interbreed with the royal lines of these kingdoms and nations. Even where another Lupine tribe claims a nation as Kinfolk, the Fangs will come and seize the breeding rights from them, usually in a series of wars between their Kinfolk (the Norman invasion is one such instance), accompanied by more individual duels and challenges to caern leadership.

The Silver Fangs are spread throughout royalty in France, Italy and the Near East. They also have achieved a foothold in Britain through the Normans, and their most ancient kingships still rule in Russia.

They, more than any other Lupine tribe of the period, know the danger of revealing their true nature to humans. They are considering adding a tenet to Lupine law (the "Litany") concerning this, a prohibition against lifting the "Veil" that hides the Garou from human knowledge.

• **Bone Gnawers** — These filthy, ill-bred scavengers are found in almost every city. They may not be nearly as numerous as in modern times, but they are present nonetheless. They are found among the lowest levels of society, among the poor, the bandits and rogues. The conscripted soldiery may even have a few Gnawers among them.

This tribe is reviled by all other tribes, especially the Silver Fangs. Concepts of tolerance and acceptance extended to them in modern times are nowhere to be found in the Dark Ages. The Bone Gnawers represent what Lupines fear to become, a weakness which threatens the purity of the race. While they are not attacked on sight, neither are they socially accepted by other Garou.

• **Shadow Lords** — This severe and hateful tribe claims Eastern Europe as its territory. The constant tread of too many conquering feet over their lands allows them no mercy or remorse. They are now the conquerors, and they aim to overthrow the Silver Fangs (such optimism is more realistic in medieval times). For now, they stay in their territory, warning all away from the misty Carpathians and old pine forests of their haunted lands — although they must fight with the Tzimisce for this territory.

• **Red Talons** — This tribe is composed entirely of Garou born as wolves. They have not a trace of human kindness, nor do they need it. They hate humans with a passion unknown to even the other tribes, for their history is full of the tragedy of human cruelty to wolves. They aim to return this cruelty tenfold. The vast majority of tales about marauding wolves and rampaging werewolves come from Red Talon activity. No matter how the

Silver Fangs try to prevent them from their depredations, they continue, sneaking into cities in packs and assaulting merchants in the squares, peasants at their hearths and even knights on the moors. Nothing can halt their anger.

• **Black Spiral Dancers** — The slanderous lies which humans perpetuate concerning noble Lupines are not always so far from the mark. They are true when concerning the deeds and deviltry of the Black Spiral Dancers, a tribe of vile werewolves who worship the "Dyvil himself in the gyse of Our Father Magnus Wyrmis." They were once a tribe of Pictish werewolves who were lured into corruption and transformed into their present, insane state. Their most dangerous Pits (holy places, similar to caerns) are in the remote regions of Scotland, and the Dancers' behavior when wearing human shape adds to the widespread medieval belief that Scots are filthy, degenerate animals. The Dancers purposefully make mischief by capturing other Lupines and branding the sign of the pentragram onto their left palms (the brand is made of silver and cannot be healed), thus revealing them as werewolves to the superstitious peasantry.

Of the other tribes, the Black Furies (an all-female tribe) are strong in the Mediterranean region; the Children of Gaia (a tribe counseling peace) can be found in the more civilized areas of Islam, Constantinople or Rome; the Silent Striders (a nomad tribe) wander Africa and the Middle East, with a few individuals roaming everywhere; some Stargazers (a philosophical tribe) have come from the East; and the Glass Walkers (a technology-oriented tribe, called the *Luperci* in Italy) can be found in the largest and most advanced cities.

CHAPTER NINE: ANTAGONISTS

Kinfolk

Werewolves are fiercely protective of their Kinfolk, both their human and their wolf families. They are also more aware of who is and who is not their Kin. In modern times, Kin are spread far and wide, but in the Dark Medieval world, when most people are born, raised and laid to rest in the same villages, it is very easy to keep track of blood ties.

This fact can spell the doom of an ignorant vampire. Looking for blood or herds among certain off-the-beaten-track villages can be dangerous. The problem is that most vampires believe all the superstitions concerning werewolves, thinking that the brutes are cursed individuals, not realizing that they are actually whole tribes or tight-knit gangs who zealously guard their own. Feeding from a tavern serving-wench may cause the vampire to become the prey as her hefty "cousins" come sniffing for revenge.

The cities are far less prone to Lupine guardianship, since they form a hodgepodge of travelers and migrants, those who have broken the rural chain of generational residency, thus losing their Lupine protectors. But in many small, unassuming villages near the deep woods, where the people don't like outsiders and avert their eyes from the traveling clerics, meddling with the residents can prove a deadly affair.

In some of these villages, especially those with ancient ties and some claim to upholding ancient ways and traditions, the villagers are even aware of their blood status, and secretly hold pride in it. In these places, only the priest who comes from the big city to set up a church is ignorant. The local sheriff's office and constabulary may be maintained by actual Garou, charged by their tribe to keep watch over their people. Tax collectors have learned to avoid these villages, and instead wring the lost revenue from other, less fortunate towns.

The case with wolves is different. Unlike today, wolves roam nearly every wilderness in medieval Europe, and have not yet been wiped out from England. These wild wolves are sometimes Kinfolk, and in medieval times, 30% of werewolves are of lupus (wolf) stock. By reason of their wolf blood, the Garou are somewhat more barbaric in this time. The voices at their fires of those who have never known what it is to be human are many, and they propose — no, demand — harsh action against the humans who harm the Lupines or their charges. Even those born of human stock are by no means civilized (with the exception of the Silver Fangs), and they counsel old justice and might as right.

The Spirit World

The world was once whole, spirit and matter as one. No longer. Spirit has been divided from matter, and now exists in a realm of its own, beyond a wall known as the Gauntlet. The origin of this division and the erection of this wall are sources of debate among werewolves, ghosts and magi.

Lupines believe in three cosmic entities: the Weaver (pattern and order), the Wyld (creation and chaos) and the Wyrm (once balance, now corruption). They believe that the Weaver went mad and drove the Wyrm to madness with her, dividing the worlds and bringing corruption and evil to them. The Lupines blame humans for much of this disaster.

The barrier separating the spirit world from the real world is thinner in medieval times than in the present. Thus, passage to and from the Umbra, or the "Invisible World," is much easier and more common, not only for werewolves but for spirits. In places where the Gauntlet is thinnest, such as the deep wilderness, spirits often emerge to frolic and play at night, sometimes possessing humans who inadvertently wander these woods.

Garou gather around caerns, sacred places of power tied to the spirit energy of the earth. The Gauntlet is extremely thin at these places, and almost nonexistent at the greatest of these sites. At a caern, Garou can open a Moon Bridge to another caern, a mystical gate between one place and another. Traveling a Moon Bridge, a Lupine can go vast distances in seconds. In modern times, Moon Bridges traverse the world in well-known paths. This is not so in medieval times; Moon Bridges here can only stretch one-third their normal, modern distances (i.e., a Level One caern can only open a bridge 300 miles distant, while a Level Five bridge can only stretch 3,000 miles — still vast for medieval Europe).

Gauntlet

Area	Gauntlet
Major cities (Rome, Constantinople).	7
Most cities or towns.	6
Villages, hamlets, rural countryside.	5
Wilderness.	4
Typical active caern.	3
Powerful caern.	2
The greatest caerns.	1

Templates

Werewolves can shapeshift into five distinct forms:

• Homid — Human shape. No Trait changes.

• Glabro — A brutish human shape, not uncommon among normal humans at this time. Extra strength but uglier appearance.

• Crinos — The dreaded half-man/half-wolf form. Extra Strength, Dexterity and Stamina, although less Social Skills. There is now a wolf-snout, so the Lupine may bite, and she has sharp claws.

• Hispo — Dire wolf. Extra Strength, Dexterity and Stamina, and a stronger bite.

• Lupus — Wolf. Extra Stamina and Perception.

RITCHIE

When in their wolfish forms (Crinos, Hispo, Lupus) they gain extra sensory skills, and can track using scent. Their hearing is also sharper.

Werewolves are blessed (it is said cursed in modern times) with Rage, a trait marking their inner anger and bestiality. The higher their Rage, the quicker they can move in combat, performing some actions at blinding speeds. However, their Rage can also undo them, causing berserk frenzies. When using **Vampire: The Dark Ages** Traits, give all Lupines a Celerity rating from 1-5. Unlike vampires, however, they can't use this every turn — they "use up" their Celerity levels. But they can get them back whenever something angers them — and just about everything does.

The legends about werewolf invulnerability are dangerously true. While their hardy physiques make it difficult to injure them, they can be hurt by swords and axes. However, they heal such wounds with astonishing speed. Grave and even mortal blows delivered onto a human will knit up and completely heal in mere seconds on a werewolf (one Health Level automatically heals per turn). The exception to this rule is silver. Its very touch pains them, and they have no defense against it (Lupines cannot soak damage from a silver weapon). Wounds delivered by silver or other supernatural damage will not heal quickly, and are the key to killing a werewolf.

Werewolves possess magical Gifts, spells of a sort which they learn from spirits. Many of these can be simulated with vampire Disciplines. In general, Fianna powers can be simulated with Auspex and Presence, Get of Fenris with Potence and Fortitude,

DRINKING WEREWOLF BLOOD

Vitæ taken from werewolves has an unusual and troublesome effect on the unwary Cainite. For every Blood Point of Lupine blood ingested, the difficulty level of any rolls to avoid frenzy increases by one. A vampire who has drunk deeply of a Lupine may find herself on the verge of frenzy all night, and even if she manages to avoid frenzy, she will be paranoid and jittery until the blood is out of her system.

In spite of the dangers, werewolf blood is very potent, twice as potent as normal kine blood. So if a vampire drinks two Points of Lupine vitæ, she receives four Blood Points for her Blood Pool. While Cainites may savor potent blood like fine wine, Lupine blood may be the drink of last resort.

Rumors abound that drinking from werewolves can temporarily grant levels of Celerity or Potence. This is not a matter of the vitæ, per se, but a factor of the Lupine's Pure Breed Background. The more pure the werewolf's lineage, the more powerful the blood to the Cainite. Some tell tales of insane Kindred deliberately hunting pure-bred Lupines for their blood.

Silver Fangs and Shadow Lords with Dominate and Presence, Red Talons with Potence and Animalism, and Bone Gnawers with Fortitude and Obfuscate.

Besides their tribal powers, werewolves also have certain roles within the tribe determined by the moon under which they were born, called "auspices." Each role also has powers associated with it. A Lupine born under the full moon is considered a warrior (Potence), one born under the Gibbous moon a bard (Auspex), the half moon a judge (Presence), the crescent moon a shaman (Thaumaturgy) and the new moon a trickster (Obfuscate).

Sample Garou

Young Werewolf

Attributes: Strength 3, Dexterity 3, Stamina 4, Charisma 2, Manipulation 2, Appearance 2, Perception 3, Intelligence 2, Wits 4

Abilities: Athletics 3, Brawl 3, Dodge 2, Intimidation 3, Animal Ken 2, Survival 3, Occult 1

Disciplines: Animalism 2, Auspex 2, Celerity 3, Fortitude 2, Potence 2

Blood Pool: 10, **Willpower:** 3

Equipment: Little of any worth. They will rely on their teeth and claws to kill their foes.

Tough Werewolf

Attributes: Strength 4, Dexterity 3, Stamina 5, Charisma 2, Manipulation 3, Appearance 2, Perception 5, Intelligence 3, Wits 4

Abilities: Athletics 4, Brawl 4, Dodge 3, Intimidation 4, Animal Ken 3, Leadership 2, Melee 3, Survival 4, Occult 2

Disciplines: Animalism 3, Auspex 3, Celerity 4, Fortitude 3, Potence 3

Blood Pool: 12, **Willpower:** 5

Equipment: A magical fetish, usually in the form of an animal part (deer hoof wrapped in leather, pouch tied with feathers, etc.). This fetish can simulate any one Discipline or a power at the Storyteller's discretion. This fetish may come in the form of a ritual klaive (a silver knife).

Elder Garou

Attributes: Strength 4, Dexterity 5, Stamina 5, Charisma 3, Manipulation 3, Appearance 2, Perception 5, Intelligence 4, Wits 4

Abilities: Athletics 5, Brawl 5, Dodge 4, Intimidation 5, Animal Ken 4, Leadership 4, Melee 4, Survival 5, Occult 4

Disciplines: Auspex 4, Celerity 5, Fortitude 5, Potence 5, **Blood Pool:** 15, **Willpower:** 7

Equipment: A number of powerful magical fetishes (see above).

Magi and Magicians

Now he goes along the darksome road, thither whence they say no one returns.

— Catullus, *Carmina*

Powerful as they are, the Cainites speak in whispers of the magus, the witch and the hermit-sorcerer. The powers such beings command frightens not only the common folk, but the undead as well. For despite their innate powers, vampires (with the exception of the newborn Tremere) know little of the mysteries of magic.

Wizards are often a secretive lot, plotting and experimenting in shadow until some commoner either seeks their aid or crosses their path. The threats magi pose are often heightened by their mysterious ways. No one dealing with a wizard knows exactly where he stands — is the magician an ally, an enemy or an observer collecting information that he might use against later? To the medieval mind, the sorcerous arts also carry an Infernal taint. After all, the Holy Word commands: "Thou shalt not suffer a witch to live." Who are the magi? What can they do? What *might* they do, given the chance? Even the Cainites have few answers.

Types of Magicians

This is, in many ways, the age of magic. Everyone believes in the mystic arts, and some practice them in various forms. While real magi (great sorcerers) are rare, every town seems to have some wise woman, minor saint, village witch, mad hermit, fortune-teller or alchemist of some degree of power. While many of those who claim to follow the craft are liars, Cainites sneer at reputed wizards at their peril.

Many vampires (and mortals, for that matter) tend to view followers of the sorcerous arts as variations on a single type. In truth, they're a bit more diverse. While each of the following general categories cover the most common medieval magicians, don't feel constrained to follow rigid "templates." Magi and their ilk are often a surprising lot.

• **Clerical miracle-workers** perform their arts in the service of the Church. While many of them belong to the vested clergy (priests, nuns, monks, etc.), others are defenders of the faith, like Crusaders, or independent blessed folk, like pilgrims, hermits and healers outside the Church's ranks. Naturally, reputed miracle-workers fall under harsh scrutiny. The hysteria of the European witch-craze, however, is still hundreds of years in the future. Although it's against policy, some parishes have Christian magi to back up God's word. The Lord works in mysterious ways, and in this age the Church can use all the allies it can find.

• **Folk magicians** are common throughout the continent. Cunning men, talented healers, Gypsies, shamans, rune-readers and wise women all seem to posses a small but potent touch of the unearthly. Some folk magicians are pagan holdovers, while others follow the Christian faith but keep the old ways alive. For the most part, these wise folk have minor powers — a bit of healing, a knack for fortune-telling, an evil eye, etc. — but underestimating the local wise woman is a dangerous business. In addition to her magical talents (which might be limited), she may have friends or debtors among the locals.

• **High magi** have studied for years, perhaps even decades or generations, to perfect the mystic arts. The forces they can command, therefore, are frightening to behold. Most of them are secretive and very, very touchy — a wrong word to one, and you might be emptying chamberpots for the Grand Duke of Hell.

The magi have mastered lore most vampires have never heard of. Many are said to belong to arcane fellowships which trade in esoteric knowledge and ancient secrets. Duels between these wizards occasionally spill into the hidden corners the Cainites call home. When that occurs, both sides lose. Magi bind spirits, command elemental powers and summon supernatural creatures to aid them. As dangerous as they are, few Cainites can best a magus on his own terms.

• **Witches** command the powers of the raw elements. Some folk view them as devil-whores, while others remember the priestesses of Diana and the Morrigan. Whatever the origin of their powers, witches are feared by the common folk, even when those same locals come to them for help — which they frequently do. Occasionally, a priest or Crusader will take it upon himself to go witch-hunting, but for the most part, these enigmatic crafters (often, but not always, women) are left to their own devices. And that's how many prefer it. Whether she belongs to a coven or lives alone with her familiar, the archetypal witch keeps her own counsel.

• **Philosopher-scientists** delve into the mysteries of nature, seeking the reasons behind every occurrence. Some only want to catalogue every phenomena they can find, but others strive to master the material world.

The differences between a modern scientist and the medieval variety is fairly significant (see Magic Types); philosopher-scientists seek the bonds that unite God, Man, the World and the Elements, and those bonds often transcend mere physical laws. Where ritual magicians tend to harness otherworldly powers, however, these rationalists prefer more practical techniques. Even so, their observations are pretty fanciful by our "modern" perceptions, and their arts often incorporate holy names, astrological charts, codes, arcane formulae and pet theories. Because of the latter, many such scientists oppose each others' efforts or guard their secrets from others. Rumor has it, however, that a cabal of like-minded philosopher-scientists conspires through a continent-wide network. The truth behind such an alliance is, as of yet, unknown.

• **Infernalists** deal with demons and evil spirits. While some ritual magi use occasional demonic aid, the Infernalist gives himself over to the darkest forces in return for raw power. These quick and simple arts do not come cheaply; the diabolist becomes a hunted man, and owes his soul to entities best left in shadow. Some folk — cultists, fallen clergymen, failed magi, frustrated peasants, bastard nobility, etc. — are perverse or desperate enough not to care. Such sorcerers are not magicians in the learned sense, but they command devastating arts just the same. Worst of all, most seek to pervert, sacrifice or control others. Of all the different types of magi, these wicked folk have most in common with the Cainites, and are those most likely to meet them in the night....

• **Familiars and assistants** are common helpers among all types of magicians. After all, someone has to watch the house while the master studies. Most familiars resemble animals, often with unusual marks or uncanny intelligence. Followers (known as "grogs" by some magi) come in all kinds, from foreign slaves to family members to warriors to mysterious servitors. Anyone who crosses a sorcerer will usually have to deal with her retainers as well. While most followers are strictly mortal, many have special weapons, talents or blessings that enable them to serve their masters better.

Magic

Magic is not easy to perform, even in this age of magical beliefs. As the section below describes, nearly all magical feats demand certain props, rituals or both, which must be utilized before the sorcerer can succeed. Even then, there are definite limits as to what a magician can accomplish. Earthshaking effects might be performed if the story demands them, but they take time and effort.

A Storyteller can handle magical feats one of three ways:

• She could utilize the Storyteller rule systems for True Magick, hedge wizardry and Infernal Arts;

• She might substitute vampiric Disciplines (especially Thaumaturgy, Auspex and Dominate) to cover the game effects of human magic, or;

• She could simply leave the whole thing up to Storytelling, and grant a wizard a certain amount of things he or she could do.

In the latter case, a simple Intelligence + Occult, Perception + Occult or Intelligence + Herbalism roll will do. Small feats (seeing in the dark, sniffing out a well or reading someone's aura) will have low difficulties (4-6), or might be done with no roll at all. Greater feats (flying, cursing someone, igniting a bonfire, becoming a wolf) might demand extended rolls (5-10 successes), higher difficulties (7-10) and painstaking, time-consuming rituals.

If a wizard's attack inflicts damage somehow, simply assume that a target takes one Health Level of damage per success rolled. Depending on the attack, this might be normal (like a cold wind) or aggravated (like hellish fire), and could take a long time to occur (like a curse). Really potent attacks might do two Health Levels instead of one. Such damage might not be soakable without Fortitude, or may not be soaked at all.

These guidelines work best when the sorcerer character belongs to the Storyteller. Magicians and magi player characters demand more structured rules, which run beyond this rulebook's scope. The following Storyteller books cover more detailed and esoteric systems for magic and similar abilities: True Magick: **Mage: The Ascension (Second Edition)**. Infernal magics and demonic Investments: **Storyteller's Handbook to the Sabbat** and **The Book of Madness**. Hedge magic: **Ascension's Right Hand** is the prime source, with variations and expansions in **The Quick and the Dead, Halls of the Arcanum, The Inquisition, World of Darkness: Gypsies** and **The Hunters Hunted**.

Magic Styles

Medieval European magic falls into a few basic categories. Cainites may be familiar with some of them, if only by rumor, but won't know many details unless they possess Occult Knowledge. There's no real difference between the styles of True Magick and hedge magic; both of them would be cast the same way. The difference between the two lies within the caster, not within the style.

Those familiar with **Mage** can assume that these styles, with the exception of Science, fit the Dark Medieval impression of coincidental magick. Since this game takes place during the High Mythic Ages, the modern paradigm doesn't restrict what a mage can do. Local paradigms still exist, however; technomagick and other alien forms (such as Do or Native American shamanism) would be considered vulgar.

All styles of magic use the same systems. These listings are presented more for Storytelling than for rules. Some styles will limit or expand a magician's abilities — a Hermetic magus will take a long time summoning a bolt of lightning from the sky, a priest won't be able to control a vampire, and a Gypsy herbalist couldn't do either one without help — but again, these differences depend more on the story than on hard rules. Use common sense; if a magus must read the True Name of the Cainite he wishes to command, he'll have to discover that name, prepare a circle, call in a few favors from his supernatural contacts and enact a ritual. All of these things take time. If a witch wants to fly on a

MAGIC AND MAGICK

In the World of Darkness, there are two kinds of magical arts available to human characters: hedge magic and True Magick. The first stirs the surface of magic reality by working through the innate power of objects, spirits and words, while the latter actually alters reality itself through a person's heightened state of being. Both kinds of magic are useless to the Cainite; she may employ slight variations on these practices through Thaumaturgy, but has lost the gift of the mystick Arts through her undead state.

Mage: The Ascension deals in depth with True Magick; the details are far too long and complicated to go into here. If you choose not to use those systems, simply assume that no distinction exists between hedge magic and True Magick, and treat all forms the same.

broomstick, she'll have to prepare that broomstick (and herself) before she can go anywhere. Few, if any, magicians can perform miracles at the drop of a hat.

Vampire: The Dark Ages is a subtle game. Magic in this setting should be mysterious, unpredictable and more than a little frightening. Magi really shouldn't become lightning-bolt machines, no matter what style they practice or how good they are at it. Wild or colorful magics may spoil the atmosphere of the game or overshadow the Cainites who stand center-stage. When running a story which features the mystic arts, use care, mood and good judgment. A shadowy hermit with enigmatic powers is far more effective than a Gandalf-in-Training with a ponderous spellbook.

Medieval folk practice a variety of arts. The following style listings aren't intended as scholarly definitions — they're merely Storyteller tools. By describing the things a magician does while working her arts, you add atmosphere, forboding and perhaps an element of suspense to a simple "The wizard begins to cast a spell...."

HIGH CEREMONIAL MAGIC

The greatest refinements of the mystic arts involve elaborate rituals, specially-prepared objects, precision and years of research. Medieval high ritual magic assimilates Egyptian, Hebrew, Greek, Roman and Arabic lore into a variety of potent styles, of which the Hermetic variety is most famous. A whole mystic order built around this style of the art dominates Western Europe's magical thought during this period, and in many ways defines the archetypal wizard — proud, learned, conspiratorial and dangerous. His is the art of binding, shaping and commanding God's creation.

Ceremonial magics take a long time to cast, but their effects can be devastating to even the most powerful Cainite. Magi versed in such magics know the Thousand Names of power, are said to call forth the elements, give life to clay, scry on their enemies, build castles from air, command angels and demons, or live for centuries. Some vampires scoff that the greatest wizardly feats come more from stories than from facts, but rumors of mighty sorcerers still persist.

In game terms, high ceremonial magic demands years of study, elaborate and exacting preparations, and objects of power (grimoires, wands, gems, element samples, specially-prepared flasks, orbs,

swords, boxes, etc.). It cannot be dashed off without severe risk (in **Mage** terms, Paradox or failure), and there must always be some source of power the magician draws from — a circle, an arcane incantation, a sacrifice, etc. Of all the medieval styles, however, high magic has the greatest effects short of divine miracles or demonic pacts. In fact, many high arts involve pacts with angels or demons to increase the power (and the risk) behind the castings.

Hermetic magi are not common, even now. Though some gather into cloisters called "covenants" and set themselves up as virtual nobility, most ceremonial magicians remain solitary, hoarding their wisdom over lifetimes and perhaps playing elaborate power-games with mortal folk — or even with the Damned.

FOLK MAGIC

The most common mystic art, folk magic taps the power of common items and occasions, and turns it to a magician's needs. Sometimes called "low magic" by highbrow sorcerers, folk magic is simple and effective, if limited in its effects. It cannot summon castles from thin air, but it can supposedly spin straw into gold if you know how to use it.

Each culture and subculture has some variant of folk magic; in Dark Medieval Europe, all of them work somewhat. These are the pagan arts, based upon nature-knowledge and an affinity with the unseen world. Many of the practices we consider superstition have their roots in folk magic. Typical spells involve using some item or relic of the intended target, calling upon spirit or faerie allies, charms or hexes passed down from wise ancestors, concoctions and bodily fluids (blood, spit, semen), the elements, and by-products like ash, dust and powder; ritual items like knives, cups, wands, runes and cards; song, music and dance; sacrifices of animals, items or people; and invocations to the gods. Their rumored effects include shapechanging, curses and blessings on people, places or things; warding, divination, weather control and potent brews which give a person some desired attribute like charisma, longevity or flying powers.

Whatever use folk magic is put to, it is a slow and subtle art. Although tales claim that witches and cunning men could perform amazing feats, they could not do so quickly or in full view. The Church claims that no division exists between folk magic and Infernalism (see page 252), but many good Christians still follow the old ways when they need a lucky break, or when some strange figure lurks by their bedsides....

CLERICAL MAGIC

No power, to the medieval mindset, approaches the power of God. Through Him, all things are possible. Thus, His chosen occasionally manifest powers beyond any mortal art. Most miracles work through True Faith (see page 236), which is capricious and unreliable. Some clergy, however, use more deliberate magics. Naturally, a variety of faiths, including pagan ones, use sacred magic. For the sake of the setting, however, we'll use the Christian viewpoint to describe its effects.

Most clerical magics invoke the direct intervention of God or His angels. The degree to which this works (or the reason for why it does) is up to the individual Storyteller, but such magic does seem valid in the Dark Medieval world. Accessing such power requires devotion, sacrifice, faith and purity. Clerical

magic is not sorcery; the magician merely becomes a conduit for the Divine Will. Thus, Church magicians are always careful not to strain God's tolerance ("Thou shalt not tempt the Lord thy God"), for such arts come only through His grace and may be removed at a moment's notice. There is a thin line between sacred magic and demonic temptation, and the holy magician is always careful to keep a clear path to Heaven in sight.

Sacred objects, prayers, chants, meditations, self-sacrifice and songs help focus a cleric's intents. The minor miracles attributed to sacred magic include healing, bursts of burning light or cleansing fire, blessings, dramatic changes of heart for the wicked, visions and prophecies of past or future events, and purification of people, places or objects which have been tainted or possessed. Whatever form they take, divine arts are rarely overt, lest the servant begin to consider himself the master.

The Church has a split view of magic. If an outsider performs a strange feat, she's using dark arts; if one of their own calls forth a miracle, she's blessed by God. A magician of the faith will still be closely watched by her peers, and even the most pious ones should beware of pride. The Devil uses a fascination with magic to lure clerics away from their intent and into arcane studies best avoided....

INFERNALISM

The Church claims all forms of magic come ultimately from Hell. The magicians themselves would argue differently. True Infernalism, diabolism and black magic, however, are deliberately chosen to invoke the darkness and learn its secrets.

Infernal powers exist; their exact nature is a mystery, but they do occasionally manifest to encourage all that's worst in humanity. Diabolist magi make pacts with such forces in return for guidance, service and sheer power. This inversion of the sacred arts is perhaps the most powerful magic mortals can attain — diabolists gain more power, more quickly, with less study, than any other form of magic. The cost, however, is considerably more than most wise folk would be willing to pay. One's soul is usually forfeit, either through a pact or through eventual corruption.

Although some high magic rituals attempt to bind demons into service, diabolic magics attempt to win a devil's favor. To do so, an Infernalist rejects the will of God or the gods, and blasphemes against all that her culture holds sacred. From there, some agent of darkness comes to secure service — first through minor favors or desecrations, then through a tithe to Hell, to final soul-binding pacts. Most such bargains begin as dabblings ("I'll only go so far, then quit"), but they soon corrupt all a magician desires. Soon after, most diabolists willingly trade light for darkness. In the process, many grow powerful, but doomed.

Demonic magicks are potent and frightening. A dark magus could conjure hellfire, fly through the air, possess others' minds or bodies, curse her enemies, summon horrific creatures, cause bodily pain at a distance, even in the undead; sour liquids or cause crops to wither, and even assume animal shapes — hares, bears, wolves, ravens, etc. Using such abilities usually requires a bloody sacrifice, a bit of the person or animal to be affected, an incantation or curse, potions, poisons or brews, or perhaps simply an ill wish or nasty gaze directed at the target. In many cases, the magician herself has little personal power, and merely conjures some being which works the magic for her.

MAGE: THE ASCENSION - THE MEDIEVAL AGE

For those familiar with **Mage**, or those who wish to incorporate that game into your Dark Medieval chronicle, here's where things stand for the years 900-1200:

• Groups

The Ascension War has not yet begun. Although groups of magi battle occasionally, the powerful factions of the modern age will not exist for centuries. The roots of the modern conflict lie in events that take place after this setting period ends. In 1210, the Craftmasons unite to storm Mistridge Covenant. The Order of Reason (the Technocracy's foundation) forms in 1325, with the Craftmasons as a focus. The Council of Nine Mystick Traditions does not form for another 140 years after that.

Only the Akashic Brotherhood, Ahl-i-Batin and Order of Hermes (which existed as a federation of separate Houses) exist as organizations in the 10th century, and few outside the Hermetic magi have ever traveled to Western Europe. The groups which later form the other Traditions and Conventions exist in scattered forms across the continent. The exceptions are the Hollow Ones and Virtual Adepts, who won't take shape for the better part of a thousand years. Although their Traditions don't exist yet, the Verbena, Celestial magi and scattered Ecstasy Cultists work their Arts in pretty much the same way as their modern counterparts. The Euthanatos and Dreamspeakers remain in distant lands, and the Solificati have just begun to take shape.

The Sons of Ether are an interesting case; although they came into being in the 1800s, the *Kitab al Alacir* (which provides their metaphysical jumping-off point) is far older. In the late 1100s, an Italian prince and Hermetic magus, Lorenzo Golo, discovers this Arabic translation of an even earlier document. Around that time, a Templar magus, Simon de Laurent, uncovers a different translation of the same work. The two men form a magickal society called the Natural Philosophers Guild; this group, though short-lived, provides the first stirrings of the Etheric Tradition. Their influence in the 1200s is negligible, but it gains momentum in the later Renaissance.

Hermetic Houses dominate the magickal politics of medieval Europe. Although they face strong rivalries with the Church-based clerical mysticks and pagan sorcerers which later formed the Chorus and Verbena, their harshest opponents often belonged to other Houses. Despite articles of Hermetic Confederation, these proud wizards quarreled often. The "witch-war" which exterminated House Diedne and the vampiric treachery of House Tremere are only the most obvious highlights of this constant intrigue. For the most part, Hermetic wizards in this period acted with great civility, then backstabbed each other when disputes arose.

Until the Convention of the White Tower (1325), the various Technocratic factions remain scattered throughout several dozen tiny societies. The most notable group during this period, the Craftmasons, have a fairly organized network throughout Spain, Normandy and Italy, where their Arts carry respect and influence. They do not, however, consider what they do "magick"; even now, such willworkers maintain that it is science, not superstition, that guides their Art.

The Nephandi and Marauders exist, and resemble their modern counterparts in many ways. The Fallen have great success during this period through Infernalist practices, while the Mad Ones skirt the fringes of medieval society, passing through towns and cities just long enough to leave disorder behind. Their organizations (such as they are) are a bit looser at this time, but the basic nature of both groups — primal corruption and dynamic madness — remain unchanged.

• Magick

The concept of the Spheres will not be defined for centuries, although the root of that metaphysic — the keystones, or prime elements — finds its way into Hermetic and Craftmasonic works. For game purposes, True Mages still use the Spheres, but define them according to their styles (see above).

The "set" of reality favors Hermetic Arts, village witchcraft, Infernalism and Christian miracles. Remote areas and the fringes of Church influence favor folk magic and pagan clerical forms. During this period, mystick magick has the coincidental edge; the slight technomagick which exists must be as subtle as supernatural Arts are in the modern era. Magick, to be coincidental, requires elaborate rituals, special objects (i.e., foci) and prayers, invocations or incantations. Fast-castings or "spells from nowhere" are sure routes to Paradox. Because the idea of demonic magick is so ingrained in the population (even in those places only recently Christianized), backlashes tend to take the form of divine punishments or infernal visitations.

The limits of "acceptable" Effect levels are largely up to the Storyteller; heavily-populated areas (like Rome or London) will not have quite the same "tolerance" for large and elaborate magicks as lonely wilderness areas. Bear in mind that large spells are still hard to pull off, and require extended rolls to perform (see **Mage Second Edition**, Chapter Eight). For those who want further details about the ways of the magi, the following books offer more information: **Mage Second Edition**, **The Fragile Path**, **The Book of Madness**, **Ascension's Right Hand** and **The Book of Shadows**.

Infernalists rarely need to study to advance in the arts. Their demonic contact (who may follow them around in some animal form) grants them greater power for greater pacts. Most of the initial learning involved in black magic covers the summoning and bargaining the magician does to win a demon's favors. Some powerful demons grant their servitors special powers called "Investments." For the sake of simplicity, assume that a diabolist with Investments can use one or more Disciplines, usually one to three dots worth, or has a single power — like turning into a raven — that she can use without preparation. Any sorcerer possessing such "gifts" will have a "devil's mark" somewhere on his body, indicating the favor of the demon he serves.

Black magic is the most despised kind. All societies forbid it, and even vampires fear those who deal with demons. Infernalists are condemned to painful deaths if they're discovered, and their masters rarely help them when the torturer binds them to his table. Nevertheless, many greedy or desperate people are drawn to the Dark Arts despite the risks.

SCIENCE

Medieval science is more art than law, and bears more resemblance to ritual magic than to modern technology. Astrological correspondences and lists of heavenly hosts replace the periodic table of elements and calculus. Even mundane technology such as smithing, building and brewing often demanded certain prayers, sacrifices and observances to be successful. Invention throughout this period was seen as little more than magic itself, and the high sciences — alchemy, medicine, mathematics, astronomy — still seemed to depend upon supernatural aid. Off to the East, wondrous technology already exists, and the ancient innovations of the Greeks, Romans and Egyptians, while lost during the Dark Ages, still survives among secret societies; such hidden lore *must* be magical! This is an age before skepticism, remember; reason bows before the unexplainable.

The medieval scientist resembles the Hermetic magus; he has mastered arcane formulae through decades of study and experimentation. More often than not, he belongs to a secret society with rituals and stringent membership requirements. With great labors, he can perform feats no mortal could match. Small wonder many consider him a magician. If magic compels the world to do the sorcerer's will, that's exactly what technology is.

Scientific magic demands constant study and some form of invention or observation. Most devices demand a fair amount of time and manpower to create. Given the resources, however, this brand of magician can detect or concoct poisons and elixirs; construct labor-saving devices, traps and war machines; create new and wondrous substances, like metal alloys or Greek Fire, assuming they lie within his expertise; cure and prevent diseases; and design wondrous devices like golems, fountains, super-forges and perhaps even flying machines (if the Storyteller doesn't mind getting a bit fanciful). Obviously, the laws of science as we understand them will determine what is and isn't possible. A scientific genius, however, might employ electricity, explosives or De Vinci-esque technology centuries before they became commonplace.

Obviously, Storytellers should beware of creating James Bondian villains in a Dark Medieval setting — it could spoil the mood and ruin the chronicle's balance. All the same, a Dark Ages Daedelus or a budding John Dee might throw an unexpected twist into your **Dark Ages** tales. What lengths might a scientific cabal go to while studying the true causes of vampirism? What surprises would a Cainite encounter if intruding upon the chambers of a mad inventor? If modern mages are to be believed, a group of Technomancers began their conquest of reality right around this time period....

TEMPLATES

These rough statistics could apply to any of the different magicians' types above. While their equipment and styles of magic will differ, the Traits remain fairly constant. Some types, of course, specialize in different skills, like those below:

Alternate/ Additional Abilities:

• Gypsies: Athletics, Larceny, Intimidation, Animal Ken, Archery, Stealth, Survival

• Philosopher-Scientists: Leadership, Crafts, Etiquette, Law, Politics, Science

• Familiars/ Followers: Athletics, Dodge, Melee, Music, Stealth, Survival

MINOR SPELLCASTER

Attributes: Strength 2, Dexterity 3, Stamina 2, Charisma 3, Manipulation 4, Appearance 3, Perception 3, Intelligence 2, Wits 4

Abilities: Alertness 3, Brawl 1, Dodge 2, Empathy 2, Subterfuge 3, Crafts 2, Herbalism 2, Melee 2, Academics 3, Linguistics 3, Medicine 2, Occult 3

Disciplines: (distribute 5 levels among several Disciplines as appropriate to the style of magic)

Blood Pool: 4, **Willpower**: 4

Equipment: Small stash of herbs or tools, minor library of lore, small group of followers, familiar, hidden weapon

ACCOMPLISHED MAGICIAN

Attributes: Strength 3, Dexterity 4, Stamina 3, Charisma 4, Manipulation 3, Appearance 2, Perception 4, Intelligence 4, Wits 4

Abilities: Alertness 3, Brawl 1, Dodge 2, Empathy 3, Intimidation 3, Subterfuge 3, Crafts 3, Etiquette 2, Herbalism 4, Melee 2, Ride 3, Academics 4, Investigation 2, Law 1, Linguistics 3, Medicine 3, Occult 4, Politics 1

Disciplines: (distribute 10 levels among several Disciplines as appropriate to the style of magic)

Blood Pool: 5, **Willpower**: 7

Equipment: Complete tools, small sanctuary or laboratory, large group of followers or strange allies, one to three magical items (crystal ball, wand or Storyteller's choice), mundane weapon nearby

ARCH-MAGUS

Attributes: Strength 4, Dexterity 4, Stamina 4, Charisma 3, Manipulation 5, Appearance 3, Perception 4, Intelligence 5, Wits 4

Suggested Abilities: Alertness 4, Dodge 2, Empathy 4, Intimidation 4, Leadership 2, Subterfuge 4, Animal Ken 2, Crafts 2, Etiquette 2, Herbalism 4, Melee 1, Ride 2, Academics 5, Investigation 4, Law 1, Linguistics 4, Medicine 4, Occult 5, Politics 3

Disciplines: (distribute 15 levels among several Disciplines as appropriate to the style of magic)

Blood Pool: 6, **Willpower**: 9

Equipment: Tower or castle (perhaps shared by a group), huge library, small army of followers or powerful supernatural allies, collection of magical devices, possibly a mundane weapon if she really feels she needs one

WRAITH IN THE DARK AGES

There are tumbled roofs, towers in ruins, rime on the limy mortar, storm-shielding tiling scarred, scored and collapsed, undermined by age. An earthy grasp holds the lordly builders, decayed and gone, the cruel grip of the ground, while a hundred generations of humanity have passed away.

— S.A.J Bradley, trans., "The Ruin"

Ghosts are very much a part of the medieval world. No one doubts their existence or their power, though their origins can be disputed. Among the living, most feel that wraiths are diabolic creatures, sent forth from the Pit to tempt or seduce souls into perdition. Those wraiths who attempt to warn the living about the horrific nature of the afterlife are seen as prophetic in the tradition of an Amos or Isaiah, leveling dire predictions of what awaits those souls who have not earned Heaven. Their tales of the rotted Shadowlands, horrific Spectres and the City of the Dead, Stygia, where human souls are given to unearthly flames to be forged into swords or worse, are easily transmuted into stories of Hell by the humans into whose minds they are poured.

The spirits of the Restless Dead move through the world (or worlds), each intent on his own mission. Potent enough to make blood rain down or rip souls from sleeping bodies, wraiths can yet be dispersed by the pounce of a cat or the fist of a child. They dwell in a realm called the Shadowlands, a dim, twisted reflection of the earth that bears the same relation to the waking world that a rubbing of a tombstone on parchment bears to the stone itself. They observe the world, tied to it by Fetters of passion and Pathos, but can touch it only rarely. At once fragile and terrifying, they can be either staunch allies or implacable foes to a Cainite.

THE WORLD OF WRAITHS

The Shadowlands in which wraiths dwell is a decayed vision of the landscape of the living world, overlaid on and woven around what mortal men and vampires see. A man and a wraith may stand in nigh unto the same place in the same cathedral and see the same nave and apse, but their vision will relate very different things. To the living man, all will be splendor and glory, polished gold and shining flame of tapers. To the wraith, all will seem to be ruin and rot, the splendor of centuries gone past. Of course, the wraith can also spy, dimly, into the so-called Skinlands, seeing the living man standing faintly in the midst of the decay.

Wraith society is not homogenous. In the late 12th century, it is divided into a number of mutually suspicious factions teetering on the verge of open conflict. The most powerful is the Hierarchy, also known as the Empire of Stygia, which extends its might from its dread capital city on the shores of the Sunless Sea. Stygia has no real-world equivalent, though it is composed of the ghosts of the stones of Byzantium and Rome, Jerusalem and Babylon, Memphis and Tyre, and every imperial city that ever was. From here Charon and his Deathlords rule, sending out their Legions for their tithes of souls. Obedient citizens of the Hierarchy are forbidden by a decree called the Dictum Mortuum from interfering with the living. This law is honored more in the breach than in the observance.

In opposition are the Fishers, Crusaders and other followers of the Cross who believe that the Far Shores across the Sunless Sea are Heaven, and whose beliefs bring them into direct conflict with Charon and his servitors. Open hostilities are infrequent, but the Crusaders (Fisher knights among the dead, and not to be confused with the living knights who took the Cross) and the Order of the Unlidded Eye (Charon's elite military force) are in frequent, violent conflict. Many Fishers who deal with the living send visions in an attempt to rescue them from the Underworld, which they view alternately as Purgatory or Hell.

A third faction is the rag-tag rabble disdainfully labeled the Renegades. Allies of convenience, not choice, the Renegades serve as a catchall for all those to whom neither obedience nor religion has any appeal. Some are dedicated freedom fighters, others are ruffians and highwaymen who prey on weaker wraiths. Renegades are frequently the worst offenders when it comes to tormenting the living. Many, through use of the shapeshifting ability known as Moliate, enjoyed appearing to mortals as demons or gods, demanding sacrifices and worship. It is these mockeries that caused the Church to take such a dim view of ghosts, and both consecration and warding techniques were perfected to combat this sort of interference.

A fourth kind of wraith, the monstrous beings called Spectres, are infrequently encountered outside of the Shadowlands, and thus pose little threat to vampires. Souls who have given over completely to their darker natures, Spectres exist to torment and tempt others into damnation with them. Some can appear quite fair, but all are foul at heart. All other conflicts between wraiths pale when Spectres raise their foul heads; in many ways they are the ultimate enemy.

Shadows

All wraiths have a dark side, known as their Shadow. A constant presence in the wraith's mind, the Shadow is equal parts tempter and trickster, destroyer and seducer. It seeks to drag the wraith down to Oblivion in a self-destructive frenzy, at the same time working toward the destruction of all the wraith holds dear as well. Simultaneously, the Shadow is the wraith's evil half, an almost distinctly separate personality, and it can come to the fore when darker emotions seize the wraith.

When the Shadow is in command of a wraith, it will either completely disregard any alliances and acquaintances the normal persona, called the Psyche, might have made. This will undoubtedly confuse and perhaps even offend those who know the wraith but who are unaware of her Shadow, for the Shadow is not a topic of polite conversation among wraiths, nor is it something the non-Restless community is generally made aware of.

The other option that Shadows sometimes take is to play along, pretending to be the Psyche and attempting to ruin whatever plans the Psyche had laid with her allies. Betrayal,

backstabbing and deliberate misinformation are not beneath a Shadow, and many have Dark Passions which are fulfilled by such damnable acts.

There is no sure way to tell when a wraith's Shadow has come to the fore. Often there will be some subtle hints in the wraith's visage — a sneer instead of a smile, an appraising gaze instead of a friendly one, a countenance that seems to be either twisted or always in darkness, the manifestation of a new ghostly relic that betrays its unholy origins — but there is no sure way to tell, and most Cainites don't even know to look for the signs.

Dealings With Cainites

There is much commerce between the Restless Dead and the denizens of the waking world, even those who no longer breathe. Indeed the Restless and the Cainites can be seen as sharing many goals, which may bring them into either pallid cooperation or undying conflict.

Wraiths depend upon the living for what they call Pathos, the spiritual energy that fuels their unearthly existence. As wraiths are driven by what they call Passions, they are fed by passions in the living that echo or mimic their own. Some of these Passions relate to specific individuals; for example, a wraith may be driven to protect his widow after his death. Should he succeed in his task, he would be rewarded with the underworld sustenance called Pathos in abundance; should he witness another working towards the same goal or even towards simple protection of another, he would also be rewarded.

In addition, those wraiths who can still visit the Skinlands are tied there by their Fetters: places, things or people whose connections to the wraith are stronger by far than the grave. Often a family member, an unrequited love or a liege lord will serve as a wraith's Fetter, and the wraith will stop at nothing to protect them. Should a wraith's Fetter be destroyed (or, in the case of an individual, killed), another tie holding the wraith to earth is loosed, and the unlucky soul may be that much closer to spiraling into Oblivion, the gaping Void that waits at the end of all things. Ergo, it is in a wraith's best interest to protect her Fetters fiercely, else the personal consequences could be disastrous.

Here, then, lie the grounds for most of the cooperation and conflict between Cainites and the Restless. Vampires also have uses for humans; however, their manipulations can be more draconian than those of wraiths whose only interest is to protect or cultivate emotion. Many Cainites have indiscriminately fed upon and discarded a wraith's Fetter, and earned the undying enmity of that spirit. Similarly, a wraith wanting to undermine another's source of Pathos may seek to burn down a building that serves as a Fetter, unaware that a Cainite slumbers within. Through this ignorance of each others' motives and needs, wraiths and vampires often come into deadly conflict.

Conversely, there are times when the Restless and the Cainites have achieved cooperation towards a mutual end. A human burgomeister may be of prime importance as a pawn to a vampire in his economic war against another of his kind; simultaneously said town official could be a Fetter for a wraith. As both beings work to advance the burgomeister's fortunes, they may notice each other's interference and become aware of each other's existence. A deal may be struck, an arrangement reached, and the two supernatural beings may combine their efforts to exalt the humble

Wraithly History

In the late 12th century, the Second Maelstrom had not yet swept across the Shadowlands. There was no clear division of the Tempest, Shadowlands and Skinlands, and the Empire of Stygia was not yet the dark and dismal place it can be in these unenlightened times. Most of the Spectral incursions following the First Maelstrom had been beaten back, and while the Renegade and Fisher presences were strengthening, Spectres were rare.

Well-kept roads run from Necropolis to Necropolis, but all roads end at Stygia. The Imperial Roads are patrolled by Charon's Knights, heavily armed and extensively trained. The Legions march to and fro keeping order, when such force as they represent is needed. Stygia itself is not yet overcrowded, but the first rumblings of dissent are beginning to be heard.

On a hill on the Isle of Sorrows stands the Fishers' Temple, from whence souls depart for the promise of the Far Shores. Patrolled by Crusaders and other, less heavily armed followers of the Cross, the Temple and its surroundings are essentially exempt from Charon's law; the dwellers within claim to follow a higher one. Fishers ride out on the roads, seeking souls to convert to their messianic vision, and as Charon has granted some legitimacy to the Fishers, these activities are tolerated. Still, tension between Hierarchy and Fishers grows daily, particularly since many Moslems slain by invading Crusaders have also been brought into the Stygian Shadowlands under the Hierarchy aegis.

Renegades, at the moment, are a far less serious threat. A rabble of bushwhackers and footpads, they hide out in the fringes of the Shadowlands, skulking to an attack here and an ambush there. There is little unified about them; some few are true idealists disgusted with the Stygian soul-trade, others are ex-Hierarchy citizens running from the restrictions of the Dictum Mortuum, still others are merely looking for the easiest existence after death they can find. Still, their numbers grow daily, and even small bands of Knights have fallen to their depredations.

The Ferrymen are long banished, working in solitude in the Darkness that will someday become the Tempest. On the other hand, the Guilds are embroiled in the midsts of their deadly war, a titan struggle for supremacy below the Deathlords in Stygia. The War of the Guilds, initiated in 1096 A.D. as an attempt to wrest away some of the power the Artificers' Guild had acquired, rapidly expanded into a free-for-all involving all 16 Guilds in a series of wildly shifting alliances. The War will grind on for another century and a half, but for the moment the forges are turned to hammering out blades from unfortunate casualties. While no battles rage in the streets of Stygia, assassinations are frequent, and often "innocent" bystanders are pulled into the morass of conflict.

For a more detailed history of the events in the Shadowlands, see **Wraith: The Oblivion**.

---

townsman. A building where a Cainite rests during the day may be a Fetter of a wraith who is not inimical towards the other tenant; they both have reason to work towards the building's preservation.

Of course, there are those not-so-rare occasions where wraiths are created by Cainites, and then bloody constraint can follow. Among the more common Passions is to avenge one's own murder, and certain incautious Cainites have attracted what might be termed "flocks" of ghosts following them, howling for blood. A Cainite who creates such dedicated enemies, who have so much to gain from his destruction, tends not to last very long in the great game. A wraith devoted to a Cainite's Final Death may whisper the vampire's eavesdropped plans to his enemies, or lead a monk to his haven at midday through a vision granted in a dream.

THE METHODS OF INTERACTION

When Cainites and the Restless interact, it is generally in the so-called Skinlands. Very few Cainites have the ability to venture into the Underworld and meet wraiths on their home ground, though there are scare-tales of a vast city of Cainites somewhere lost in the swirling mists of the lands of the dead.

Not all vampires can see wraiths; only those with Auspex can generally glimpse them as they flit through the Shadowlands. Once a Cainite knows what he is looking for, he can generally spot wraiths quite easily; it's knowing what to look for the first time that presents the difficulty. The scholars of the Cappodocian clan, by virtue of their studies into life and death, and the sorcerers of the

Tremere often have greater insights into the ways of the Restless Dead than most other vampires, and both clans have at their disposal certain rituals and incantations that can bind, dispel, summon or even on rare occasions destroy wraiths. A subtle detente exists between Cainites of these two clans and the Restless; neither side wishes the war that an abuse of such powers as the Cappodocians or Tremere have at their disposal would precipitate.

WAR AMONG THE DEAD

Wraiths and vampires do inevitably come into conflict. Direct combat between the two is almost impossible as wraiths are essentially "not there," and thus are more or less invulnerable to fang and claw. Any blow struck on a wraith, no matter how well placed, does only one level of damage and sends the wraith into a noncorporeal state, where it cannot be further harmed by physical attack. Conversely, most wraiths cannot strike vampires; any attempt to do so almost inevitably damages the wraith as well as the Cainite, and sends the attacker back into noncorporeal status. Only certain wraiths have the ability to actually materialize at all, and even these can be returned to the Shadowlands with a minimum of effort by the most callow Cainite.

Wars between the two, then, are fought in ways other than hand-to-hand. Both sides have at their disposal certain abilities which can neutralize the other's advantages. Disciplines such as Thaumaturgy or the budding study of Necromancy can affect wraiths, and Chimerstry can befuddle them. Less directly, Cainites can target

Notes on Wraith: The Oblivion

Many wraith situations and powers, especially the Arcanoi, have no readily convertable equivalent in **Vampire: The Dark Ages**. With that in mind, Storytellers are encouraged to be creative and liberal in their treatment of Arcanoi when having their Cainite characters interact with the Restless dead. In essence, the Arcanoi cover the gamut of "classic" ghostly powers, from poltergeists flinging crockery to blood dripping from the walls to horrific nightmares being inflicted by the dead. For anything a ghost in a piece of fiction can do, there exists an Arcanos equivalent.

Most Arcanoi that directly affect the psyches of the denizens of the Skinlands can be reduced to contested Willpower rolls; should the roll call for the loser to lose Pathos, temporary Willpower should be substituted. Corpus directly converts to Health, and it is possible for a wraith to use such Arcanoi as Usury to directly damage Cainites.

Several arts and Arcanoi function primarily within the Shadowlands and Tempest, particularly Argos, and as such are unlikely to be useful in a crossover **Vampire: The Dark Ages/Wraith: The Oblivion** chronicle. Some other Arcanoi, especially most uses of Inhabit, are anachronistic for the late 12th century, and as such should be replaced with acceptable period equivalents. Some sample alternate arts are available in **Guildbook: Artificers**; Storytellers are invited to invent their own as their chronicle requires.

wraiths' Fetters and by annihilating them, banish the offending wraith from the Skinlands. Wraiths counter with certain of their skills, called Arcanoi, which allow them to affect the physical world. A stake hurled by the force of a ghostly will will strike as hard as one hand-driven; a coffin possessed so that it opens and closes at inconvenient times can also severely damage a Cainite's peace of mind.

HAUNTS

Wraiths commonly haunt those places most eldritch and feared by the local peasantry, where acts of great passion and rage have been committed. Old battlefields, graveyards, gallows, castles and gaols are places where acts of a sort to tie the dead to earth have oft been performed. Conversely, those domiciles that have, through long association, become more home than house may also bind the spirits of their owners through strength of association.

Cainites who venture into Haunts are generally not welcomed there, though some wraiths welcome more corporeal protectors for their homes. The barrier between worlds is thin in a Haunt, and there are stories of Cainites being drawn into the Shadowlands while intruding on a Haunt populated by particularly unfriendly wraiths. Other tales claim that Disciplines and even the use of vitae are corrupted oddly in Haunts, and that a Cainite cannot count on even his most basic abilities in one. Regardless, Haunts are most often unfriendly territory for vampires, and any who venture in had best possess either an invitation or a hidden trump.

A PARCEL OF WRAITHS

Below are some statistics for standard wraith characters. Approximation has been made between wraithly Arcanoi and vampiric Disciplines whenever possible. All wraiths should have at least one level of Auspex, due to the fact that they are much more sensitive to external stimuli than almost anything in the Skinlands.

LEMURES

Lemures are the youngest members of wraith society, acclimated but not yet powerful. They are familiar with the ways of the Underworld, and have some understanding vis-a-vis their situation. Most Lemures have been dead for less than a century, and are strongly Fettered to the Skinlands. As they are the wraiths who frequent the lands of the living most often, they are the wraiths with whom Cainites are most likely to come in contact.

Attributes: Strength 2, Dexterity 3, Stamina 2, Charisma 3, Manipulation 4, Appearance 3, Perception 3, Intelligence 2, Wits 4

Suggested Abilities: Alertness 3, Brawl 1, Dodge 2, Empathy 3, Intimidation 2, Subterfuge 2, Animal Ken 1, Archery 1, Crafts 1, Melee 1, Stealth 1, Academics 1, Bureaucracy 2, Investigation 1, Law 2, Occult 2, Politics 1

Suggested Disciplines: Dominate 1, Chimerstry 1, Auspex 1, Vicissitude 1

Willpower: 8

Equipment: Ghostly blades, tattered clothing

GAUNTS

Gaunts are more experienced wraiths. They have settled into the society of the dead, and are more potent than Lemures. Most Gaunts are still somewhat attached to the Skinlands, but their Fetters have been weakened, or in some cases, resolved or destroyed. Gaunts tend to look at the bigger picture when dealing with mortals and Cainites, and are more patient and more dangerous than Lemures. Most Knights are either older Lemures or Gaunts; most Legionnaires are Lemures.

Attributes: Strength 3, Dexterity 4, Stamina 3, Charisma 4, Manipulation 3, Appearance 2, Perception 4, Intelligence 4, Wits 4

Abilities: Alertness 3, Brawl 2, Dodge 3, Empathy 3, Intimidation 3, Subterfuge 3, Animal Ken 1, Archery 2, Crafts 1, Melee 2, Stealth 3, Academics 2, Bureaucracy 4, Investigation 1, Law 2, Linguistics 1, Occult 2, Politics 1

Suggested Disciplines: Auspex 2, Chimerstry 1 Dominate 2, Presence 1, Vicissitude 3

Willpower: 9

Equipment: Noble banner and ghostly (but outdated) armor, spectral weapons and rich clothing, often Roman or earlier artifacts

DOMEMS

Domems are wraiths, of an age with Gaunts but without any Fetters. Thus, they cannot return to the Skinlands and dwell instead within the city of Stygia. It is highly unlikely that a Cainite will deal with a Domem.

THE FAERIE

They are known by many names: the Fair Folk, the wild ones, the mad ones. Yet no matter what name the Cainites give them, little is known of these enigmatic and mercurial beings who seem to answer to no power but their own whim. Because of their unpredictable nature, they are considered best avoided as few who have dealings with them come out ahead in the bargain. Still there are those who dare treat with them — of these most are never seen nor heard from again. Some return years later, changed or altered in some way, often addle-minded and confused, though some seem to possess a peculiar insight and sagacity.

TYPES OF FAE

There are certain "facts" that have been ascertained about the fae by those vampires who have chosen the precarious task of studying them. Faeries are incredibly varied in physical appearance. They come in a wide variety of shapes and sizes, and many believe that they can change their shape at will. Their powers and abilities are also known to be exceedingly diverse. Still, loremasters have separated the fae into several distinct categories. Many argue over the veracity of these findings, though none have been able to refute these findings with any degree of credence.

SIDHE

The noble sidhe are considered to be the ruling class of the fae, much as the Ventrue and Lasombra are among Cainites. They are seldom encountered by vampires for they only rarely venture forth from their beloved Arcadia. They are known to be extremely tall and possess a beauty so intense it is nearly alien. It is rumored that a Toreador who encountered one of these beings was so awestruck by the sight of her that he burned out his own eyes, for he knew that he would never see such magnificence again.

NYMPHS AND FOREST FAERIES

These mysterious beings are only slightly more common that the sidhe. They are usually only encountered within the boundaries of a faerie forest or glade. These creatures have some sort of deep, recondite connection with nature — indeed they most often resemble that which they have the strongest association with. Most of these fae have a relation with a particular facet of nature: trees, flowers, plants, waterfalls, rock. Usually, their nature is reflected in that which they are associated with. A faerie associated with rock is likely to be very secretive and silent, while one of water would be capricious and have a silver laugh.

Though these faeries keep mostly to themselves, they are well-known for waylaying or harassing those who have offended them. Though exactly what constitutes an offense to these fae is usually unknowable. When perturbed, these fae, as with most others, fall into the Trickster category.

HOUSEHOLD FAERIES

Known as brownies, boggarts, gremlins or bwca, these helpful sprites are the most likely to be glimpsed for they live in close proximity with mortals. These fae are well-known for performing various household tasks in exchange for food. They only work at night, and will permit no one to watch them work. They are also

known for having many strange customs, and are easily offended. When dealing with one of these faeries, it is best to know for certain what customs it follows, lest you inadvertently offend it. Once angered they can become quite malicious, and are not easily appeased.

TRICKSTERS

These fae are always best avoided. Though they may often appear harmless or even helpful, interaction with these fae will almost always spell certain doom for the mortal (or vampire) involved. They are mischievous creatures intent only on causing havoc. These faeries come in many varieties, each possessing its own peculiar method of leading mortals astray. Among the many varieties of tricksters are the pooka, willow o' the wisp, kelpie, leprechaun and the lamia.

Other types of faeries are often known to become tricksters, especially if they have been offended in some manner. Once a faerie has taken offense with someone, they will taunt and harass the offender until they believe the affront has been paid for.

CHANGELINGS

Little is known about changelings as they appear to be mortals, at least to one who does not know what to look for. It is said that occasionally one of the fae will snatch a mortal from this world in order to take their place and live among mortals. Though this "kidnapping" is most common among babies, it is rumored that at times an older mortal may be replaced in this manner. There are many rituals and customs which are said to be able to cause a changeling to reveal its true nature. Whether there is any veracity to these customs is up for debate. Certainly, some of them have been known to be effective at times, though it is possible that some changelings have merely decided to reveal themselves at the time.

It is unknown why the fae practice this strange custom. Some say that ancient faeries need to live among mortals to experience a sort of rebirth, allowing them to become young again. Others take a dimmer view, recalling the tradition that the fae must pay a tithe to Hell every seven years. These pessimists believe that mortals are taken away to Arcadia for just this purpose. Some say that both these views are correct, and there are still many more conjectures on the subject. In the end it seems the only ones who know the truth are the fae, if indeed even they do.

THE UNSEELIE COURT

The fae are believed to be divided into two courts, the Seelie who rule from Beltaine to Samhain and the Unseelie who rule from Samhain to Beltaine. Either may be encountered throughout the year, though the Seelie are said to be most often encountered during twilight and the Unseelie are found mostly during the depths of night. Most of the fae discussed here are of the Seelie court, and while some of these can be said to be largely unfriendly, nothing can compare to the evil of the Unseelie court.

The Unseelie seem to exist only to torment others. A band of the Unseelie known as the Host fly over the lands at night, assaulting any undefended mortals they encounter. Such unfortunate souls are often found the next day, their bodies shattered by the indescribable punishments inflicted by the Host. Lone vampires who are not in some way protected are also subject to such harassment.

Faerie Customs

The fae seem to have innumerable customs and traditions, some of which can seem paradoxical. Still there are several constants upon which most loremasters agree. These have been collected from the reports of travelers, stories and legends, and from others who have had firsthand encounters with faeries. The most commonly accepted rule is that faeries are unpredictable, and one should always use caution when dealing with them.

Glamour

No one can truly define what Glamour is, for it has no "real" substance. Some would say that it is the magical energies with which the fae fuel their spells; it is that and much more. The Glamour is an intrinsic part of faerie nature. With it they can fashion whatever they desire from thin air, and they can alter their appearance. Some even say that the very forms they take are fashioned from the stuff of raw Glamour. Whatever the truth, its uses certainly provide them with a great deal of power. There are those who can pierce these illusions, allowing them to see the truth behind the fiction (though it is considered bad form to inform a faerie that you have done so).

Piercing the Glamour

Characters who posses the Discipline Auspex may see through a faerie Glamour. For purposes of the game the Discipline Chimerstry is used to represent the illusionary ability of the fae. Though normally not the case, a character may roll one die for each level of Auspex possessed (difficulty 8) any time they encounter a faerie illusion. Normally, only one success is needed to pierce this veil, though a Storyteller may deem that more successes are needed depending upon the nature of the illusion.

Possession

Most faeries have a very different concept of ownership and property than do mortals. From their point of view, humans have a great number possessions of which they are able to give freely. The fae regard this human generosity as one of their highest features. They believe that anything which is not intrinsically a part of another person to be free for the taking. In fact they do not really view this as stealing, since as far as they are concerned, the item in question never really belonged to the mortal anyway.

The possessions of the fae are another matter entirely, however. Anything possessed by the fae is most often considered to be intrinsically a part of them. This means that stealing something from a faerie implies stealing something that is a very part of her — in a sense a part of her "soul." For obvious reasons this can evoke great anger from a faerie, inciting him to hunt down the offender in order to retrieve the stolen object and exact retribution on the offender. Those guilty of stealing from a the fae are likely to find themselves the victim of a faerie curse, or worse. The fae do not extend this peculiar attitude of ownership to some things possessed by mortals, particularly works of art. No scrupulous faerie would dare "borrow" a work of art created by a mortal, as it would be tantamount to stealing from another faerie.

Faerie Places

There exist in the world places where the realm of faerie, Arcadia, overlaps our own. These places are often known by those who live near them as faerie forests or glades. In these places faerie magic can be truly awesome. Even the most powerful Tremere warlock would think twice before challenging the most lowly of the fae in one of these places.

Why these places exist is a subject for debate. The most common belief is that these are places where Arcadia connects with Earth; this would explain why faeries and fae creatures are often found in these areas. Most faerie forests are well-known by the peasantry who live in the surrounding lands and so are easily located. Often it is not the entire forest which is under faerie enchantment, instead only a portion a of a forest or even just a single glade.

A faerie forest can usually be traveled with little or no worry, with the exception of the usual threat of Lupines, though it is often best to be alert. In fact one may travel such a forest dozens of times without ever encountering a fae creature. Especially those who go in search of the fae are unlikely to find them, for faeries are very private creatures, and prefer to deal with others on their own terms.

Cainites and the Fae

Encounters with the fae can create a very different feel for a **Dark Ages** chronicle. A brush with faerie can add an element of fantasy and mystery to a story. In this sort of story the fae should always remain enigmatic and mysterious, their motives never known and often confusing. Alternately, dealings with the Fair Folk could be an ongoing part of the chronicle. This may have a much more high fantasy feel to it than the typical **Dark Ages** chronicle, though some Storytellers and players may prefer this sort of setting. In this type of chronicle, encounters with the fae and mythic beasts would be more common, if not exactly commonplace. The Storyteller should still try to maintain an aura of mystery about the fae.

The fae are mostly unknowable to vampires. Their wild ways and capricious whims are beyond the comprehension of Cainites. However, the Malkavians claim to have close ties with them. Exactly what the nature of these ties are is unknown to most other Cainites, though many would certainly like to know more.

According to faerie legend, vampires are descendants of the fae. Indeed there is some evidence to support this, at least among faerie-kind. There are several varieties of faeries who behave in much the same manner as vampires, with few distinguishing features other than that they do not create more of their kind through the Embrace. Most notable of these is the leanan sidhe, a beautiful fae woman known for inspiring poets to brilliance even as she drains them of their essence.

Sample Fae

Sidhe Warrior

The sidhe warrior is perhaps the most dangerous faerie a Cainite could expect to encounter. When seen, these beings are resplendent in shining armor, with long flowing hair. A bright nimbus surrounds them. The sidhe are renowned for their haughty manner and arrogance. Any who cross them or show them the slightest discourtesy will be quickly dispatched. These are truly beings to be feared.

Drinking Faerie Blood

Drinking the blood of the fae can be a chancy prospect for a vampire, though, because of its potency it is one many are willing to take. Each point of blood taken from a faerie equals two Blood Points. However, any character imbibing fae blood risks certain dangerous side-effects. First, the character risks frenzy. Any vampire who drinks faerie blood must immediately make a Self-Control/ Instincts roll (difficulty 4 + the number of Blood Points ingested). Failure indicates that the character is overcome by the heady rush of the powerful blood, and will seek to gorge himself with blood. The character will not stop drinking until the frenzy has subsided. Even if he has drunk to his capacity, he will continue to drink, though no benefit will be gained by this extra blood.

Assuming the character makes the frenzy roll (or even if she didn't), she must then make a Stamina roll (difficulty 8) to avoid suffering any side-effects. Side-effects are always determined by the Storyteller — they can be chosen randomly or assigned, whichever seems most appropriate. Some possible side effects from drinking faerie blood are:

• The character begins to violently eject blood from the ears, eyes, nose and mouth. All the blood consumed is lost, plus an additional 1-10 Blood Points.

• The character suffers violent hallucinations. These hallucinations last for approximately 10 minutes for every Blood Point ingested.

• The character becomes bound to the faerie in question. This has the same effects as a Blood Oath.

• The character falls completely in love with the next person they see (other than the faerie).

• The character immediately enters torpor.

• The character immediately gains one point of Appearance, but loses a point of Perception. These effects are permanent.

• The character gains all the effects of Heightened Senses (see Auspex, page 143), though these senses cannot be turned off. Increase the difficulty for any roll involving Wits by two. This effect last for one hour for each point of blood consumed.

• The character begins to glow with a golden light. This light has the same effect as sunlight to any others nearby, though the character is immune to the effects.

• The character will be overcome by emotion, and breaks out into tears of blood every time he hears music. This effect lasts one night for each Blood Point consumed.

• The character can see through all faerie Glamours. This allows a character to see faeries who are invisible and recognize them in their true form. The character had best keep his knowledge secret, lest he anger the faeries — they do not take kindly to having their secrets revealed. This effect lasts one hour per Blood Point consumed.

Attributes: Strength 3, Dexterity 5, Stamina 3, Charisma 4, Manipulation 3, Appearance 6, Perception 5, Intelligence 2, Wits 4

Abilities: Archery 6, Athletics 2, Etiquette 4, Dodge 3, Melee 5, Intimidation 4, Leadership 3, Music 4, Occult 3, Ride 4

Disciplines: Auspex 3, Celerity 3, Chimerstry 3, Obfuscate 4, Presence 3

Blood Pool: 15, **Willpower:** 8

Pooka Trickster

The pooka are a relatively benevolent variety of trickster. They usually cause no harm to their victims, instead preferring to place them in embarrassing or otherwise uncomfortable situations. A favorite prank of a pooka is to transform into the shape of a beautiful horse. Once a knight or other individual has mounted him, the pooka will take off at a wild gait with the rider unable to stop him or get off. This ride will usually end with the pooka leaping over a cliff, into a pond, or throwing the rider into a ditch and shapechanging into bird.

Attributes: Strength 2, Dexterity 5, Stamina 2, Charisma 2, Manipulation 5, Appearance 4, Perception 3, Intelligence 2, Wits 4

Abilities: Acting 3, Alertness 3, Brawl 3, Dodge 5, Music 4, Larceny 3, Occult 2, Stealth 5, Subterfuge 4

Disciplines: Animalism 2, Auspex, 2, Chimerstry 3, Celerity 2, Obfuscate 4, Protean 4

Blood Pool: 10, **Willpower:** 6

Powers: Shape Change — A pooka may instantaneously change into any creature it desires, from the size of a small bird up to a large horse.

Brownie

These household faeries generally appear as small, wizened brown men. They are among the most helpful of faeries, performing tasks for the owners of the home they inhabit and expecting only a small gift in return, usually a bowl of cream and honeyed bread. These tasks often include housecleaning, milking cows, shucking wheat and cutting wood. These tasks are usually performed with absolute stealth and secrecy. They are extremely fickle, however, and must be dealt with carefully, lest the brownie turn against its host. One should never give too great a gift or offer direct thanks to the brownie; to do so is to risk offending it.

Attributes: Strength 1, Dexterity 5, Stamina 4, Charisma 2, Manipulation 2, Appearance 1, Perception 4, Intelligence 3, Wits 4

Abilities: Crafts 5, Dodge 5, Music 2, Larceny 4, Occult 2, Stealth 6

Disciplines: Animalism 1, Celerity 4, Fortitude 3, Obfuscate 4

Blood Pool: 10, **Willpower:** 4

Powers: Industry — A single brownie can perform the tasks of several men in a single night. These tasks are performed in complete silence, and should never be disturbed. A brownie who is disturbed while working will never complete the task, and will often curse it so that it can never be completed.

Vampire: The Dark Ages precedes the Shattering, generally precluding much possibility for crossover stories featuring changelings, at least as they are described in **Changeling: The Dreaming**. It is only after the Shattering, which occurs just prior to the Renaissance, that the majority of the fae take on mortal form. During the medieval period most fae encountered would be of the true fae, though it would be possible to encounter a changeling of the traditional variety, a faerie who has kidnapped a mortal and taken his place. Such changelings often do not even realize their true nature.

Though it would certainly be possible to play this type of changeling in a medieval setting, drastic changes would have to be made to the rules to provide for the fact that Banality is nearly non-existent, Glamour is plentiful, and Bunks would probably be a lot easier. Players could also play one of the true fae, though it is not recommended that these characters be available to players. These enigmatic beings should remain in the hands of the Storyteller.

Storytellers who wish to include the more traditional variety of changelings in their stories can use the following modifications to the rules provided in **Changeling: The Dreaming**.

• Character Abilities should be assigned per the rules in **Vampire: The Dark Ages**.

• Backgrounds should be chosen from **Changeling** or **Vampire: The Dark Ages** as the Storyteller deems appropriate. All characters should take at least one dot of Gremayre as this is their innate connection to Faerie. The number of dots possessed determines how much of her fae heritage a character recalls.

• The character's Court should still be selected, though it is recommended that most characters be of the Seelie Court (see below). Legacies should be selected as usual. A character's Seeming determines the age of the mortal who has been kidnapped and taken to Arcadia, thus determining the character's starting age. Though the most common kidnapping is that of a human babe, the character cannot begin play until the age of six.

• A kith may still be chosen for the character, though it will not affect the character much in the way of outward appearance. Instead of appearing to have actual horns, a satyr may just have extremely hairy legs, while one of the sidhe may have fine features and almond-shaped eyes. The Storyteller may decide whether the kith's Birthrights and Frailties apply.

• In the time before the Shattering, Banality was not nearly the threat that it is today. This does not mean, however, that it did not exist, only that the presence of so much Glamour made the fae on Earth much more resistant to it. Though true fae are immune to the effects of Banality, changelings have attuned themselves to humanity, thus making them somewhat susceptible to its ravages. Obviously, many of the reasons that would cause a character to gain Banality that are listed in **Changeling** would not be appropriate to a medieval setting, leaving it up to the Storyteller to determine exactly what its effects are. When, and if, a character reaches 10 permanent Banality, the character is forced to return to Arcadia. The following are suggestions for how a character may gain Banality in a medieval setting:

— Getting married. Gain one permanent point of Banality.

— Advancing in age. A character gains one permanent point of Banality for every seven years they spend as a mortal.

— Any time the character tells a lie she gains one temporary point of Banality. (Characters of the pooka kith are exempt from this).

— Breaking an oath. This may cause the character to gain one or more temporary or permanent points of Banality at the Storyteller's whim.

• Glamour should be readily available in this day and age. The difficulty for gaining Glamour through any means should always be lowered by two. Additionally, places of Glamour are much more common. A character may recover Glamour just by being within the confines of a faerie forest. In such cases Glamour is usually gained at the rate of one per hour and there is no limit to the amount of Glamour which may be gained.

• Cantrips function almost exactly as in **Changeling**, though it is never necessary to roll to overcome the Banality of a mortal. When casting a cantrip, the character need only fulfill the requirements of the Bunk, no matter how fantastic the effect.

• Changelings heal at an amazing rate, at least as compared to mortals. A changeling recovers one Health Level every hour, with the exception of aggravated damage. Anything which would cause a vampire aggravated damage, with the exception of sunlight, causes aggravated damage to a changeling. This damage is recovered at a rate of one Health Level per day.

• It should be particularly noted that chimera do not exist during the Dark Ages; rather, anything that would normally be chimerical is real. A flaming magical sword is indeed a flaming magical sword, and a unicorn is a living, breathing beast. Such things should be extremely rare during the Dark Ages as they are not really appropriate to the setting, but they do exist.

Care should be taken by any Storyteller opting to allow a player to portray one of these beings as the power one of these changelings wields could easily unbalance a chronicle.

CROSSOVER RULES

Some suggested default rules to use in Storyteller games with two or more types of supernatural creatures are given below. These are general rules. Particular rules should supersede generalizations, but should still take these guidelines into account. The details given for any particular Discipline, Gift, Sphere or Arcanos should override any statement made below. Storytellers should use their best judgments in such matters, realizing that their decision overrides any rule. Use discretion, and let the story be your guide.

POWER LEVELS

When one character uses a power against another, and the issue of whether the character is powerful enough to pull it off comes up, use this scale: compare a vampire's Discipline rating, a werewolf's Rank, a mage's Sphere rating or a wraith's Arcanos rating. The supernatural with the highest score wins. In the case of ties, a resisted roll is then made.

Note: The scores compared are the being's own ability, not necessarily the level or rating of the power used. In other words, a vampire with Dominate 4 will use the level one Dominate ability Observance of the Spoken Word more effectively than a vampire with Dominate 1. Elements like duration, damage and range do not change, but the effect's potency over other supernaturals does.

DIFFICULTIES

Sometimes, one game will call for a character to defend with a Trait she does not have. For instance, some werewolf Gifts have the Rage of the target as the difficulty for the activation roll. Mages don't have Rage. What does the character use instead?

When all else fails, the default difficulty is 6. If the target is actively resisting, the Storyteller can choose to use the character's Willpower rating instead. Willpower is another handy default in the system; it is a Trait shared in all the Storyteller system games. Use common sense; your games should be evocative stories, not math tests.

Discipline	Werewolf Rank	Sphere Rating*	Arcanos
1	(Cliath)	1	1
2	(Fostern)	2	2
3	(Adren)	3	3
4	(Athro)	4	4
5	(Elder)	5	5
6+	(Elder)	—	—

* In the case of conjunctional effects, use the highest Sphere rating of the effect that mage is attempting.

DEMONS AND THEIR INFERNAL KIN

Through envy of the Devil came death into the world.
— The Wisdom of Solomon, 12:24

As all good Christians know, demons were once angels who conspired with Lucifer and fell to Earth, and from there to Hell. Jewish and Muslim scholars speculate that these entities began either as perversions of God's handiwork, or as ghosts of the wilderness sent to test the will of God's chosen. Still older faiths speak of the spirits of darkness that glut themselves on death and misery, of evil gods and primordial survivors. All sources agree, however, that infernal beings wait in the night, tempting and corrupting foolish folk, then feeding upon their souls.

According to medieval demonology, Hell's ranks form a complex hierarchy which resembles the social structure of the time. Satan, of course, sits at the top of a vast network of dukes, archdemons, consorts, lords, tempters, warriors, lesser fiends, monsters and slaves. Naturally, these entities spend most of their time in Hell, corrupting humanity from afar and scheming to overthrow God and Satan both. Each demon has its own name, identity and place in the infernal ranks. Hermetic lore lists literally hundreds of demons by name, title and purpose, though few Cainites outside the scholarly Tremere will know or care about such niceties. Supposedly, each purpose under Heaven has a corrupter in Hell.

Souls seem to be a demon's greatest prize; he'll spend years cultivating a "pupil" — nurturing her hatred, encouraging her sins, perhaps granting her some small power before the mortal's (or Cainite's) death brings her soul into the demon's hands. Perhaps advancement in Hell is measured in souls; maybe they just make good currency, slaves or food. In any case, a demon will go to great lengths to obtain a human soul.

Few characters will ever see a demon, or at least notice it for what it is. A demon's true form, it is said, remains chained in Hell. Many send their spirits wandering to Earth, however, and inhabit mortal forms. Unlucky Cainites might encounter either these infernal host creatures or the human cultists who serve the corrupters themselves. When they do, the vampires are in for a fight.

Demons rarely appear overtly; it's safer and more effective (both for the demon and for the Storyteller) for infernal beings to manifest in subtle, eerie forms: a flock of black birds, a handsome or beautiful stranger with an otherworldly taint, a cloud of insects, a sudden wind whispering with an undercurrent of damned-soul screams, etc. Despite their power, all but the lowest devils consider physical conflict beneath them. Instead, they try to lead characters into greater and more elaborate sins. A tainted innocent, it is said, is worth more than a butchered sinner.

Storytellers should be careful when working infernal powers into a chronicle; demons, if they appear at all, should seem more like forces of nature than monsters to be killed. Subtle bits of weirdness — odd sounds, sudden weather shifts, a vague whiff of brimstone — will inspire more terror than a horned beast wreathed in hellfire. If the Storyteller builds unease through atmosphere and omen (see Chapter Eight), the sudden appearance of the same horned beast will be that much more effective. Making demonology seem too cool is probably a bad move as well; people might get the wrong idea....

DEMONIC POWERS

Though bound in Hell, demonic entities can send their spirits to Earth. There they inhabit material bodies, or pass through the spiritual reflection of our world, doing what they will. The powers they can use reflect their purpose and demonic origin; a tempter will have high levels of Dominate, Obfuscation and Presence, while a warrior would have Potence, Fortitude and Auspex. For game purposes, assume that an encountered demon

EXAMPLE

A Nosferatu vampire has Obfuscate 3, and is using Obfuscate 2, **Unseen Presence** 2. A Rank Four werewolf nearby is attempting to use the (level one) Gift: **Sense Wyrm** to find any corruption in the area. The Storyteller knows the Nosferatu bears the scent of the Wyrm (the Nosferatu has a low Road of Humanity rating). If the vampire is using Obfuscate, can the werewolf sense him? The werewolf is Rank Four, and the vampire's Discipline rating is only 3, so the werewolf has a chance of spotting him.

"Has a chance" is the operative phrase here. This system does not override the existing systems: the ability is not automatic. In other words, the werewolf must still roll Perception + Occult (just like any other werewolf using **Sense Wyrm**); if he has no successes, then corruption is not detected. With one success, he will find the Nosferatu.

Now, what if the werewolf were Rank Three? He would have power equal to the Nosferatu's Obfuscate 3. The result would depend on a resisted roll. The werewolf would roll Perception + Occult, while the Nosferatu would roll Wits + Stealth (just like any other Cainite using **Unseen Presence**). Whoever has the most successes wins. If the Nosferatu won, he would remain unseen and undetected. If the werewolf won, he would sense the Nosferatu. Ties go to the defender; in this case, the Nosferatu would remain hidden. Since the werewolf is the one actively searching, the Nosferatu gains the benefit of a tie.

What if the werewolf was only Rank Two? His Gift would not be powerful enough to penetrate the Obfuscate. However, the Storyteller should let the player roll anyway and simply tell him he senses nothing.

wears its material form and uses **Vampire: The Dark Ages** Disciplines when using the statistics below. Storytellers with **Mage: The Ascension**, **The Book of Madness** or **Werewolf: The Apocalypse** should feel free to use those books' spirit rules to reflect demonic spirits.

Most demons wield the following powers:

• **Healing:** Demons and their host creatures can heal one Health Level per turn without effort. Really powerful manifestations can heal two or even three Levels per turn.

• **Fortitude:** The Infernal are notoriously hard to hurt. Assume that any demon-form has Fortitude ranging from 1 to 5.

• **Domination:** Those who meet infernal manifestations know it; even the lowliest demons have at least two dots of Presence, and many have comparable levels of Dominate as well. Powerful demons and hosts can cow an entire room of mortals with a glance.

• **Daimoinon:** An innate demonic power (see Chapter Five). Lords can go as high as 8 with this Discipline (which allows them to summon others of their kind or curse a large area), and dukes and their betters can attain any level.

• **Immunity to fire:** Flames are demons' natural element; no fire-based attack can harm them except for their own infernal flames (which hurt but inflict no damage).

- **Investments:** Tempters and more powerful devils can grant favors to their mortal servants in exchange for slavery, sacrifice or soul-pacts. For simplicity, assume that a tempter can grant 1 or 2 dots in any one Discipline — for a price. Lords and dukes may grant up to 4 dots in two to three Disciplines, but the cost will be high…and eternal.

Demons themselves rarely manifest upon the Earth; instead, their spirits inhabit lesser forms, mortal beings with supernatural powers, which are here called the infernal hosts. Occasionally possessed, often created from scratch in an imperfect mockery of the Lord's own creations, host creatures exist a short time before decaying. Unlike a demon's true form, these creatures can be hurt or killed.

Occasionally, some ritual or rift between Hell and the Earth allows a demon to create a material aspect of its true form. These manifestations are very rare and exceedingly powerful. No mortal, and few immortals, could stand and fight one on its own terms. Those who would bind or traffick with the Infernal must resort to elaborate magics or divine aid. The latter requires more faith than most Cainites can muster, while the former leaves a magician's soul at risk (see "Magi and Magicians"). Even if a demon's material form is slain, the entity itself is only banished back to the Inferno. This banishment may hurt, but will not prevent the Fallen One from coming back at another time to avenge itself. This can be especially problematic for a vampire; after all, you can accumulate a lot of enemies in a century, and not all of them reckon their lives in mortal years.…

WEAKNESSES

Although they carry hellbound powers, infernal beings are subject to the power of God's creation. While few Cainites could (or would) beseech the Almighty for help, the following things can harm or repel a demonic manifestation:

- **True Faith:** Faith has double its normal effect on infernal powers. A character with Faith can inflict one die of aggravated damage for each point of Faith she possesses. Faith can come from beliefs other than Christianity; Islam and Judaism have long histories of divine favor, and even good pagans can resist the lure of darkness.

- **Pride and greed:** Demons are a crafty lot — sometimes too clever for their own good. Because they consider themselves superior to humanity, some can be tricked into leaving or performing short services. This is exceedingly dangerous, however; many tempters will play dumb, let a character believe she has the best end of a deal, and then spring the trap.

- **The barriers:** God does not allow demons free reign on Earth; they must be summoned, bound or brought into the mortal world through human evil or stupidity. Once they're there, most demons choose to stay awhile. Some magical charms might raise a similar barrier at the Storyteller's discretion.

TEMPLATES: INFERNAL HOSTS

Cainites might encounter these demon-ridden monsters at Devils' Sabbats, around remote gathering-sites or in an Infernalist's service. They don't tend to wander around, although the occasional demon might create such a creature as a means to a greater end. Infernal hosts rarely last long; the beasts' innate corruption erodes their flesh until the mortal remains themselves curdle and

INFERNAL IDENTITIES

Modern mystics generally divide infernal beings into four classifications. Although most Dark Ages folk consider all supernatural beasties to be Satan's handiwork, the World of Darkness Storyteller knows them best as:

- **Banes and fomori:** The elemental spirits of corruption personified;

- **astral demons, or devils:** Umbrood spirits given shape and purpose by conceptions of evil;

- **outsiders, or demon hordes:** Mind-shattering devourers from deep space; and…

- **Bygones:** Mythic creatures with especially nasty dispositions.

Vampire: The Dark Ages characters know nothing about such classifications; they are offered for system clarification only. For all practical purposes, the medieval vision of Hell's ranks is more true in this time period; spirits tend to assume the form humans expect to see. The following books offer more in-depth treatments of demonic entities: **The Book of Madness**, (Mage); **Book of the Wyrm** (Werewolf); **The Storyteller's Handbook** and **Storyteller's Guide to the Sabbat** (Vampire).

An Infernal Hierarchy

An exhaustive listing of even one version of the infernal ranks would go beyond this chapter's scope, and each culture sees these beings a little differently. For the sake of general classification and power levels, assume that demons follow this basic hierarchy:

- Lucifer, the Great Satan
- Arch-Dukes
- Dukes
- Lords
- Minor Lords
- Tempters
- Servitors
  Warriors
  Infernal Hosts

Storytellers who use **Mage** or **Werewolf** rules can consider the first three ranks to be Greater Entities, Celestines and Incarna; lords, minor lords and tempters would be Umbrood Lords and Preceptors or Totem Avatars, while servitors would be Minions or Gafflings.

dissolve. Unless noted, infernal hosts have no demonic powers, but share all of their weaknesses except for "barriers"; they already exist in the mortal world (though they may enter Hell or the Penumbra with help). Hosts cannot pump blood to help them; their Blood Pool Trait is offered for Cainites who might try to drink from one. Storytellers may feel free to do horrible things to anyone stupid enough to do so.

Infernal hosts tend to be intelligent, deceptive and utterly ruthless; the demons who command them are proud, clever, self-absorbed and often cowardly in the face of some superior force.

Many know far more than they have a right to, and will reveal secrets, drop ominous hints or make morbid jests just to unnerve their opponents. Storytellers are advised to be discreet when using demonic manifestations; even the weakest of them can turn a subtle tale into a high-fantasy adventure. The appearance of some infernal host or entity will almost always signal your troupe that worse is to come, and might symbolize some greater conflict your characters face — the struggle for humanity, an impending betrayal, the lure of the Beast, etc. With good build-up and a weird atmosphere, a simple meeting with a hellcat could become an unnerving chapter in your **Dark Ages** chronicle.

DEMONHOUND

Dogs possessed, these creatures often turn night-black and grow to disturbing proportions. Their eyes reflect the flames that wait beyond, and spit sizzles on their massive fangs. Shadows seem to thicken in their presence. Some Infernalists cultivate entire demonhound packs, feeding them with serfs, enemies and careless travelers. Others have them guard worship sites or private chambers. No matter how it may appear, however, no human actually commands a demonhound; the spirits inside only bide their time, awaiting a signal from their true infernal masters....

Attributes: Strength 4, Dexterity 3, Stamina 5, Charisma 1, Manipulation 4, Appearance 1, Perception 5, Intelligence 2, Wits 3

Health Levels: OK, OK, -1, -1, -3, -5, Incapacitated.

Attack: Bite for 5 dice + Potence; claw for 4 dice + Potence

Abilities: Alertness 4, Brawl 3, Dodge 2, Intimidation 3, Stealth 3, Occult 2

Disciplines: Auspex 2, Celerity 1, Fortitude 3, Potence 1

Blood Pool: 3, **Willpower:** 4

Doppelganger

Old tales tell of the demonic double who appears in your place, commits crimes, then leaves you to take the blame. Such is the doppelganger's art — to "become" a person for a short time, disrupt her life and vanish. Such doubles rarely appear in front of their subjects, although some have been known to torment them from mirrors, shadows or pools of water before disappearing.

A doppelganger dosen't often fight; it prefers to drive the character's loved ones or foes into a rage, then go off to find another victim. The doppelganger can do inestimable damage to a Cainite's reputation, or to her sanity. With Telepathy, the creature can inject its own memories into its victim, making her wonder if she really *had* done the things she was accused of!

Confronting and destroying the creature on your terms (if you can) may be the only way to rid yourself of a doppelganger's influence. Of course, it's also said that killing your double dooms you as well....

Attributes: (As the character duplicated)

Health Levels: (see above)

Attack: (see above)

Abilities: Acting 5, Alertness 3, Athletics 2, Brawl 3, Dodge 3, Empathy 4, Subterfuge 5, Etiquette 3, Melee 2, Stealth 4, Survival 3, Knowledges: (as the character duplicated)

Disciplines: Auspex 5, Celerity 3, Obfuscate 4, Presence 1

Blood Pool: 10, **Willpower:** (see above)

IMPS

The traditional demonic familiar, an imp can change its shape to suit its purpose. Black cats, dogs, goats, mice, rams or ravens and hunched little man-creatures are infamous imp forms. Regardless of its guise, an imp can speak in a variety of human tongues, see into the soul and access uncanny wisdom. Most solitary demon worshippers find themselves with an imp for company. Some of these hosts even gain a real affection for their chosen people. Each imp has a pet name, like "Bramblefur," "Skittlebones" or "Sagebelly," to which it answers; a stranger who speaks that name aloud can cause the imp to depart forever.

While physically weak, an imp is tougher than it appears, and can be damnably hard to hit. In a pinch, it can grow wicked claws and shred an attacker, giving the imp time to escape. With a thought, the host can join the shadows, or become a bat or bird and fly away. Sometimes the creature may return to help its "mistress" escape captivity; such salvation, however, is a bad thing to count on.

Attributes: Strength 2, Dexterity 4, Stamina 2, Charisma 3, Manipulation 4, Appearance 2, Perception 4, Intelligence 3, Wits 3

Health Levels: OK, OK, -1, -3, -5, Incapacitated.

Attack: Claw, bite or both for 4 dice (aggravated)

Abilities: Alertness 3, Athletics 3, Brawl 2, Dodge 5, Empathy 3, Subterfuge 3, Animal Ken 2, Etiquette 3, Stealth 6, Survival 2, Academics 3, Investigation 2, Linguistics 3, Occult 4

Disciplines: Animalism 1, Auspex 2, Fortitude 3, Obfuscate 4, Protean 4, Vicissitude 1

Blood Pool: 4, **Willpower:** 5

INCUBI/SUCCUBI

The irony of a vampire seduced by one of these legendary tempters should be obvious. Nevertheless, Cainites find such unearthly beauty as alluring as any mortal would, perhaps moreso.

Unlike most infernal hosts, an incubus or succubus may exist indefinitely, so long as she stays sexually active. The life-force she draws to the surface during sex sustains her at the expense of her victim. Regardless of its gender (they may actually be the same thing in different disguises), one of these hosts can entrance almost anyone he, she or it pleases, enticing the target into a whirlpool of carnal sins far beyond mere lust. When the creature has had its fun, it leaves a herd of shattered victims behind.

Tales tell of sexual demon-things who have existed since time began, although these may be actual tempter devils, not mere hosts. As unearthly as her beauty may appear, a succubus still pales compared to a tempter demon in full form. By human standards, she is a vision no mortal can match, and her skills extend beyond her looks. With supernatural perceptions, the infernal seducer gauges her target, then acts appropriately. Her behavior may be shockingly blatant, quietly seductive or passively virginal — whatever works best. Male incubi prefer to deflower virgins and spoil them for any mortal lover, while female succubi incite men to betray everything they hold sacred. Many seduce their own sex, then drag the affair into the open and leave.

The secrecy and shame with many Europeans regard sex adds to the damage the seducer himself can do. The Church advises believers to deny the wills of the flesh; pagan mystics, however, have more effective ways of dealing with sexual predators. By performing pure sexual rituals — Great Rites — they drive incubi and succubi away by sanctifying the act which the demons would debase. If physically threatened, these creatures either transform into clawed horrors, beg bystanders to come to their aid or simply hide.

Attributes: Strength 3, Dexterity 3, Stamina 3, Charisma 6, Manipulation 6, Appearance 7, Perception 3, Intelligence 3, Wits 4

Health Levels: OK, OK, -1, -1,-1, -3, -5, Incapacitated.

Attack: Claw for 5 dice (aggravated)

Abilities: Acting 3, Alertness 3, Athletics 2, Brawl 3, Dodge 4, Empathy 5, Intimidation 4, Subterfuge 4, Etiquette 4, Melee 2, Music 2, Ride 1, Stealth 2, Linguistics 2, Occult 3

Disciplines: Auspex 2, Dominate 4, Fortitude 1, Obfuscate 3, Presence 5, Protean 2

Blood Pool: 10, **Willpower:** 5

TEMPLATES: DEMONS

When the impossible happens and a demon creates a material reflection of itself, all Hell really breaks loose. Unlike a monster, the demon will not stand stupidly in place while a vampire or priest pounds its body into hash. It will trick mortals when it can, avoid them if possible and destroy them when no other options exists. A demonic master often leavens his cruelty with affection and generosity. To many serfs, a devil will be the kindest master they might ever know — for a while.

Demons should be roleplayed for all they're worth. Silence falls, winds gust (or cease), sudden freezes or bursts of fire greet the infernal one's appearance, and any mortal or undead thing around becomes almost nauseous with primal terror unless the devil somehow cloaks itself. A demon's voice is velvet, sandpaper, garlic or seawater; it smells of brimstone, honey or decay, and sends ripples through the air itself. In most cases, an infernal power disguises itself in some form a person could bear to see; it may choose to become a seductive princess, a charming warrior or a slavering horned thing, but most humans could look upon it without flinching. When revealed in a shade of its true form, however, *any* demon shocks *any* observer.

As stated above, all demons have powers they may use in their material forms. Storytellers are advised to add any talents they prefer; each devil is unique. The templates below offer some options for general types. Drinking infernal blood can have whatever freakish effects the Storyteller desires.

WARRIOR SERVITOR

The foot soldiers of Hell, these brutal servitors fight whenever possible. Although not stupid, they aren't subtle either. When summoned, demon warriors prefer to disguise themselves as powerful animals — lions, bears, bulls — or charismatic human fighters, like berserkers or knights. It is said that many leave bloody footprints wherever they go. In their true forms, they appear as many-handed jumbles of thrashing limbs, staring eyes and fanged maws. Their common names, like Kahlhil the Eater of Babes, Ablu the Render and Tleesha the Flayed Patron of Spiders, give blunt portraits of the demons' favored pastimes.

Attributes: Strength 7, Dexterity 5, Stamina 8, Charisma 2, Manipulation 6, Appearance 0, Perception 6, Intelligence 4, Wits 5

RITCHIE

Health Levels: OK, OK, OK, OK, OK, -1, -1, -1, -1, -3, -3, -5, Dispelled

Attack: Claw for 9 dice + Potence; attack with weapons; bite for 8 dice + Potence

Abilities: Alertness 3, Athletics 3, Brawl 5, Dodge 3, Intimidation 5, Subterfuge 3, Melee 5, Stealth 2, Academics 2, Occult 5

Disciplines: Auspex 2, Celerity 3, Daimoinon 3, Domination 3, Fortitude 4, Obtenebration 2, Potence 2, Presence 3, Protean 2

Blood Pool: 15, **Willpower:** 8

TEMPTER

Attacking such a creature, it should be noted, would be suicide. Fortunately for those who meet them, most tempters are too finicky to fight personally. Instead, they prefer to corrupt mortals and immortals alike with their many Knowledges, unearthly beauty and infernal talents. Almost vain to a fault, they clothe themselves as gorgeous humans or wondrous beasts, like unicorns, swans, panthers, white lions and such. Even their most infernal forms contain elements of unapproachable beauty. These demons prefer noble names — Acaos Gamblegold or Dia the Vine Queen — to the coarse monikers of their cousins.

Tempters are charming, diplomatic and sincere. To them, the investment of a few mere months of behaving like one's best friend is more than worth the eventual prize. Many actually enjoy human company, and seem to regret consigning their "partners" to eventual damnation. The human spirit fascinates most tempters; the hope people have on Earth is far better than Hell's despair. Perhaps they loathe that hope for the same reason. What they cannot themselves have, they destroy in others.

Attributes: Strength 4, Dexterity 5, Stamina 6, Charisma 8, Manipulation 10, Appearance 10, Perception 6, Intelligence 7, Wits 7

Health Levels: OK, OK, OK, -1, -1, -1, -3, -3, -3, -5, -5, Dispelled

Attack: Rend or bite for 7 dice + Potence; attack with weapons + Potence

Abilities: Acting 6, Athletics 4, Brawl 4, Dodge 5, Empathy 8, Intimidation 8, Leadership 4, Subterfuge 10, Etiquette 10, Melee 5, Ride 3, Stealth 4, Academics 5, Bureaucracy 6, Linguistics 5, Occult 6.

Disciplines: Auspex 4, Celerity 3, Chimerstry 5, Dementation 2, Daimoinon 5, Dominate 5, Fortitude 5, Obfuscate 5, Obtenebration 3, Potence 2, Presence 5, Serpentis 2

Blood Pool: 25, **Willpower:** 10

Appendix

Like one that on a lonesome road
Doth walk in fear and dread,
And having once turned round walks on,
And turns no more his head;
Because he knows a frightful fiend
Doth close behind him tread.
– Samuel Taylor Coleridge, The Rime of
the Ancient Mariner

Merits and Flaws

Merits and Flaws are optional Traits that add color and flavor to your Vampire: The Dark Ages chronicle. Merits provide characters with some benefit, while Flaws act to their detriment. Some of these Traits will have little effect on a game beyond a dash of style; others could unbalance a chronicle, completely change its direction or create new plot devices.

When you create a character, you are given 15 "freebie" points to assign to whatever Traits you like, in order to give your character the finishing touches that make her unique. The system of Merits and Flaws expands on this idea, allowing you to further personalize your character.

Merits may be purchased only with freebie points and only during character conception. Flaws provide additional freebies to spend, again, only during initial conception. You may take a maximum of seven points of Flaws, limiting potential freebie points to a total of 22. Some Merits and Flaws have variable point costs; these Traits offer more options for character creation.

Merits and Flaws are provided to flesh out a character and add new story hooks and details, not to allow power-gamers to mini-max their characters into war machines. Players should make sure that the Storyteller allows these options in the chronicle before creating characters based around these options. The Storyteller is perfectly entitled to disallow any Merits or Flaws he feels would be unbalancing, inappropriate or just plain silly.

APTITUDES

These Merits and Flaws establish your vampire's special capacities and abilities, or modify the effects and powers of his other Traits.

AMBIDEXTROUS: (1 PT MERIT)

You have a high degree of off-hand dexterity, and can perform tasks with the "wrong" hand at no penalty. The normal penalty for using both hands at once to perform different tasks (such as fighting with a weapon in each hand) is a +1 difficulty for the "right" hand and a +3 difficulty for the other hand.

EAT FOOD: (1 PT MERIT)

You can still eat food, an aptitude you picked up early in your undead existence. Although your peers may find this disgusting, you can pass for living with much greater ease.

NATURAL LINGUIST: (2 PT MERIT)

You have a flair for languages. This Merit does not allow you to learn more languages than the number permitted by your Linguistics score, but you may add three dice to any Dice Pool involving languages (both written and spoken).

FAST LEARNER: (5 PT MERIT)

You learn very quickly, and pick up on new things faster than most. You gain one extra experience point at the conclusion of each story (not each game session).

JACK-OF-ALL-TRADES: (5 POINT MERIT)

You have a large pool of miscellaneous skills and knowledge obtained through your extensive travels, the jobs you've held or just all-around knowhow. You automatically have one dot in all Skill and Knowledge Dice Pools. This is an illusory level, used only to simulate a wide range of abilities. If the character trains or spends experience in the Skill or Knowledge, he must pay the point cost for the first level a "second time" before raising the Skill or Knowledge to 2. This is obviously a rare Merit in the Dark Medieval world, as so few people have a chance to learn more than their trade.

INEPT: (5 PT FLAW)

You are not attuned to your natural aptitudes, and therefore have five fewer points to spend on your Talents (the most you could take on your Talents would be eight, and the least would be 0). Of course, you can still spend freebie points to take Talents. However, you cannot, at the start of the game, have any Talent at 3 or higher.

UNEDUCATED: (5 PT FLAW)

You have received absolutely no education, and have five fewer points to spend on your Knowledge Abilities (with eight being the greatest you could have, and zero being the least). You can still spend freebie points to take Knowledges. As part of this, you cannot have any Knowledge higher than 3 at the beginning of the game.

UNSKILLED: (5 POINT FLAW)

You have never trained extensively in any skill or craft, and therefore have five fewer points to spend on your Skills (your Skills would have eight points maximum, with zero as the minimum). While freebies can be spent to raise your Skills, no Skill may be higher than 3 at the beginning of the game.

AWARENESS

These Merits and Flaws involve perception (or the lack thereof).

ACUTE SENSE: (1 PT MERIT)

You have exceptionally sharp hearing, smell, vision or taste. The difficulties of all dice rolls that relate to the sense in question (e.g., Perception + Awareness to hear a faint noise, taste poison in food or see an oncoming attacker) are decreased by two. Combined with Auspex, this Merit can grant truly superhuman senses. This Merit can be purchased multiple times (a Cainite could have Acute Vision and Acute Taste, for instance).

COLOR BLINDNESS: (1 PT FLAW)

You can only see in black and white. Color means nothing to you, although you are sensitive to color density, which you perceive as shades of gray. Note: color blindness actually indicates an inability to distinguish between two colors, but we fudged a bit for the sake of playability.

HARD OF HEARING: (1 PT FLAW)

Your hearing is defective. The difficulties of all dice rolls related to hearing are increased by two. You may not take Acute Hearing if you take this Flaw.

BAD SIGHT: (2 PT FLAW)

Your sight is defective. The difficulties of all dice rolls related to vision are increased by two. This Flaw is neither nearsightedness nor farsightedness — it is a minor form of blindness. The impairment is not correctable. You may not take Acute Vision if you take this Flaw.

ONE EYE: (2 PT FLAW)

You have lost an eye, and cannot regenerate it You have no peripheral vision on your blind side, and must roll two fewer dice for any feat requiring depth perception (including missile combat).

DEAF: (4 PT FLAW)

You cannot hear sound and automatically fail any rolls that require hearing

BLIND: (6 PT FLAW)

You automatically fail all dice rolls involving vision. You cannot see — the world of color and light is lost to you.

CAINITE TIES

These Traits reflect your status among your vampiric fellows, and any capabilities or drawbacks that result.

BOON: (1-3 PT MERIT)

An elder owes you a favor because of something either you or your sire once did for him. The extent of the boon owed to you depends on how many points you spend. One point would indicate a relatively minor boon, while three points would indicate that the elder probably owes you his life.

SPECIAL GIFT: (1-3 PT MERIT)

For some reason, your sire gave you a valuable gift after your Embrace. The Storyteller should create something suitable. You are free to make suggestions, but the final choice of item (as well as how many points it is worth) lies with the Storyteller.

REPUTATION: (2 PT MERIT)

You have a good reputation among the vampires of your city. You may have earned this reputation, or inherited it from your sire. Add three dice to any Dice Pools involving social dealings with the city's Cainites. A character with this Merit may not take the Flaw *Notoriety*.

PAWN: (3 PT MERIT)

You have a measure of control over another vampire, one of higher generation than you. Your control might lie in the Blood Oath, blackmail or some other means of coercion. Your pawn might not even realize he's being controlled. In any event, you must keep a careful eye on him, lest he slip his leash.

ENEMY: (1-5 PT FLAW)

Sometime in your life, or after your death for that matter, you offended an unknown being with the power to cause you grief. The power and influence of this enemy are determined by the Flaw's value. Someone about your equal would be 1 point, while a Methuselah or archwizard would be worth 5. You and the Storyteller should discuss the severity of your enemy's hatred, and whether or not you are aware of what is pursuing you. The Storyteller awards the freebie points for this Flaw.

INFAMOUS SIRE: (1 PT FLAW)

Your sire is distrusted and disliked by the Cainites of your home city. Perhaps he was dangerously insane, or perhaps he slew his kin without remorse or good reason. The vampires in your city will distrust and dislike you by association, and this burden is not easily shed; the sins of the fathers, after all….

SIRE'S RESENTMENT: (1 PT FLAW)

Your sire dislikes you and wishes you ill. Given the smallest opportunity, your sire will seek to do you harm, and may even attack you if provoked. Your sire's friends will also work against you. Good luck!

ROBINSON 1.9.9.5

NOTORIETY: (3 PT FLAW)

You have a bad reputation among your peers; perhaps you violated the Traditions once too often, or you belong to an unpopular coterie. You have a two dice penalty to all dice rolls for social dealings with other Cainites. A character with this Flaw may not take the *Reputation* Merit.

MENTAL

These Merits and Flaws deal with the mind — its strengths, weaknesses and special capacities.

COMMON SENSE: (1 PT MERIT)

You have a significant amount of practical, everyday wisdom. Whenever you are about to do something contrary to common sense, the Storyteller should alert you to how your potential action might violate practicality. This is an ideal Merit if you are a novice player; it allows you to receive advice from the Storyteller concerning what you can and cannot do, and (even more importantly) what you should and should not do.

CONCENTRATION: (1 PT MERIT)

You have the ability to focus your mind and shut out any distractions or annoyances, above and beyond normal vampiric discipline. Any penalty to a difficulty or Dice Pool arising from a distraction or other inauspicious circumstance is limited to two points or dice. No extra benefits are gained if only one penalty die or difficulty point is imposed.

CELESTIAL ATTUNEMENT: (1 PT MERIT)

You have an innate link to the passage of time and the movement of celestial bodies. You can estimate the time until sunrise or sunset within a minute or two, and can follow the phases of the moon in your head. Those with some training in astrology and this Merit can even foretell certain astrological conjunctions without access to charts. You can accomplish any of these feats with only a minimum of concentration.

EIDETIC MEMORY: (2 PT MERIT)

You can remember things seen and heard with perfect detail. By gaining at least one success on an Intelligence + Alertness roll, you can recall any sight or sound accurately, even if you heard it or glanced at it only once (although the difficulty of such a feat would be high). Five successes enable you to recall an event perfectly. The Storyteller relates to you exactly what was seen or heard.

LIGHT SLEEPER: (2 PT MERIT)

You can awaken instantly at any sign of trouble, and do so without any sleepiness or hesitation. Your dice usable are not limited by your Via rating, as actions during the day normally would be.

CALM HEART: (3 PT MERIT)

You are naturally calm and composed, and do not lose your temper easily. Raise the difficulty of all frenzy rolls by two, no matter how the incident is provoked.

Iron Will: (4 pt Merit)

When you are determined and your mind is set, nothing can divert you from your goals. You cannot be Dominated, and supernatural creatures using mental attacks or magic against you add three to their difficulties if you are aware of them and resisting. However, the additional mental defense costs you one Willpower per turn. Even if you are unaware of them, mages and others seeking to influence you with magic or other abilities add one to their difficulties.

Self-Confidence: (5 pt Merit)

When you spend a point of Willpower to gain an automatic success, your self-confidence may allow you to gain the benefit of that expenditure without actually losing the Willpower point. When you declare that you are using a point of Willpower and roll for successes, you do not lose the point of Willpower unless you fail. This will also prevent you from botching, but only if you declare that you are spending the Willpower point before you roll. This Merit may only be used when you need confidence in your abilities in order to succeed. You can use it only when the difficulty of your roll is 6 or higher. You may spend Willpower at other times; however, if the difficulty is 5 or less, this Merit will not help you.

Deep Sleeper: (1 pt Flaw)

You find it very difficult to awaken. Raise the difficulty by two on any such roll, and roleplay your constant tardiness when meeting with your coterie or trying to keep early evening appointments.

Amnesia: (2 pt Flaw)

You are unable to remember anything about your mortal life. Your past is a blank slate, and may come back to haunt you. You may, if you wish, take up to five other points of Flaws without specifying what they are. The Storyteller can supply the details. Over the course of the chronicle, you and your character will slowly discover them. Amnesia can be a dangerous Flaw; your Storyteller is under no obligation to be merciful.

Confused: (2 pt Flaw)

You are often confused, and the world seems to be a very distorted and twisted place. Sometimes you are simply unable to make sense of things. You need to roleplay this behavior all the time to a small degree, but your confusion becomes especially strong whenever stimuli surround you (such as when a number of different people talk all at once, or you enter a cavern with an overpowering stench). You may spend Willpower to override the effects of your confusion, but only temporarily.

Weak-Willed: (2 pt Flaw)

You are highly susceptible to Dominate and intimidation; you are, in fact, unable to use your Willpower freely. You can employ your Willpower only when survival is at stake or when it is appropriate to your Nature.

Absent-Minded: (3 pt Flaw)

This Flaw may not be taken with the Merit *Concentration*. Though you do not forget such things as Knowledges and Skills, you do forget such things as names, titles and the last time you fed. In order to remember anything more than your own name or the location of your haven, you need to make a Wits roll or, as a last resort, spend a Willpower point.

Mortal Society

Church Rank: (1-3 pt Merit)

You were part of the Church in life, and somehow maintain the illusion that you still live, thereby still possessing some of the advantages of church rank. You can influence local politics to some extent, and locals respect you as a representative of God. One point of this Merit might mean you are a summoner or deacon; 2 a monk, nun or pardoner. Three points represents a local friar or ranking monk. Higher rank (abbess, bishop and so on) should only be allowed with the Storyteller's permission (and an even higher cost) — these ranks carry a great amount of influence, and a grave level of responsibility.

Nobility: (1-3 pt Merit)

You possessed a mortal title before your Embrace and have somehow managed to pass yourself off as alive. Consequently, the advantages of nobility are open to you. You are presumed to be landless unless you purchase the Resources Background. One point of this Merit translates roughly as a minor title with little prestige (a knight, say). With 2 points, you could be a baronet, and with 3 you might be a minor baron. Higher titles should be given to players only at the Storyteller's discretion. In the Dark Medieval world, they represent great power, but require an equally great amount of work to maintain.

Manse: (2 pt Merit)

You own a large manor — a home with 25 or more rooms — as well as the surrounding estate. The servants, if you have any, are provided for if you choose this Merit, although they cannot be used as Herd or Retainers unless you purchase the appropriate Background. The mansion is assumed to be fenced or walled in, and makes an excellent haven. While the mansion can be in as poor or as good repair as you wish, the more inhabited it appears to be, the more attention (from taxmen and the like) it will garner. Similarly, superstitious mortals will go out of their way to avoid a "haunted" manor....

Institutional Control: (2-5 pt Merit)

You begin play with absolute control over one mortal institution of your choice. Either you are the head of this institution, or you have mastered its leader. In the first case, think about how you will retain control without being able to appear to your followers during the day (it may be impossible to remain in command for long). If you control the mortal leader, then think about how you keep him loyal. (Blackmail? The Blood Oath? Dominate? Presence?) The cost of the Merit depends upon the size and power of the institution. Control of a small hermitage with six monks is a 2-point Merit. To control an opulent monastery with 200 brothers is a 5-point Merit. Plausible institutions include: monasteries and friaries (3-5 points), cathedral chapters (monks attached to a cathedral; 5 points), hermitages (2 points), hospitals (hostels for the poor or sick; 3 points), city guilds (2 to 5 points, depending on size and power), city law courts (3 points), etc.

Spy Network: (2 pt Merit)

You begin play with access to a group of mortals who frequently bring you information on the daylight world or on faraway places. Their information is both up-to-date and fairly reliable, and they are not likely to lie to you. However, these cannot be used as Allies or Retainers (unless you have that Background, too); they have their own aims. Why do they keep you informed? Do you pay them? Perform occasional "favors" for them? Dominate their leader? Or are they mortal friends and family? Also, how much do they know about you? (The more they know, the better they can search out relevant information and pursue useful rumors — but the more damage they could do if they ever betrayed you.) A spy network might be anything from a peasant family to a coven of witches, a merchant family's underlings to a network of wandering lepers. What they can discover will depend upon who they are; different people move in different circles, after all.

Known to be Dead: (2 pt Flaw)

Communities are small, and deaths and disappearances are known to all. You originally lived in the area where the chronicle is set, and the locals know that you are dead. Perhaps they saw you die, or you were discovered in torpor and pronounced dead (perhaps even buried). At the moment this causes you no problems — but if you use your real name or are spotted by people who knew you, then you can expect problems. Exorcists, pious knights and others (perhaps even local Lupines) will seek to destroy you; demons, mages and others may come to offer you "assistance."

Ward: (3 pt Flaw)

You are devoted to the protection of a mortal. You may describe your ward, though the Storyteller will actually create her. This character is often a friend or relative from your living days. Retainers do not count as wards, as they "pay their own way." Wards have a talent for getting caught up in the action of stories, and are frequent targets of a character's enemies.

Hunted: (4 pt Flaw)

You have come to the attention of a witch-hunter, or some similar individual who now seeks your destruction. This hunter is beyond reason and has some form of power, influence or authority that puts you at a disadvantage. Your friends, family and associates are likewise endangered. Sooner or later, this Flaw will result in a confrontation. The resolution should not be an easy one, and until then, you are in for a hellish time.

Second-Class Citizen: (2 pt Flaw)

The simple happenstance of birth has made you a second-class citizen in medieval Europe. This tends to come in two forms. First, you might simply be female. Mortal men treat you as a natural inferior, and many male Cainites also discriminate against you. Furthermore, you must rationalize taking any combat-oriented skills (Brawl, Melee or Archery) or certain Knowledges (Bureaucracy, Finance, Academics) during character creation. Being a woman usually precludes tuition in these typically exclusively male areas.

Alternately, you might be a member of a disliked or persecuted social group, and your appearance, speech or local reputation marks you as a member of this group. You are excluded from local politics,

and are distrusted and hated by most local mortals. (Remember, too, that many Cainites retain the prejudices of the societies which bore or sustain them.) You may be an Arab in Western Europe, or a Jew. Or perhaps you were a convicted thief, with a brand on your face or forehead attesting to your conviction, or an infamous local prostitute. You also might be a member of a resented immigrant group (like a wealthy Norman in Wales). Either way, you can be targeted by angry mobs needing a scapegoat….

Bear in mind that you need not take this Flaw! A female vampire without this Flaw is simply assumed to be able to overcome societal pressures and garner respect. Take this Flaw only if you want to roleplay a vampire at a social disadvantage.

PHYSICAL

These Merits and Flaws deal with your health and physical makeup, and the unusual physiology of the undead.

DOUBLE-JOINTED: (1 PT MERIT)

You are unusually supple. Reduce the difficulty of any Dexterity roll involving body flexibility by two. Squeezing through a tiny space is one example of a use for this Merit.

SANGUINE HUMOR: (2 PT MERIT)

The flush of life still seems to fill your veins; therefore, you appear more human than other vampires. Your skin never paled with death, you never really stopped breathing, and even sneezing comes naturally. You can make your heart beat as long as you have at least one Blood Point. Nosferatu may not take this Merit.

MISPLACED HEART: (2 PT MERIT)

Your heart has actually moved within your body, though no farther than two feet from its original position. You cannot be staked unless your attacker knows the right location of your heart. Obviously, you will want to keep this highly secret.

EFFICIENT DIGESTION: (3 PT MERIT)

You can draw more nourishment than usual from blood. You increase your Blood Pool by three for every two Blood Points you ingest, rounding down. For instance, taking four Blood Points increases your Blood Pool by six, and so does drinking five Blood Points.

HUGE SIZE: (4 PT MERIT)

You are abnormally large in size, possibly over seven feet tall and 400 pounds in weight. You therefore have one additional Health Level and are able to suffer more harm before you are Incapacitated. Treat this as an extra Health Level, with no penalties to rolls.

SHORT: (1 PT FLAW)

You are well below average height and have trouble seeing over high objects and moving quickly. You suffer a two-dice penalty to all pursuit rolls, and you and the Storyteller should make sure your height is taken into account in all situations. In some circumstances, this will give you a concealment bonus.

WEAK BLOOD: (1 PT FLAW)

You are of the 13th generation, the product of a liberal bloodline. As such, you are both less powerful than normal medieval Cainites, and are looked down upon by them. You may only rise in generation through diablerie, and will likely be hunted if you do so.

DISFIGURED: (2 PT FLAW)

A hideous disfigurement makes you ugly and easy to notice or remember. You therefore have a zero Appearance, much like the Nosferatu (who cannot take this Flaw).

SELECTIVE DIGESTION: (2 PT FLAW)

You can only digest certain types of blood. You may choose whether you can only drink cold blood (that from a corpse), or blood with the taste of a strong emotion (fear, joy, and so on) or possibly only the blood of animals. This Flaw may not be taken by Ventrue, who are already similarly limited by their clan weakness.

CHILD: (3 PT FLAW)

You were a small child at the time of your Embrace. Precocious or not, you are still only a youngster. You have the Flaw *Short* (see above), and find it difficult to be taken seriously by others (two-dice penalty to all relevant rolls). Additionally, traveling on your own may prove difficult, to say nothing of wandering into a tavern or brothel to feed.

DEFORMITY: (3 PT FLAW)

You have some kind of deformity (a misshapen limb, a hunchback, whatever) that affects your interactions with others and may inconvenience you physically. The difficulties of all dice rolls related to physical appearance are raised by two. Your deformity will also raise the difficulty of some Dexterity rolls by two, depending on the type of deformity you possess.

LAME: (3 PT FLAW)

Your legs are injured or otherwise prevented from working effectively. You suffer a two-dice penalty to all dice rolls related to movement. A character may not take this Flaw along with the Merit *Double-Jointed*.

LEPER: (3 PT FLAW)

Before you were Embraced you suffered from leprosy or a skin disease which might be easily confused with leprosy. Your Appearance may be no higher than 2, and your flesh is marred by rashes, pale patches, festering sores, scars, etc. Your skin disease, whatever it actually is, is obvious to any who look upon you. Mortal authorities refuse you entry to any city, and you will be treated with fear and revulsion. Very likely (Storyteller's discretion) your condition is still contagious, though being undead it cannot have any further effects on you, and you may transmit it to those upon whom you feed. This Flaw is worth only 1 point to Nosferatu, and then only if their disease is contagious.

ONE ARM: (3 PT FLAW)

You have only one arm — choose which, or determine randomly at character creation. This could be a battle scar, birth defect or other form of injury (which cannot be regenerated). It is assumed that you are accustomed to using your remaining hand, so you suffer no off-hand penalty. However, you do suffer a two-dice penalty to any Dice Pool wherein two hands would normally be needed to perform a task. A character may not take this Flaw along with the Merit *Ambidextrous* (of course, there's little need).

PERMANENT WOUND: (3 PT FLAW)

You suffered injuries during or just before the Embrace, which your sire did nothing to repair. You start each night at the Wounded Health Level. This can be healed like normal damage, but each evening, after sleep, your wounds always return.

MUTE: (4 PT FLAW)

Your vocal apparatus does not function, and you cannot speak at all. You must communicate through other means, through writing or signing. (American Sign Language obviously did not exist during the Middle Ages, but there is an early form of fingerspelling available to monks living under vows of silence and deaf nobility. Remember that literacy is irregular in these times, and only the educated would be able to read your messages.)

THIN-BLOODED: (4 PT FLAW)

You have weak blood, and are unable to use it for anything but sustaining yourself and healing your wounds. Blood cannot be used to add to your Physical Attributes, to fuel blood Disciplines or to enact the Blood Oath. Moreover, you will not always be able to create a new vampire. Half the time the Embrace will simply not work.

PERSONALITY

These Merits and Flaws deal with the personality of your character, and may describe ideals, motivations or pathologies. Some Personality Flaws can be temporarily ignored by spending Willpower points, and are so noted. If you possess such a Flaw and do not roleplay it when the Storyteller thinks you should, then she may tell you that you have spent a point of Willpower for the effort. Flaws cannot be conveniently ignored.

CODE OF HONOR: (1 PT MERIT)

You have a personal code of ethics to which you strictly adhere. You can automatically resist most temptations that would bring you in conflict with your code. When battling supernatural persuasion (Dominate, mind magic, etc.) that would make you violate your code, you gain three extra dice to resist, or your opponent's difficulties are increased by two (Storyteller's choice). You must construct your own personal code of honor in as much detail as you can, outlining the general rules of conduct by which you abide.

HIGHER PURPOSE: (1 PT MERIT)

Everyone has "reason to live," but you have a special commitment to your existence. Your chosen goal drives and directs you in everything. You do not concern yourself with petty matters and casual concerns, because your higher purpose is everything. Though you may sometimes be herded along by this aim and find yourself forced to behave in ways contrary to the needs of personal survival, it can also grant you great inner strength. You gain two extra dice on any roll that has something to do with your particular goal. You will need to decide what your higher purpose is; make sure you talk it over with the Storyteller first. (You cannot take both this Merit and the Flaw *Driving Goal*.)

BERSERKER: (2 PT MERIT)

You can direct the Beast better than most, and can frenzy at will (thus ignoring wound penalties). However, you must still pay the consequences of your actions in frenzy, and your chance of unwillingly entering frenzy is unaffected.

DUAL NATURE: (2 PT MERIT)

You have two distinct yet compatible Natures, both of which influence your personality. You may regain Willpower using both Natures. You may still choose a Demeanor, one as different from your Natures as you like. This Merit is not the same as having multiple personalities (which is a Derangement).

COMPULSION: (1 PT FLAW)

You have a compulsion of some sort, which can cause you a number of different problems. Your compulsion may be for cleanliness, perfection, bragging, stealing, gambling, exaggeration or just talking too much. A compulsion can be temporarily avoided at the cost of a Willpower point, but it is in effect at all other times.

INTOLERANCE/HATRED: (1 - 3 PT FLAW)

You have an unreasoning dislike of a certain thing. You may loathe a species of animal, a class of person, a situation or just about anything else, and you constantly pursue opportunities to harm the hated object or to gain power over it. If you are merely intolerant (the 1-point version of this Flaw), the difficulties of all your dice rolls involving the subject are increased by two. If you hold actual hatred (worth 3 points), you must make a frenzy roll whenever confronted with the subject of your hate. Note that some things are just too trivial to be angered by — intolerance of Chinese cooking or hatred of red-haired Sicilian cobblers will have little effect on most Dark Ages chronicles. The Storyteller is the final arbiter on what you can pick to dislike or hate.

NIGHTMARES: (1 PT FLAW)

You experience horrendous dreams every time you sleep, and memories of them haunt you during your waking hours. Sometimes the nightmares (or daymares, if you prefer) are so bad they cause you to lose one die on all your actions for the next night (Storyteller's discretion). Some of the nightmares may be so intense that you mistake them for reality. A crafty Storyteller will be quick to take advantage of this.

PHOBIA: (1 OR 3 PT FLAW)

You have an overpowering and irrational fear of something. You instinctively and illogically retreat from and avoid the object of your fear. Common objects of phobias include certain animals, insects, crowds, open spaces, confined spaces and heights. You must make a Willpower roll whenever you encounter the object of your fear. The difficulty of this roll is determined by the Storyteller, and depends on the circumstances. The consequences of failure depend on the severity of the Flaw. If you have taken a 1-point phobia, you must retreat from the object upon failure. If the fear is worth 3 points, you will not approach the object with fewer than three successes (even if the roll succeeds). If you fail the roll, you will enter Rötschreck and flee in terror. The Storyteller has final say over which phobias she will allow in a chronicle.

PREY EXCLUSION: (1 PT FLAW)

You refuse to feed from a certain class of prey. For example, a pacifistic hermit might avoid feeding from humans, or an erudite vampire might decide to spare scholars or musicians. You become angry when others prey on this class, and might enter frenzy (Storyteller's discretion). If you accidentally feed upon this class of prey yourself, you will automatically frenzy and will need to make a Via roll (difficulty 8 or higher) to avoid losing ground to the Beast. This Flaw is not as restrictive as the Ventrue limitation, and therefore cannot be taken by Ventrue characters.

OVERCONFIDENT: (1 PT FLAW)

You have an exaggerated and unshakable opinion of your own worth and capabilities — you never hesitate to trust your abilities, even in situations in which you risk defeat. Because your abilities may not be enough, such overconfidence can be very dangerous. When you do fail, you quickly find someone or something else to blame. If you are convincing enough, you can infect others with your overconfidence.

LOW SELF-IMAGE: (2 PT FLAW)

You lack self-confidence and don't believe in yourself. You have two fewer dice in situations in which you don't expect to succeed (at the Storyteller's discretion, though the penalty might be limited to one die if you help her by pointing out times when this Flaw might affect you). At the Storyteller's option, you may be required to make Willpower rolls to do things that require self-confidence, or even to use a Willpower point when others would not be obliged to do so.

SOFT-HEARTED: (2 PT FLAW)

You cannot stand to see others suffer; perhaps you are very compassionate, or perhaps you simply dislike the intensity of emotion. If you are the direct cause of suffering, and you witness it, you will experience nights of nausea and days of sleepless grief. You avoid situations in which you might have to witness suffering, and will do anything to protect others from it. Whenever you must witness suffering, difficulties of all rolls are increased by two for the next hour.

TERRITORIAL: (2 PT FLAW)

You do not like to leave your territory, nor do you like to have strangers enter it. In fact, you get so nervous and disoriented while outside your territory that the difficulties of all your rolls are increased by one. In addition, you must make a frenzy roll when other vampires enter your territory, unless they obtain your permission to pass through.

VENGEANCE: (2 PT FLAW)

You have a score to settle — a friend was corrupted, a parent was slain, whatever. You are obsessed with wreaking vengeance on the guilty party. Revenge is your first priority in all situations. The need for vengeance can only be overcome by spending Willpower points, and even then, it only temporarily subsides. Some day you may have your revenge, but the Storyteller won't make it easy.

DRIVING GOAL: (3 PT FLAW)

You have a personal goal, which sometimes compels and directs you in startling ways. The goal is always limitless in depth, and you can never truly achieve it. It could be to overthrow the Church or achieve total enlightenment. Because you must work toward your goal throughout the chronicle (though you can avoid it for short periods by spending Willpower), it will get you into trouble and may jeopardize other actions. Choose your goal carefully, as it will direct and focus of everything your character does.

SUPERNATURAL

These Merits and Flaws are different kinds of supernatural benefits or detriments. Although rare in the extreme, they are still more common in this superstitious age than in other times. Because of the potential of these particular Traits, the Storyteller might not allow you to pick from this category; ask before you choose one. Furthermore, you should not select such Traits unless they firmly fit your character concept, and you can explain why your character possesses them. In general, we do not recommend that anyone have more than one or two supernatural Merits or Flaws — they should be strictly controlled by the Storyteller.

TRUE LOVE: (1 PT MERIT)

You have discovered, and possibly lost (at least temporarily) a true love. Nonetheless, this love provides joy in an existence usually barren of such enlightened emotions. Whenever you are suffering, in danger or dejected, the thought of your true love is enough to give you the strength to persevere. In game terms, this love allows you to succeed automatically on any Willpower roll, but only when you are actively striving to protect or come closer to your true love. Also, the power of your love may be powerful enough to protect you from other supernatural forces (Storyteller's discretion). However, your true love may also be a hindrance and require aid (or even rescue) from time to time. Be forewarned: this is a most exacting Merit to play over the course of a chronicle.

DANGER SENSE: (2 PT MERIT)

You have a sixth sense that warns you of danger. When you are in danger, the Storyteller should make a secret roll against your Perception + Alertness; the difficulty depends on the remoteness of the danger. If the roll succeeds, the Storyteller tells you that you have a sense of foreboding. Multiple successes may refine the feeling and give an indication of direction, distance or nature.

FAERIE AFFINITY: (2 PT MERIT)

Your presence does not frighten faeries; indeed, it attracts them, and you are naturally attuned to their ways. You may even share some small amount of faerie blood. Of course, God only knows what will happen to you should you traffic overmuch with the Fair Folk....

UNBONDABLE: (3 PT MERIT)

No matter how much blood you drink from other vampires, you can never fall under the Blood Oath. You will never live the life of the Thrall.

LUCK: (4 PT MERIT)

You were born lucky, or maybe the Devil looks after his own. Either way, you can repeat three failed rolls per story. Only one repeat attempt may be made on any single roll.

TRUE FAITH: (7 PT MERIT)

You have a deep-seated faith in and love for God, or whatever name you choose to call the Almighty. You begin the game with 1 point of Faith (a Trait with a range of 1-10). This faith provides you with an inner strength and comfort that continues to support you when all else betrays you. Perhaps you hold this faith from before your Embrace. Perhaps, incredibly enough, you gained your faith in spite of the adversity of your undead existence.

Your Faith adds to Willpower and Virtue rolls, giving +1 to the Dice Pool for each point in Faith. The exact supernatural effects of Faith, if any, are completely up to the Storyteller, although it will typically repel vampires. (Basically, the character must make a Faith roll against a difficulty of the vampire's Willpower to repel him. Each success forces the Cainite to take one step back; if the character places her holy symbol against the vampire's body, she inflicts one Health Level of damage on him per success.) The effects will certainly vary from person to person, and will almost never be obvious — some of the most saintly people have never performed a miracle greater than managing to ease the suffering of an injured soul. The nature of any miracles you do perform will usually be tied to your own Nature, and you may never realize that you have been aided by a force beyond yourself.

No one may start the game with more than 1 Faith point. Additional points are only awarded at the Storyteller's discretion, based on appropriate behavior and deeds.

TAINT OF CORRUPTION: (1 PT FLAW)

Plants wither at your approach and die at your touch. Some vampires believe that Caine himself possesses this Flaw.

DEMON-HOUNDED: (1-4 PT FLAW)

A demon has taken a special interest in your soul. She appears to you occasionally, using threats, bribes and honeyed words to win you to her cause. Sometimes she just asks you to perform innocuous favors for her. Sometimes she asks you to sell your soul. Sometimes she offers favors or information without any apparent catch. In any case, it is not your interests she serves, but those of her diabolical masters. All of her plots are ultimately designed to ensnare you and win your soul. A minor demon (1-point Flaw) may be an annoying imp, incapable of no more than distracting you, thieving small items and pleading for your soul; its plans are unimpressive, but can be frustrating. A greater creature (4 points) is your physical equal and can concoct horribly devious plans to win your soul. In either case the Storyteller creates the character for the demon, and keeps track of its plots.

REPULSED BY GARLIC: (2 PT FLAW)

You cannot abide the smell of garlic, and the tiniest whiff of its scent will drive you from a room. The full force of its odor will bring bloody tears to your face, nearly blinding you, while its touch can cause boils and even wounds (Storyteller's discretion for damage). In these times, most peasants believe that garlic drives away evil spirits, so it can be fairly commonly encountered. Be careful.

HAUNTED: (3 PT FLAW)

You are haunted by a ghost that only you (and mediums) can see and hear. It actively dislikes you and enjoys making your life miserable by insulting, berating and distracting you, especially when you need to keep your cool. It also has a number of minor powers it can use against you (once per story for each power): hiding small objects; bringing a "chill" over others, making them very ill at ease with you; causing a loud buzzing in your ear or the ears of others; moving a small object such as a knife or quill; breaking a fragile item such as a bottle or mirror; tripping you or making eerie noises, such as chains rattling. Yelling at the ghost can sometimes drive it away, but it will confuse those around you. The Storyteller will likely personify the ghost in order to make things all the more frustrating for you. (More ideas for this Flaw can be obtained from **Wraith: The Oblivion**.)

DARK FATE: (5 PT FLAW)

You are doomed to experience a most horrible end or, worse, suffer eternal agony. In the end, all your efforts, your struggles and your dreams will come to naught. Your fate is certain, and there is nothing you can do about it. Even more ghastly, you have partial knowledge of this, for you occasionally have visions of your fate — and they are most disturbing. The malaise these visions inspire in you can only be overcome through the use of Willpower, and the malaise will return after each vision. At some point in the chronicle, you will indeed face your fate, but when and how is completely up to the Storyteller. Though you can't do anything about your fate, you can still attempt to reach some goal before it occurs, or at least try to make sure that your friends are not destroyed as well. This is a difficult Flaw to roleplay; though it may seem as if it takes away all free will, we have found that, ironically, it grants freedom.

ADDITIONAL BACKGROUND

In the following section you will find more detailed information on subjects which may crop up in your chronicle (such as the medieval money system).

MONEY

Medieval Europe has a pretty strange system of coinage. The subject gets very complicated, and it usually isn't going to be important. What do the characters want to buy? Just describe goods and services in relative terms (e.g., "it isn't expensive," "it's out of your reach," "if you buy this, you'll be broke for a month"). But for those interested in the nitty-gritty details of the monetary system, read on.

The basic currency is the penny, a coin supposedly made of silver but heavily debased, even in this period. The value of a penny varies wildly, depending on the quality of the latest harvest, the purity of the silver in the coin, etc. Some countries' pennies use much purer silver than others; some coins are so debased that they are virtually made of copper (called "black money" as it blackens with age). Everything is more expensive when harvests are poor, and prices fall when food is plentiful. On average, assume that a laborer would earn about three pennies per day, just enough to feed himself and pay his rent. Few medieval people have money to spend on luxuries.

Large amounts are figured in shillings and Librum. There are 12 pennies to one shilling, and 20 shillings (or 240 pennies) per Librum. Shillings and Librum coins do not physically exist, however — they are just accounting conventions. Only pennies, half-pennies and quarter-pennies circulate.

And of course, most people have little or no contact with money. Most medieval people are farmers, who grow their own food and often make their own pots, clothes, tools and shoes. If they need to buy anything they barter — two chickens for that pair of shoes, one cow for that bolt of cloth, and so on.

Dark Ages Equipment

Possession and ownership in the Dark Medieval world are not rights but privileges, and ones reserved for those of status. The lowly serf owns nothing, not even his own body. A freeman owns a scant amount, probably only that which he requires to scavenge sustenance from the soil.

A parish priest is usually from common stock, and lives barely more comfortably than his peasant brethren, if not on an even par should he be true to his vows of poverty. A monk or scribe might have access to larger funds, whether his own that have been squirreled away or those belonging to the monastery or church. A bishop has considerable funds of both kinds at his disposal.

The nobility is easily the wealthiest group among the social classes. Lowly knights may be lean on money and could lack any holdings, but are still better off than peasants. Lords and overlords hold moderate to grandiose estates, ranging from small manors to countries, with all appropriate access to currency or trade goods.

The following is a list of objects that vampires may wish to acquire or have their proxies purchase. It's based on the Resources Background Trait. Simply find the item that the character is interested in and compare his Resources score (if any) to the Resources Requirement. If the character's score is equal or higher, the item is available — in theory. No actual coins are counted. Indeed, objects could be acquired through barter of goods or services as quickly as purchased with coin.

Rarity is an indication of how difficult it is to acquire an item, whether based on local population, economy, natural resources or demand. Characters might find a barge at a river wharf, but probably don't find any large ships. The storyteller may adjust the availability of items as suits the story. Rarity is simply a benchmark. If a desired item seems completely out of place for a setting, increase its Resources Requirement. If the item should be readily available, decrease its rating.

If an item is common to everyone or can be acquired without making a purchase, it has a Resources Requirement of zero — even a serf could have one.

Equipment List

Item	Resource Requirement	Rarity	Item	Resource Requirement	Rarity
Armor, heavy	•••	Rare	Hammer	•	Common
Armor, light	•	Common	Hatchet	••	Common
Armor, composite	••	Uncommon	Holy water, pint	•••• or 0	Rare
Armor, knights'	•••••	Very Rare	Horse tackle and bags	••••	Uncommon
Arrows, dozen	••	Uncommon	Horse, good quality	••••	Rare
Banquet, extravagant	•••	Rare	Horse, poor quality	••••	Uncommon
Banquet, simple	••	Common	Inn room, one night	••	Common
Battle axe	•••	Uncommon	Jewelry, homemade	0	Common
Boat, merchant	•••••	Very Rare	Jewelry, ornate	•••	Rare
Boat, river	••••	Rare	Jewelry, simple	••	Uncommon
Boat, row	•••	Uncommon	Mace	•••	Uncommon
Book, blank	•••	Rare	Meal for one, extravagant	••	Uncommon
Book, illuminated	•••••	Very Rare	Meal for one, simple	•	Common
Bow	••	Uncommon	Mining gear	•••	Uncommon
Bribe, guard	••	Common	Mule	•••	Uncommon
Bribe, knight	•••	Rare	Ox	••	Uncommon
Bribe, scribe	•••	Uncommon	Pig	••	Common
Chain	••	Uncommon	Plow	••	Common
Chicken	••	Common	Rope	0	Common
Clothes, extravagant	•••	Uncommon	"Saint's relic"	••	Rare
Clothes, ragged	0	Common	Salt, bag	••	Uncommon
Clothes, simple	•	Common	Serfs	•••••	Common
Club	0	Common	Servants	••••	Common
Coach	••••	Rare	Shield, knight's	••••	Rare
"Companionship"	••	Common	Shield, simple	•••	Uncommon
Crossbow bolts, dozen	•••	Uncommon	Spear	•	Common
Crossbow	•••	Uncommon	Staff	0	Common
Crucifix, ornate	•••	Uncommon	Sword	•••	Uncommon
Crucifix, simple	•	Common	Traveling gear	••	Common
Dagger	••	Common	Wagon	••	Common
Great sword	••••	Rare	Warhammer	•••	Uncommon
Halberd	•••	Uncommon	Wooden Stake	0	Common

Index

VAMPIRE
THE DARK AGES

NAME:　　　　　　　　NATURE:　　　　　　GENERATION:
PLAYER:　　　　　　　DEMEANOR:　　　　HAVEN:
CHRONICLE:　　　　　CLAN:　　　　　　　CONCEPT:

═══ ATTRIBUTES ═══

PHYSICAL
Strength_____ ●○○○○○
Dexterity_____ ●○○○○○
Stamina_____ ●○○○○○

SOCIAL
Charisma_____ ●○○○○○
Manipulation_____ ●○○○○○
Appearance_____ ●○○○○○

MENTAL
Perception_____ ●○○○○○
Intelligence_____ ●○○○○○
Wits_____ ●○○○○○

═══ ABILITIES ═══

TALENTS
Acting_____ ○○○○○○
Alertness_____ ○○○○○○
Athletics_____ ○○○○○○
Brawl_____ ○○○○○○
Dodge_____ ○○○○○○
Empathy_____ ○○○○○○
Intimidation_____ ○○○○○○
Larceny_____ ○○○○○○
Leadership_____ ○○○○○○
Subterfuge_____ ○○○○○○

SKILLS
Animal Ken_____ ○○○○○○
Archery_____ ○○○○○○
Crafts_____ ○○○○○○
Etiquette_____ ○○○○○○
Herbalism_____ ○○○○○○
Melee_____ ○○○○○○
Music_____ ○○○○○○
Ride_____ ○○○○○○
Stealth_____ ○○○○○○
Survival_____ ○○○○○○

KNOWLEDGES
Academics_____ ○○○○○○
Hearth Wisdom___ ○○○○○○
Investigation_____ ○○○○○○
Law_____ ○○○○○○
Linguistics_____ ○○○○○○
Medicine_____ ○○○○○○
Occult_____ ○○○○○○
Politics_____ ○○○○○○
Science_____ ○○○○○○
Seneschal_____ ○○○○○○

═══ ADVANTAGES ═══

DISCIPLINES
_____ ○○○○○○
_____ ○○○○○○
_____ ○○○○○○
_____ ○○○○○○
_____ ○○○○○○

BACKGROUNDS
_____ ○○○○○
_____ ○○○○○
_____ ○○○○○
_____ ○○○○○
_____ ○○○○○

VIRTUES
Conscience/Conviction_ ○○○○○

Self-Control/Instinct_ ○○○○○

Courage_____ ○○○○○

OTHER TRAITS
_____ ○○○○○○
_____ ○○○○○○
_____ ○○○○○○
_____ ○○○○○○
_____ ○○○○○○

ROAD
_____
○ ○ ○ ○ ○ ○ ○ ○ ○ ○

WILLPOWER
○ ○ ○ ○ ○ ○ ○ ○ ○ ○
□ □ □ □ □ □ □ □ □ □

BLOOD POOL
□ □ □ □ □ □ □ □ □ □
□ □ □ □ □ □ □ □ □ □

HEALTH
Bruised		□
Hurt	-1	□
Injured	-1	□
Wounded	-2	□
Mauled	-2	□
Crippled	-5	□
Incapacitated		□

COMBAT
Weapon	Difficulty	Damage

EXPERIENCE

CRY HAVOC!

And Let Slip The Dogs Of War.

The Clash of Magic, Faith and Science begins in June of 1498.

Featuring fiction by Storm Constantine and illustrations by the artists who brought you...